AMTA Monograph Series

Effective Clinical Practice in Music Therapy:
Medical Music Therapy for Adults in Hospital Settings

Deanna Hanson-Abromeit, Monograph Editor
Cynthia M. Colwell, Series Editor

The American Music Therapy Association is a non-profit association dedicated to increasing access to quality music therapy services for individuals with disabilities or illnesses or for those who are interested in personal growth and wellness. AMTA provides extensive educational and research information about the music therapy profession. Referrals for qualified music therapists are also provided to consumers and parents. AMTA holds an annual conference every autumn and its seven regions hold conferences every spring.

For up-to-date information, please access the AMTA website at www.musictherapy.org

ISBN: **978-1-884914-27-0**

Monograph Editor: **Deanna Hanson-Abromeit**
University of Missouri–Kansas City
Kansas City, Missouri

Series Editor: **Cynthia Colwell**
University of Kansas
Lawrence, Kansas

Technical Assistance: **Wordsetters**
Kalamazoo, Michigan

Cover Design: **Tawna Grasty/Grass T Design**

cover photo (center): James D. Battin, Music Medicine Institute, www.musicmedicine.org
Printed in the United States of America

List of Contributing Authors

Soozie Cotter-Schaufele, MA, MT-BC
Music Therapist
Advocate Lutheran General Hospital
Park Ridge, Illinois

Judy Nguyen Engel, MM, MT-BC
Music Therapist
Florida State University/Tallahassee Memorial HealthCare
Tallahassee, Florida

Deanna Hanson-Abromeit, PhD, MT-BC
Assistant Professor of Music Therapy
Conservatory of Music and Dance
University of Missouri–Kansas City

Joanne V. Loewy, DA, MT-BC, LCAT
Director, The Louis Armstrong Center for Music and Medicine
Beth Israel Medical Center
New York, New York

Dawn McDougal Miller, MME, MT-BC, FAMI
Music Therapist, Oncology and Hospice
Park Nicollet Health Services
Minneapolis, Minnesota

Clare O'Callaghan, PhD, RMT
Peter MacCallum Cancer Center and St. Vincent's Health
Clinical Associate Professor, Dept. of Medicine, St. Vincent's Health
Fellow, Faculty of Music, University of Melborne
Melbourne, Australia

Jessica Shaller Gerweck, MM, MT-BC, CLP
Music Therapist
Willamette Valley Hospital
Salem, Oregon

Xueli Tan, MM, MT-BC
Clinical/Research Music Therapist
The Cleveland Music School Settlement
MetroHealth Medical Center Comprehensive Burn Care Center
Cleveland, Ohio

Joey Walker, MA, MT-BC
Music Therapist
Iowa City Hospice
Iowa City, Iowa

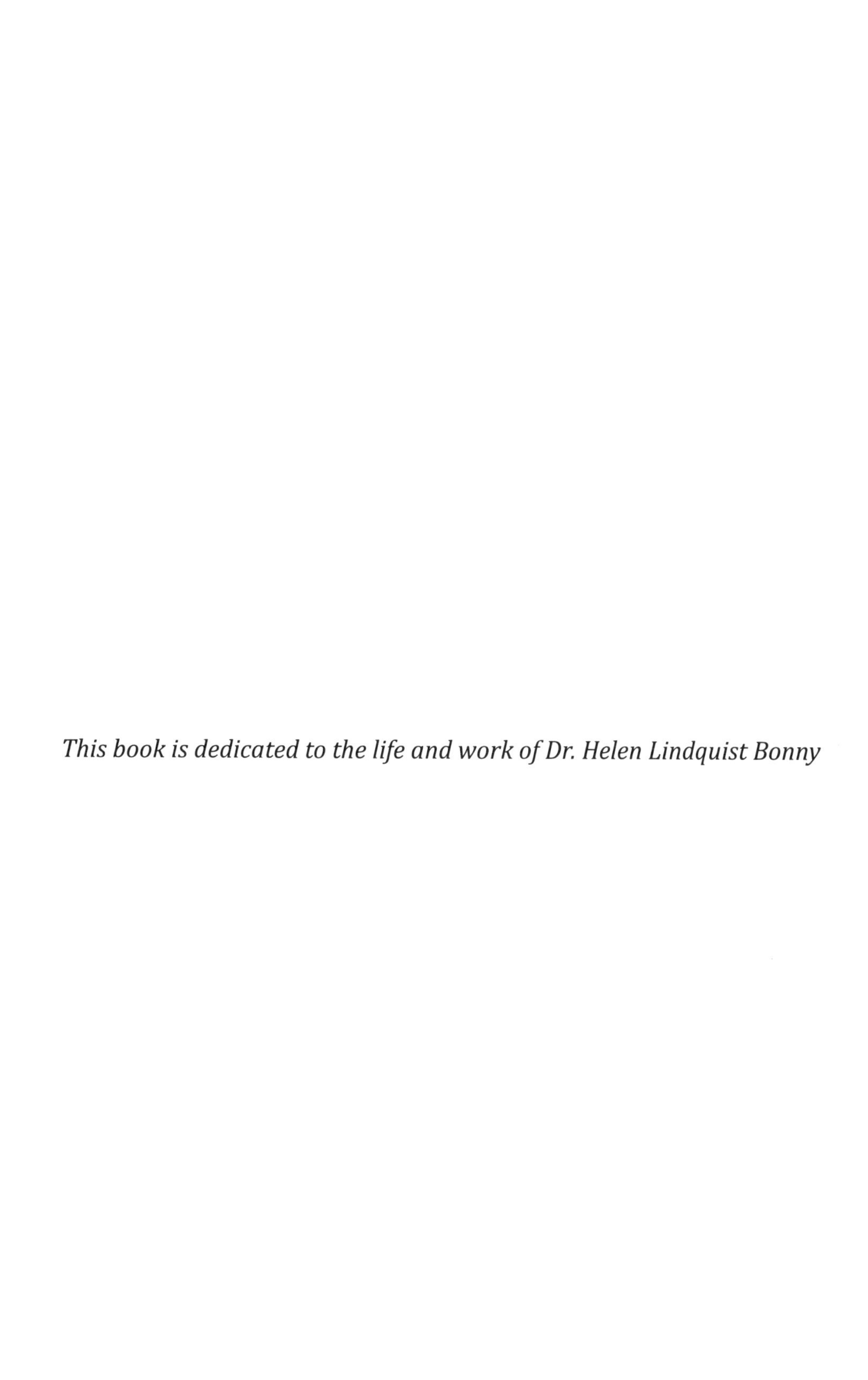

This book is dedicated to the life and work of Dr. Helen Lindquist Bonny

Acknowledgments

The editors would like to acknowledge the following individuals with the University of Missouri–Kansas City and the University of Kansas for their assistance in preparing the manuscript of this monograph.

V. Carol Dale
Kirsten Meyer
Whitney Ostercamp
Kelli Koberlein

Contents

Section III: Resources

Section I:

Music Therapy in Hospital Settings

CHAPTER I

Introduction to Adult Medical Music Therapy

Deanna Hanson-Abromeit

June was a woman in her mid-50s with a pulmonary complication requiring a tracheotomy and hospitalization. She had been on the Pulmonary Intensive Care Unit (P-ICU) for several weeks when she was referred to music therapy. The unit clerk paged the music therapist to refer June, stating that several of the nurses were concerned about her state of mind and felt that music therapy might be helpful. The music therapist's caseload was particularly heavy that day, but she promised to stop by the unit before the end of the day. The music therapist finished with her regularly scheduled patients; only 15 minutes were left of her scheduled workday, so she stopped by the P-ICU on her way back to the office. There had been a shift change since the referral had been placed, but it was evident that the nursing staff was expecting the music therapist based on their comments indicating a sense of relief at her arrival. Without an opportunity to review June's chart, a nurse led the music therapist to June's room and from the doorway said, "June, the music therapist is here to see you."

The P-ICU had a centrally located nurses' station with private rooms surrounding the perimeter. Each room had a glass front wall and sliding glass doors facing the nurses' station. Curtains that could be closed lined the front panel to allow for privacy. Windows with blinds constructed the back wall. June's front panel curtains were partially drawn, her door was open, and the window blinds were tightly closed. The lights were off and June offered no response to the nurse's introduction of the music therapist. The nurse turned to leave and said to the music therapist, "I know she'll enjoy this." The music therapist felt a little unsure about the situation, but sensing the nurses' urgency for music therapy, the therapist proceeded to June's open door.

At the doorway, the music therapist greeted June and introduced herself, stating that she would like to come in and play some music for June if that was all right. The music therapist could see June open her eyes and look in the general direction of the hospital room door. Due to the tracheal tube, the music therapist did not expect June to vocalize and knew she would have to depend on nonverbal communication cues. Because June was looking in the direction of the music therapist and did not look away, the therapist proceeded into the room with her guitar and a thick songbook.

As the music therapist moved into the room, she asked June if it would be all right to sit at the side of the bed. June continued to stare blankly towards the music therapist, without clear indication of consent or denial, so the music therapist proceeded to move a straight-backed chair next to the bedside. The music therapist sat down, put the songbook on the floor, and gently began to strum the guitar. As she strummed, she spoke softly, telling June that she was going to play and sing a few songs. She also set some parameters for communication—head nod for "yes" or a shake for "no"—and instructed June to turn her head away from the music therapist if she wanted her to finish or leave. The music therapist ended the instructions by asking June if she understood and wanted to continue. June nodded her head up and down indicating "yes," she wanted the music therapist to stay and play. The music therapist proceeded to play and sing several popular songs from the 1950s and 1960s in a steady, medium-paced tempo and quiet volume. After singing the song's first verse or chorus, the music therapist would pause the singing and ask June if the song met with her approval. Each time she nodded "yes." After about 20 minutes of singing, the music therapist noticed that tears were forming in June's eyes. The music therapist watched June carefully as she transitioned to a pause in the song, and then asked June if she wanted the therapist to stop. June shook her head "no." The music therapist then commented that sometimes music moves one to tears because it triggers a memory or a feeling. The music therapist asked June if the song had triggered a memory. June shook her head "no." Then the music therapist asked if June was feeling sad; she again shook her head "no." The music therapist finally asked June if the music was helping her to feel better. June slowly nodded her head "yes" and offered the music therapist a small smile. The music therapist smiled back and said, "Well, I suppose I should just keep singing then," and finished the song.

At this point, the music therapist decided to try and increase June's involvement in the session. She asked June for permission to slightly raise the lights so that they could use the songbook. Using the table of contents from the songbook, the music therapist offered June two choices for the next song; June was asked to lift one finger for the first song or two fingers if she wanted to hear the second song. The song selected by June was sung and the other song was included in a later choice. This allowed the therapist to get a better sense of June's music preferences based on the songs she did and did not select, and allowed June greater autonomy and control.

The session had been going for approximately 45 minutes when June began to show signs of fatigue; she was closing her eyes during the songs and was taking longer to make her choices. The therapist began the transition to end the session by offering songs that were slower in tempo, ending the session by pointing out to June that she looked tired. June nodded in agreement and sighed. The music therapist asked June if she would like her to return the following day. June looked directly at the music therapist, smiled, nodded "yes," and offered her hand to the therapist. The music therapist gently squeezed June's hand and thanked her for allowing the therapist to spend time with her. The music therapist stood, gathered her materials, dimmed the lights, and left the room. As the therapist returned to the nurses' station to chart on the session, June's nurse thanked the music therapist and inquired when she would be back. The nurse then offered that they were concerned that June was becoming depressed because she always wanted to be in the dark, slept most of the day, rarely communicated with staff or family, and was not progressing medically toward discharge. The music therapist thanked the nurse for the referral and shared the session outcomes with him.

Over the next few weeks, the music therapist continued to see June. With each visit, June had a brighter affect and was more involved with the session. She even began to vocalize over her tracheal tube so that she could sing a bit with the music therapist. June was often found sitting up with the curtains open and the lights on, waiting for the music therapist to arrive. On the day she was discharged to an assisted living facility, she verbally thanked the music therapist and said that the music therapy sessions gave her something to look forward to and helped her feel better, both physically and emotionally.

This vignette illustrates how music therapy influenced both the emotional and physical well-being of the patient and its value to the staff. It also represents one role of the music therapist in the medical setting. Medical music therapists serve adult patients in a variety of settings, including outpatient clinics and inpatient units, and for acute (short-term, one or two visits) or chronic (long-term, from weeks to years) hospitalization. Medical music therapists also address an array of patient needs along a continuum that requires the medical music therapist to adapt to changing medical requirements, be flexible in the fast-paced environment of the medical setting, and be a sensitive and astute responder to patients and their families.

Medical music therapists may work with patients and families who have experienced a traumatic event, have a serious life-threatening diagnosis, or are going through a life-changing transition, such as the birth of a child. In the adult medical setting, music therapists will serve a wide range of patient ages, from adolescents to older adults. Therapists must be knowledgeable in medical terminology, equipment, procedures, and the characteristics of common and sometimes rare diseases and disorders, not to mention a vast musical repertoire spanning various genres, styles, and eras. They also must be advocates for the benefits and application of music therapy within the medical community, as well as demonstrate patient outcomes and cost effectiveness in an ever-changing health care system.

The information in the adult medical music therapy monograph compiles evidence from the nursing, medical, and music therapy research and clinical practice literature, and the wisdom derived from many years of clinical experience. The relationships between the therapists, their patients and families, and the staff with whom they work are emphasized, as well as the importance of understanding and supporting the unique individual patient needs and the characteristics of each unit. Practical knowledge and guidelines for increasing successful experiences are documented through the descriptions of the treatment process. Case studies illustrate the efficacious nature of music therapy in the medical environment.

This adult medical music therapy monograph includes four chapters highlighting various units in the general hospital: obstetrics (**antepartum** and labor and delivery), intensive care, general medical/surgical, and cancer care. Each chapter is self-contained in that unique contributions are relevant to the specific unit and chapter authors, yet much of the information in each chapter is relevant across the adult medical setting. The content has a central focus on inpatient services with frequent mention of applicability to outpatient services. The final section of the monograph includes helpful resources.

Each chapter contains words in boldface type with which the reader may not be familiar. In the Resources section, the Glossary of Terms defines these words. A Comprehensive Bibliography lists additional resources specific to the monograph chapters. Sample application descriptions of typical intervention strategies will be particularly helpful to the music therapy student, intern, or professional new to the medical setting. Finally, the Appendices contain reprints of the AMTA Fact Sheets relevant to adult medical music therapy.

This chapter will highlight several concepts that are helpful to contextualize music therapy in the hospital setting: a historical perspective of medical music therapy, a definition of medical music therapy, and an overview of evidence-based practice. In addition, other considerations for the medical music therapist, such as quality assurance, program funding and reimbursement, and cost/benefit effectiveness issues, and, finally, future directions for adult medical music therapy, will be briefly discussed.

Medical Music Therapy

The roots of medical music therapy can be traced back to pre-literate societies when it was believed that music could change both mental and physical health (Davis & Gfeller, 2008). These beliefs continued through the development of early civilization and the Middle Ages. The scientific approach to medicine emerged during the Renaissance, at which time music was prescribed as a treatment for a variety of mental health concerns and as a preventative intervention (Davis & Gfeller, 2008). By the 19th century, music therapy was used in medical facilities, primarily as a treatment for mental illness. Music therapy and its connection to health continued to emerge following World Wars I and II as treatment for veterans. During the early 20th century, music therapy in the medical setting expanded beyond concerns of mental health to include procedural support.

Published accounts document positive outcomes in reducing anxiety during surgical procedures, promoting sleep, acting as a recreational activity, and reducing medication and length of hospitalization (Davis & Gfeller, 2008).

From these early developments, music therapy in the medical setting has become an area of rapid growth in both clinical practice and research, with 10% of music therapists currently working in the medical environment (American Music Therapy Association, 2008; Standley & Walworth, 2005a). This increased interest in music therapy is evidenced by the frequent use of music as a nursing intervention to reduce anxiety, promote sleep, and diminish agitation or depression (Gagner-Tjellesen, Yurkovich, & Gragert, 2001), similar to how music was used in the past. But the clinical use of music by a music therapist has expanded beyond these parameters.

Music activities can contribute to a person's quality of life by creating a more positive experience than it would be without the use of music. Such music activities are therapeutic in that they can be goal-directed toward a desired outcome and are measurable (Clair & Davis, 2008). However, therapeutic music activities differ from music therapy. Music therapy requires a relationship between the therapist and patient or client to address an established goal that is facilitated through the therapeutic function of music. The therapeutic function of music can be defined as the systematic manipulation of the musical elements (e.g., tempo, dynamics, melodic contour, lyrics, timbre, etc.) specific to the desired outcomes. The therapeutic function of music is key to the definition and role of music therapy in treatment environments, including the medical setting.

Medical music therapy has been defined as the use of music-based interventions that are applied within a therapeutic relationship between the board-certified music therapist, the patient, and the patient's family (Dileo, 1999). Music therapists can be trained to practice using a variety of philosophical and theoretical viewpoints. Sometimes, depending on the patient and setting, clinical interventions may incorporate a number of philosophies, theories, and approaches (Dileo, 1999). In medical music therapy, a distinction between the different philosophical orientations is complex due to the difficulty in isolating the various components of music therapy and the role of the treatment in the physical, social, psychological, or spiritual needs of the patient and family (Dileo, 1999).

The chapters in this monograph exemplify skilled medical music therapists in the adult setting. Despite having different educational backgrounds and philosophical orientations, the collective wisdom of these therapists is evident. The authors convey their understanding of the medical setting and its potential impact, both negative and positive, on the patient. There is value in the integrative collaborations with nursing and medical staff to address the health and well-being of the whole patient. Through the descriptions of patient and family interactions and how common techniques of music therapy are applied and adapted in the medical environment, the reader will gain a clear sense of how medical music therapy functions in the hospital with adult patients.

Medical music therapy has dramatically evolved from the early uses of music as a healing modality. The hospital setting is a fast-paced, constantly evolving health care system. Continued advocacy and development for medical music therapy will ensure its continued growth and relevance in the medical community. Research that promotes clinical practice and identifies the mechanisms of music will provide a consistent distinction between music therapy and therapeutic music activities used in medicine. Based on a meta-analysis, Dileo and Bradt (2005) have identified a research agenda for medical music therapy. A focused research agenda will support the sustainability of clinical programs. Strong clinical programs established within an evidence-based framework and implemented in a collaborative and integrative environment will provide the foundation for the future of medical music therapy research and practice.

Research Agenda

Dileo, C., & Bradt, J. (2005). *Medical Music Therapy: A Meta-Analysis and Agenda for Future Research.* Cherry Hill, NJ: Jeffrey Books.

Goal 1: *To clearly distinguish music therapy from music medicine in research endeavors and to increase the amount of music therapy research within all medical specializations.*

Obj. A – To actively investigate the influence and components of client–therapist relationship, music, and process on research outcomes.

Obj. B – To investigate the effectiveness of a broad range of music therapy approaches, besides receptive.

Goal 2: *To define specific characteristics of the music as well as types of music therapy approaches required for specific therapeutic purposes, e.g., stress reduction, pain management.*

Obj. A – To identify specific musical elements (rhythm, harmony, melody, timbre, tempo, meter, etc.); instrumentation (vocal vs. instrumental, lyrics vs. no lyrics, type of instruments); and performance methods (live vs. recorded) which affect health parameters of the listener.

Obj. B – To identify specific music therapy experiences that are most effective in addressing common clinical needs of medical patients, e.g., stress reduction, pain management, mood enhancement, emotional expression, sensory stimulation, etc.

Goal 3: *To investigate more completely music's ability to entrain with biopsychosocial phenomena.*

Goal 4: *To identify specific intra-subject variables that impact on the effectiveness of treatment.*

Goal 5: *To identify social context variables that may impact on the effectiveness of treatment and to investigate the influences of music medicine and music therapy in enhancing aspects of social relatedness.*

Goal 6: *To utilize a variety of research paradigms as well as more rigorous research designs to best understand the effects of music medicine or music therapy interventions.*

Goal 7: *To investigate directly various treatment delivery specifications and their comparative effectiveness (e.g., how much, how long, how many, when, where?).*

Goal 8: *To investigate the effectiveness of music listening or music therapy alone versus its combination with other approaches for a variety of research outcomes.*

Goal 9: *To identify, through collaboration with medical professionals, the most significant and meaningful outcome variables to be studied for each clinical specialization.*

Obj. A – To determine the most significant outcome variables within each clinical specialization.
Obj. B – To continue to assess the outcomes that appear to be influenced significantly and consistently by music medicine or music therapy interventions within and across medical specializations and to determine the generalizability and predictability of these effects.
Obj. C – To continue to investigate the interrelationships among various outcome measures.
Obj. D – To investigate more fully the effects of music medicine or music therapy on outcome measures that impact on cost-effectiveness issues.

Goal 10: *To investigate the effects of music medicine or music therapy on important medical conditions that have received little or no attention in the literature.*

Goal 11: *To investigate the long-term and developmental effects of music medicine or music therapy interventions.*

Goal 12: *To investigate the impact of music therapy or music medicine on the larger and most significant health issues.*

Goal 13: *To investigate the potential role of music therapy or music medicine in the prevention of illness.*

Evidence-Based Practice

Ask any music therapist and he or she will be able to describe countless examples of effective outcomes in music therapy in the hospital setting. The clinical narratives presented throughout this monograph clearly describe the efficacy of music as a therapeutic modality in the hospital setting. But clinical examples are not enough to validate the role of medical music therapy. Current clinical practice and research paradigms, particularly in medical settings, require an understanding and utilization of evidence-based practice.

Evidence-based practice emerged from the standards created for evidence-based medicine, a methodology to organize and synthesize the vast volume of research available in the international medical community to inform quality patient health care and outcomes (Davidson et al., 2003; Elphick & Smyth, 2004; Haynes, 2002). Evidence-based practice combines the most current, rigorous, and significant clinical research outcomes with the expertise of the clinician and the needs, rights, and desires of the patient to determine the best course of treatment (Sackett, Rosenberg, Gray, Haynes, & Richardson, 1996; University of Minnesota, n.d.; Yale University, 2005). Evidence-based music therapy practice paired with the emerging relationship between the brain and music will transform how music therapy is utilized and viewed within the medical community (Thaut, 2005).

Evidence-based practice in music therapy is a systematic method in which clinicians can articulate the value of their work in a language and manner understood by other professionals (Edwards, 2005). The literature related to medical intervention strategies is vast and can be overwhelming. The clinician who designs and implements treatment intervention strategies within an evidence-based practice framework creates successful prescriptive practices (Hanson-Abromeit, 2008) that can be adapted for specific needs of individual patients and their families. Music therapists understand the challenges of and techniques for collecting data for treatment outcomes. It is important for music therapists to consistently provide measurable, evidence-based outcomes (Clair & Davis, 2008). Evidence-based medical music therapy allows for better understanding of outcome effectiveness and what specific aspects of music therapy contribute to such efficacy (Hillecke, Nickel, & Bolay, 2005).

Documentation of music therapy outcomes in an evidence-based framework will further validate music therapy in the medical setting and expand knowledge concerning the therapeutic function of music in the context of music therapy. At a minimum, music therapists should be reporting specifics regarding the content and elements of the intervention, who provided the intervention and who received it, the format and environment of the intervention implementation, the duration and frequency of the treatment, and the fidelity of the intervention (i.e., method of how intervention was monitored and measured) (Davidson et al., 2003). Documentation of these parameters will serve to inform future clinical interventions not only for the specific patient, but also potentially for the general patient population with the particular diagnosis. Consequently, the potential for predictable outcomes and treatment cost effectiveness increases.

Familiarity with the music-based intervention literature suggests that few music therapists are documenting all of the recommended minimum intervention details, particularly related to the elemental qualities of the selected music. These qualities, considered the therapeutic function of music, are the primary components that differentiate music therapy from other intervention treatments. Further investigation and encouragement is required to ensure future compliance with such documentation strategies. At this time, only one study has systematically investigated how music-based interventions are described in the literature, revealing noteworthy limitations in documentation (Robb & Carpenter, 2009).

Additional Considerations for Medical Music Therapy Programs

Most medical music therapy programs begin small. Music therapists may be hired on a contractual basis for a specific unit or service, or begin part-time on the behavioral health unit. Much of the limited beginnings and ability to expand services are related to funding concerns. In addition, expansion can be impeded without a clear vision for the direction of the music therapy program. Limitations can be minimized with careful planning and articulation of a program plan and implementation strategy. While a comprehensive program development scheme is beyond the scope of this chapter, there are several foundational attributes of a music therapy program that will be briefly discussed. These concepts include quality assurance, funding and reimbursement, and cost/benefit effectiveness of music therapy services.

Quality Assurance

Quality assurance is defined as a method to monitor and evaluate the components of a program, service, or project to ensure principles of excellence (Merriam-Webster Online, 1973). Quality assurance is, first and foremost, considered a method to improve patient care. It is also relevant for patient satisfaction and serves to educate others on the aspects and outcomes of a program, service, or project (MacLean, 1991). A well-defined medical music therapy program will articulate how the various aspects of a program and treatment will be implemented in the context of the hospital units and the policies and procedures of the medical facility, as well as the professional standards of practice.

Primary characteristics of quality assurance include identifying the aspects of care to monitor, how to determine if patient care is meeting standards, the criteria for levels of care, how the data will be collected, and how it will be evaluated (MacLean, 1991). Once the characteristics have been established, the quality assurance methodology should be documented in a written format for accessibility and accountability. In addition, it should be reevaluated periodically and used to provide feedback for modifications to the music therapy program (MacLean, 1991).

The first step is to identify the critical aspects of care for the various components of the service (MacLean, 1991). This would include consideration for each aspect of the treatment process (referral, assessment, treatment plan, implementation, documentation), as well as educational and training (e.g., supervision) components. In some cases, the implementation of the treatment process will differ depending on the unit, patient needs, and how best to integrate into the services and characteristics of the unit, the staff, and hospital. For example, the chapters in this monograph discuss the referral process, but have subtle nuances due to the different diagnoses and hospital experiences of the authors. Such variations should be taken into account when establishing quality assurance requirements.

In order to determine if the patient care standards are being met, the specific components that will be evaluated and monitored should be identified. In addition, observable, measurable, and clinically valid indicators will be included for each component being monitored (MacLean, 1991). Established criteria with preset thresholds of measurements (e.g., adequate, minimum, excellent) will provide a method for determining levels of accountability for standards of care (MacLean, 1991). Data can be collected from a variety of sources, most frequently from already existing records such as hospital charts and clinical documentation. Once the data are collected, evaluation concludes the quality assurance process.

The music therapist can conduct internal quality assurance reviews of the program. This is highly recommended in order to monitor the program on an ongoing basis. Internal quality assurance allows the music therapist to correct any deficiencies or create program enhancements in anticipation of external feedback. External evaluation can be conducted to ensure excellence in the various aspects of the music therapy program. External evaluations can be patient and family surveys, questionnaires presented to nursing and medical staff, and other ancillary therapies, as well as auditing of documentation and program implementation by program or hospital administrators (Abbott, 2006; MacLean, 1991). Little has been written on quality assurance of clinical music therapy programs; however, this is a valued aspect of medical music therapy.

It is important to keep in mind that some units may have quality assurance requirements already in place that the music therapist will be expected to follow. There will also most likely be general hospital guidelines that all hospital employees must adhere to in order to fulfill the hospital quality assurance policies. These policies will often relate to safety and security of employees and patients (e.g., fire safety training), issues of confidentiality (e.g., Health Insurance Portability and Accountability Act of 1996 Privacy Rule, or HIPAA), universal precautions and infection control, and requirements for accreditation approval (e.g., Joint Commission on Accreditation for Healthcare Organizations or JCAHO). Music therapists are encouraged to integrate the music therapy program's quality assurance criteria with the requirements, expectations, and the policies of the hospital, as well as the specific requirements of the units being serviced by music therapy. In addition, medical music therapists should integrate the American Music Therapy Association *Standards of Clinical Practice* (www.musictherapy.org) and the Certification Board for Music Therapists *Scope of Practice* (www.cbmt.org).

Program Funding and Reimbursement

Music therapy programs in the hospital setting are funded in a variety of ways. Some programs are incorporated into the general operating budget of the facility. In this situation, music therapy is an umbrella category under ancillary services. Grants and endowments are another way to fund music therapy services. It is common for music therapy programs to find support from corporate, physician directed, or internal or external philanthropic organizations, as well as private foundations. One hospital program was developed through collaborative funding sponsored by a university's school of music and the hospital's foundation (Standley & Walworth, 2005a).

Reimbursement of music therapy services is not yet widespread; however, it is being pursued, and in some cases is successful. According to the American Music Therapy Association (2001, 2008), between 20 to 25% of music therapists in the United States receive third party reimbursement. In the medical setting, music therapy has been a reimbursable service for over 10 years within Medicare for Partial Hospitalization Programs. In order to qualify for Medicare reimbursement, interventions must be individualized, address treatment plan goals, and provide active treatment. To qualify as active treatment, music therapy must (a) be physician-prescribed; (b) be a reasonably necessary treatment for the patient's diagnosis; (c) be goal-directed, based on the documented treatment plan; and (d) demonstrate improvement in the patient (American Music Therapy Association, 2001).

Third party reimbursement with private insurance companies continues to grow. Insurance companies are responding to the increasing demand for greater variety in health care services and are awarding reimbursement to providers on a case-by-case basis (American Music Therapy Association, 2001, 2008). For example, Ireland Cancer Center reported that insurance companies reimbursed 20% of music therapy services provided to medical surgical patients (Petterson, 2001). Pre-approval is often required for reimbursement, and the treatment must be medically necessary for the patient to reach his or her treatment goals (American Music Therapy Association, 2001). Music therapists are encouraged to work closely with their hospital administrators and billing department to fully understand how to obtain reimbursement for their services. In addition, familiarity with reimbursement issues and resources within the music therapy profession is strongly encouraged. The American Music Therapy Association offers information through publications and their website member area (www.musictherapy.org).

Cost/Benefit Effectiveness

Cost-effectiveness analysis (CEA) is supported by the medical community as a means in which to compare effectiveness of treatment. The American Medical Association, in a letter to President Obama, stated that access to comparative-effectiveness research is one of the key components of achieving a health care culture that is patient-centered (Cassel et al., 2009). Standard measurement criteria of a program's benefits, related to the resources necessary to implement services, create a dependable benchmark for administrators to evaluate a program (Weinstein, Siegel, Gold, Kamlet, & Russell, 1996). However, a cost-effectiveness analysis is an economic-based ratio that is not infallible and should not be the only consideration for efficacious treatment. Understanding the relationship between the cost of a service and its benefits will support better and less expensive health care (Dark, 2009).

Programs and services in the medical setting must be able to demonstrate financial viability in addition to other valued aspects, such as positive patient satisfaction, beneficial outcomes, and positive marketability in the competitive and costly health care environment. Careful documentation of patient services and outcomes, as well as documentation of music therapy in comparison to standard medical treatments, will facilitate financial feasibility and program stability. Documentation of program effectiveness can be integrated into patient documentation and detailed record keeping of daily services that can be used for analysis, thus making it an integrated part of normal documentation procedures. Music therapists are encouraged to work with their program administrators to develop standard measurement criteria appropriate to their facility.

Published accounts of cost effectiveness in medical music therapy are emerging (Standley & Walworth, 2005b; Walworth, 2005). Published documentation of beneficial outcome, particularly meta-analysis and statistically derived results, can be integrated or included as additional support for a hospital music therapy cost/benefit evaluation, to estimate intervention effectiveness (Weinstein et al., 1996), or as a basis for evaluating how the program's cost/benefit effectiveness can be improved. While published documentation of cost-to-benefit effectiveness will be helpful to an individual program, most medical facilities will also be interested in ascertaining these outcomes for their own facility. It is important to note that published accounts of cost effectiveness may be regionally based, so what may be cost-effective at one location may not be cost-effective at a different medical facility (Ghetti, 2008).

Future Directions for Adult Medical Music Therapy

Health care in the United States may be on the verge of unprecedented changes. Health care reform, economic uncertainty, and an aging population are leading to careful examination of the traditional practices of medicine. Professional organizations are making recommendations for the future that will likely influence the type of services provided in this changing health care system. The American Hospital Association advocates a framework for change that provides better health care for all Americans. The *Healthy for Life* initiative has five points: health care for all with equally distributed costs, services that are efficient and affordable, provision of the best information, focus on the highest quality care, and a concentration on wellness and prevention (American Hospital Association, 2009). The American Medical Association (2009) has also issued a statement regarding their desired changes in health care reform policy. As the largest professional organization of U.S. physicians, the American Medical Association advocates for affordable health care options, third party reimbursement that does not limit the choices for health care options, provider–patient relationships that are not interfered with by insurance companies or government, and quality programs for prevention and wellness (American Medical Association, 2009).

Medical music therapists have always been challenged with the rapidly changing hospital environment due to vast patient diagnoses and needs, variety of units, and the education and advocacy of music therapy to a wide range of professionals in the medical setting. Now, medical music therapists must be prepared for the changes coming to the health care system. Proactive program development initiatives that align with the vision of leaders in health care, evidence-based research and practice, and predictable outcomes will position music therapy as a valuable and respected resource in the future of health care. As both an art and a science, medical music therapy can break down barriers, enhance relationships, and integrate into the medical setting to provide services that promote wellness, prevention, and health.

References

Abbott, E. A. (2006). The administration of music therapy training clinics: A descriptive study. *Journal of Music Therapy, 43*(1), 63–81.

American Hospital Association. (2009). *2009 AHA advocacy issue papers.* Retrieved August 9, 2009, from http://www.aha.org/aha/advocacy/annual-meeting/09-issue-papers.html

American Medical Association. (2009). *Our vision for health system reform.* Retrieved August 9, 2009, from http://www.ama-assn.org/ama/pub/advocacy/health-system-reform.shtml

American Music Therapy Association. (2001). *Resources for reimbursement.* Retrieved August 3, 2009, from http://www.musictherapy.org/membersonly/gr/reimbursement.html

American Music Therapy Association. (2008). *AMTA member sourcebook 2008.* Silver Spring, MD: Author.

Cassel, C., Crosby, J., Henley, D., Kahn, N., Lewis, F., Nielsen, N., Puffer, J., Rosof, B., Russell, T., & Tooker, J. (2009, February 28). Letter to United States President Barak Obama regarding *The Profession of Medicine's Commitment to and Vision for Improving Patient Outcomes and the Efficiency of Health Care Delivery.* Retrieved August 4, 2009, from http://www.ama-assn.org/ama1/pub/upload/mm/399/clinical-quality-joint-letter.pdf

Clair, A. A., & Davis, W. B. (2008). Music therapy and elderly populations. In W. B. Davis, K. E. Gfeller, & M. H. Thaut (Eds.), *An introduction to music therapy theory and practice* (3rd ed., pp. 181–207). Silver Spring, MD: American Music Therapy Association.

Dark, C. K. (2009, May 19). Cost effectiveness/comparative effectiveness: Rationing or priority setting? *Policy Prescriptions.* Retrieved August 4, 2009, from http://www.policyprescriptions.org/?p=362

Davidson, K. W., Goldstein, M., Kaplan, R. M., Kauffman, P. G., Knatterud, G. L., Orleans, C. T., Spring, B., Trudeau, K. J., & Whitlock, E. P. (2003). Evidence-based behavioral medicine: What is it and how do we achieve it? *Annals of Behavioral Medicine, 26*(3), 161–171.

Davis, W. B., & Gfeller, K. E. (2008). Music therapy: Historical perspective. In W. B. Davis, K. E. Gfeller, & M. H. Thaut (Eds.), *An introduction to music therapy theory and practice* (3rd ed., pp. 17–39). Silver Spring, MD: American Music Therapy Association.

Dileo, C. (1999). Introduction to music therapy and medicine: Definitions, theoretical orientations and levels of practice. In C. Dileo (Ed.), *Music therapy and medicine: Theoretical and clinical applications* (pp. 3–10). Silver Spring, MD: American Music Therapy Association.

Dileo, C., & Bradt, J. (2005). *Medical music therapy: A meta-analysis and agenda for future research.* Cherry Hill, NJ: Jeffrey Books.

Edwards, J. (2005). Possibilities and problems for evidence-based practice in music therapy. *The Arts in Psychotherapy, 32*, 293–301.

Elphick, H., & Smyth, R. (2004). Research: The principles of evidence-based medicine. *Current Paediatrics, 12*(4), 325–330.

Gagner-Tjellesen, D., Yurkovich, E. E., & Gragert, M. (2001). Use of music therapy and other ITNIs in acute care. *Journal of Psychosocial Nursing & Mental Health Services, 39*(10), 26–37.

Ghetti, C. (2008, November). Special issues in medical music therapy panel discussion. Presenter at the AMTA Conference Institute: *Medical Music Therapy: Pediatrics and Adults in the Medical Setting*, St. Louis, MO.

Hanson-Abromeit, D. (2008). Introduction to pediatric medical music therapy. In D. Hanson-Abromeit & C. Colwell (Eds.), *AMTA monograph series: Medical music therapy for pediatrics in hospital settings: Using music to support medical interventions* (pp. 3–11). Silver Spring, MD: American Music Therapy Association.

Haynes, R. B. (2002). What kind of evidence is it that evidence-based medicine advocates want health care providers and consumers to pay attention to? *BMC Health Services Research, 2*(3), 3–15. Retrieved from http://www.biomedcentral.com/1472-6963/2/3

Hillecke, T., Nickel, A., & Bolay, H. V. (2005). Scientific perspectives on music therapy. *Annals of the New York Academy of Sciences, 1060,* 271–282.

MacLean, B. (1991). Developing a meaningful quality assurance program. *The Arts in Psychotherapy, 18,* 51–58.

Merriam-Webster Online. (1973). *Quality assurance*. Retrieved July 31, 2009, from http://www.merriam-webster.com/dictionary/quality%20assurance

Petterson, M. (2001). Music for healing: The creative arts program at the Ireland Cancer Center. *Alternative Therapies, 7*(1), 88–89.

Robb, S. L., & Carpenter, J. S. (2009). A review of music-based intervention reporting in pediatrics. *Journal of Health Psychology, 14*(4), 490–501.

Sackett, D. L., Rosenberg, W. M. C., Gray, J. A. M., Haynes, R. B., & Richardson, W. S. (1996). Evidence-based medicine: What it is and what it isn't. *British Medical Journal, 312*, 71–72.

Standley, J., & Walworth, D. (2005a). Overview. In J. Standley et al., *Medical music therapy: A model program for clinical practice education, training, and research* (pp. 3–10). Silver Spring, MD: American Music Therapy Association.

Standley, J., & Walworth, D. (2005b). Cost/benefit analysis of the total program. In J. Standley et al., *Medical music therapy: A model program for clinical practice education, training, and research* (pp. 31–40). Silver Spring, MD: American Music Therapy Association.

Thaut, M. (2005). The future of music in therapy and medicine. *Annals of the New York Academy of Sciences, 1060*, 303–308.

University of Minnesota. (n.d.) *Evidence-based practice* (Online tutorial). Retrieved August 1, 2009, from http://www.biomed.lib.umn.edu/learn/ebp/index.html

Walworth, D. D. (2005). Procedural support music therapy in the healthcare setting: A cost-effectiveness analysis. *Journal of Pediatric Nursing, 20*(4), 276–284.

Weinstein, M. C., Siegel, J. E, Gold, M. R., Kamlet, M. S., & Russell, L. B. (1996). Recommendations of the panel on cost-effectiveness in health and medicine. *The Journal of the American Medical Association, 276*(15), 1253–1258.

Yale University. (2005). *Evidence based practice*. Nursing Library and Information Resources, updated on January 17, 2007. Retrieved August 1, 2009, from http://www.med.yale.edu/library/nursing/education/ebhc.html

Section II:

Music Therapy with Adult Units

CHAPTER 2

Obstetrics

Deanna Hanson-Abromeit
Jessica Shaller Gerweck

Pregnancy can be described as a developmental transition that requires adequate coping skills, supportive social structures, and a variety of resources. This transitional period is a necessary experience for growth in the woman's psyche and personal structures in preparation for parenthood as she redefines her self, her relationships, and her environment (Wohlreich, 1986). For the woman who is hospitalized during pregnancy, the learning environment will be altered from that of a normal pregnancy, putting a greater emphasis on the changes she is experiencing. Supportive services within the medical setting should address the unique needs of women preparing for childbirth in both the inpatient and outpatient setting. Music therapy may be a complementary service that can assist the pregnant woman in attaching meaning to her environment, adapting to the changes she will be experiencing, and providing a supportive and interactive environment, based on her individual learning style and self-identified needs.

The use of music in obstetrics has been documented in the latter half of the 20th century. Interest in music as an **audioanalgesia** in obstetrics emerged in the 1960s (McDowell, 1966). Initial studies, theoretical frameworks, and recommendations for the systematic use of music during labor and delivery emerged in the 1980s and 1990s (Allison, 1991; Clark, 1986; Clark, McCorkle, & Williams, 1981; Durham & Collins, 1986; Geden, Lower, Beattie, & Beck, 1989; Gonzalez, 1989; Goroszeniuk & Morgan, 1984; Hanser, Larson, & O'Connell, 1983; Kershner & Schenck, 1991; May, Young, & Conant, 1996; McKinney, 1990; Sammons, 1984; Stein, 1991) with additional studies on the therapeutic use of music in obstetrics being conducted in the last 10 years (Browning, 2000, 2001; Chang & Chen, 2005; Federico & Whitwell, 2001; Phumdoung & Good, 2003; Robinson, 2002). In general, the literature on the therapeutic use of music in obstetrics tends to be anecdotal and focus on music-therapy assisted childbirth, with little attention given to the specialized needs of women experiencing at-risk pregnancies, either as a result of age or complications. There is also limited research documenting significant benefits of music therapy in obstetrics and few comprehensive clinical programs in the hospital setting designed specifically to meet these needs. Nevertheless, nurses have continued to validate an interest in the use of music in obstetrics, particularly during labor and delivery, reflected by the body of literature prescribing music as a complementary intervention (Adams & Bianchi, 2008; Gentz, 2001; Olson, 1998; Zwelling, Johnson, & Allen, 2006).

Music therapists can be valuable contributors to the support of women during pregnancy as well as collaborative colleagues to nursing staff on the maternal care unit. Using an evidence-based approach, an obstetrics music therapy program can support nursing care while providing a constant element in the continuum of care for the parent–newborn dyad. Music-based interventions can be applied during the various stages of pregnancy as both an inpatient and outpatient service. The role of the music therapist can take two forms: that of a consultant and a therapist. As a consultant, the music therapist can develop and teach strategies to the pregnant woman and her partners (e.g., spouse, labor coach, family members) that will provide emotional and physical support throughout pregnancy and the **postpartum** period. The nursing staff can benefit from consultative services from the music therapist for music-based complementary and alternative pregnancy and labor support behaviors (Adams & Bianchi, 2008). Referrals for direct music therapy service can result from more critical needs, such as elevated blood pressure, anxiety, coping strategies, or emotional support throughout pregnancy and into labor and delivery.

It is recommended that music therapists who are working on the obstetrics unit be knowledgeable about the stages and characteristics of pregnancy, types and methods of childbirth techniques, issues related to high-risk pregnancy and childbirth, and how music can be used to support the learning needs and issues related to pregnancy and childbirth. This chapter will describe the characteristics and special issues of pregnancy and how music therapy can address the needs of pregnant women in three contexts: normal healthy pregnancy, high-risk pregnancy, and teen pregnancy.

General Obstetrics Care

For most women, learning that they are pregnant initiates contact with a family practice physician, **obstetrician, nurse-midwife** or **midwife**, and a **doula**. Prenatal care is important for the well-being of the **fetus** and the mother-to-be. Proper nutrition, physical exercise, plenty of sleep, decreased stress and avoidance of toxins (e.g., alcohol, cigarettes, recreational drugs, caffeine, toxic fumes) are lifestyle considerations that the woman must make for the best growth and development of her unborn child. Most prenatal care occurs with monthly appointments in a clinic setting. These appointments consist of a full health history of the maternal and paternal families. Regular visits include monitoring/checking the infant's heart rate, maternal blood pressure, weight gain, and urine samples for signs of diabetes. Additional screening tests for suspected birth defects or health concerns may be warranted (National Women's Health Information Center, n.d.). If there are concerns with the pregnancy, more frequent appointments and testing are required. In the final stages of pregnancy, the clinic visits will become more frequent, resulting in weekly visits in the last month of pregnancy.

The location of the birth may occur in a variety of settings dependent on the personal preference and health of the pregnant woman. Labor and delivery may occur in a traditional hospital, a specialized hospital (e.g., one focused on women and children), a freestanding birthing center, or at home. The environment within the hospital may also differ. Labor and delivery may occur in one room with the recovery process happening in another postpartum room. Some hospitals and birthing centers offer birthing suites that allow for the labor, delivery, and immediate postpartum recovery to occur in one room. The environmental setting and care services provided by the nursing and medical staff are often seen as valuable marketing tools by the facility in an effort to attract childbearing families. Two concepts that medical facilities are integrating into their obstetrics programs are family-centered maternity care (FCMC) and labor support behaviors (LSB).

Family-Centered Maternity Care

The concept of family-centered care emerged within pediatric settings and is gaining wide acceptance and adaptation to other settings and ages within the hospital context. This chapter will address the unique aspects of family-centered maternity care.

Historically, all stages of having a baby (pregnancy, labor, and birth) occurred in the family home and involved immediate and extended members of the family. This changed with modern medicine and a shift to viewing labor and delivery as a medical condition, with birthing taking place in the medical environment (Zwelling & Phillips, 2001). Traditionally, maternity care was characterized by an emphasis on safety and the physical requirements of the mother and baby; by organized procedures to support the mother–child safety and physicians' successful care; and with a mindset that pregnancy, labor, and delivery were of a pathological nature rather than a healthy and normal biological process. More recently, hospitals are recognizing that this mindset is not conducive to the respectful care of healthy adults experiencing a major transition in their lives. This recognition has caused a shift not only in the physical structure of the maternity unit, but also in the mindset of how the pregnant woman and her family are supported within the context of the hospital environment (Ecenroad & Zwelling, 2000; Gramling, Hickman, & Bennett, 2004; Zwelling & Phillips, 2001).

Currently, the two most common physical environment models for maternity care are labor/delivery/recovery units (LDRs), which are separate units for the mother–baby dyad, or labor/delivery/recovery/postpartum units (LDRPs), also known as single-room maternity care (Zwelling & Phillips, 2001). The changes in the physical environment create a warm and inviting hospital unit; however, practicing in a family-centered manner on the maternity unit extends beyond the physical environment. It involves a shift in philosophy of care and careful and conscientious implementation in the delivery of services based on the needs of the individual family.

Family-centered maternity care (FCMC) is representative of the needs and desires of the family unit, in collaboration with the family and the medical, nursing, and support services staff. It promotes care that is safe and of high quality within the context of the family's beliefs, values, cultural expectations, and/or desires (Zwelling & Phillips, 2001). FCMC may begin with changes to the physical environment of the maternity units; however, there are 10 guiding principles that evolved to support the philosophy of family-centered care on maternity units (Ecenroad & Zwelling, 2000; Zwelling & Phillips, 2001). These principles are illustrated below.

Principles of Family-Centered Maternity Care (FCMC)
(Phillips, 2003a, 2003b)

http://www.pandf.com/
http://www.pandf.com/vision.htm

1. Childbirth is seen as wellness, not illness. Care is directed to maintaining labor, birth, postpartum, and newborn care as a normal life event involving dynamic emotional, social, and physical change.
2. Prenatal care is personalized according to the individual psychosocial, educational, physical, spiritual, and cultural needs of each woman and her family.
3. A comprehensive program of perinatal education prepares families for active participation throughout the evolving process of preconception, pregnancy, childbirth, and parenting.
4. The hospital team assists the family in making informed choices for their care during pregnancy, labor, birth, and postpartum/newborn care and strives to provide them with the experience they desire.
5. The father and/or other supportive persons of the mother's choice are actively involved in the educational process, labor, birth, and the postpartum and newborn care.
6. Whenever the mother wishes, family and friends are encouraged to be present during the entire hospital stay, including labor and birth.
7. Each woman's labor and birth care are provided in the same location unless a cesarean birth is necessary. When possible, postpartum and newborn care is also given in the same location and by the same caregivers.
8. Mothers are the preferred care providers for their infants. When mothers are caring for their babies, the nursing role changes from performing direct newborn care to facilitating the provision of care by the mother/family.
9. When mother–baby care is implemented, the same person cares for the mother and baby couplet as a single-family unit, even when they are briefly separated.
10. Parents have access to their high-risk newborns at all times and are included in the care of their infants to the extent possible given the condition of the newborn.

The implementation of the FCMC principles is dependent on the philosophy of the medical setting and maternity unit. Some hospitals may apply only certain characteristics of the guiding principles, such as open visiting hours or the availability of rooming with the baby while taking the infant away only for baths or shots. From the pregnant woman's perspective, value was found in FCMC when the understanding and availability of necessary material goods (e.g., car seats, infant supplies) and resource staff were evident (Gramling et al., 2004). Whether or not the facility is practicing FCMC in its truest form, complementary resource persons, such as music therapists, should use these principles to guide their clinical practice within obstetrics.

The perspective of the family, particularly the spouse or partner, is an important consideration in FCMC. Pregnancy offers a time when women are naturally open to learning. Traditionally, there has been little concern for men's learning related to pregnancy and childbirth, and their health behaviors are rarely considered as part of the equation for prenatal care. Approaching prenatal care in a comprehensive manner, which includes the birthing partners, may encourage a change in behaviors that benefits not only the partners, but also the pregnant woman and the developing infant (Everett et al., 2006; Martin, McNamara, Milot, Halle, & Hair, 2007).

Paternal involvement in prenatal care can have a significant influence on the likelihood of prenatal care received by the mother early in pregnancy and can contribute to healthier maternal patterns of behavior during pregnancy, such as decreased smoking (Martin et al., 2007). Socioeconomic status and level of education can be predictors of the level of father involvement in the pregnancy and birthing process. Those with lower socioeconomic status and education tend to participate less than those with higher levels of education and economic security. Those who select not to participate in family labor may be fearful and lack knowledge of the birth process. Fear, for both the mother and father, may be based on concerns that paternal experiences in labor and delivery may negatively impact the couple's relationship and sexual intimacy. For these couples, knowledge and education about pregnancy and the birthing process is generally derived from the woman herself and/or the popular media (Condon, 2006; Martin et al., 2007; Wielgos et al., 2007).

Family labor is generally viewed as a positive experience. Motivation to participate in the labor is mostly due to a desire to be helpful, with pain of the laboring woman being indicated as the worst part of the birthing process for the partner (Capogna et al., Camorcia, & Stirparo, 2007; Wielgos et al., 2007). The use of **epidural analgesia** has been shown to reduce paternal stress and anxiety. It also appears to increase the father's sense of involvement, participation, and satisfaction in the birthing experience (Capogna et al., 2007). Other support services may also provide these positive benefits. Thus, education on pregnancy and childbirth directed at men should be available in a variety of formats, offer multiple support strategies, and appeal to their age, level of education, socioeconomic status, and desire for knowledge.

Pregnancy and the ensuing birth may complicate the relationship between the mother and father. Pregnancy can be more stressful for fathers than the postnatal period, with fathers experiencing their own adjustment period leading up to and following the birth of a new child (Condon, 2006). Some pregnancies add to the complexity of the intimate personal relationship due to complications from a high-risk pregnancy or postpartum depression. Some specific concerns for the partner and family are related to maternal postpartum depression and **antepartum** bed rest.

Maternal postpartum depression may increase the father's risk of experiencing depression. The father may also find challenges to coping with maternal postpartum depression that may result in anger, resentment, and maladaptive behaviors (Condon, 2006). Preterm labor and/or medically ordered bed rest due to complications also impacts the father. Some may find that they are surprised that the pregnancy is not progressing as normally expected. This creates concerns for the safety of his partner and fetus, in addition to feelings of uncertainty and confusion (Hsieh, Kao, & Gau, 2006). In addition to these feelings, fathers must assume multiple roles and provide support for their pregnant partners. Coping strategies may involve accepting help from others, communicating their concerns, and shifting their thinking and education about the situation. Many have found little help from the medical community, an indication that the paternal perspective should be an important component of family-centered maternity care (Hsieh et al., 2006; Maloni & Ponder, 1997). Incorporating labor support behaviors in the context of a family-centered maternity care philosophy may also support the roles of the caregivers in the obstetrics unit, providing strategies that can be useful to the families, nursing staff, and other caregivers.

Labor Support Behaviors

Labor support behaviors (LSB) are nursing strategies that are intentional human interactions provided by the **intrapartum** (labor and delivery) nurse to the laboring woman to support her coping strategies in a positive way during the birthing process (Sauls, 2004). Labor support behaviors are typically non-pharmacologic pain relief and support concepts (Adams & Bianchi, 2008). While a variety of definitions for LSB exist in the literature, most recently LSB have been categorized in six dimensions: tangible or physical support; advocacy; emotional support in the form of reassurance; emotional support that creates a sense of control, security, and comfort in the environment; emotional support in the form of caring nursing behaviors; and informational support (Adams & Bianchi, 2008; Sauls, 2006). Based on Watson's Theory of Human Caring, care modalities have been identified as being multisensory, in other words, auditory, visual, olfactory, tactile, kinesthetic, and caring consciousness (Hottenstein, 2005).

Labor Support Behaviors
(summarized from Adams & Bianchi, 2008)

Tangible/Physical Support
- Creating a comfortable environment through temperature, lighting, and music
- Positioning – alternative positions, such as sitting or squatting, that are appropriate for the woman's desires, labor phase, and fetal position
- Touch
- Use of cold and heat
- Partner Care – ensuring partner environmental comfort, respite time, encouraging regular food/drink

Advocacy
- Conveying respectful and nonjudgmental care
- Acknowledgment of mothers' expectations (e.g., birth plan)
- Conflict resolution
- Partner Care – determination of the partner's expectations of birth experience

Emotional Support
- Caregiver presence
- Caring attitude from caregiver
- Distraction – focal point, guided imagery
- Spirituality
- Partner Care – caregiver presence, encouragement, praise, and reassurance directed to the partner

Informational Support
- Clear verbal and nonverbal communication and information with regards to the birth experience
- Instruction for relaxation
- Instruction for breathing
- Instruction during pushing
- Patient care information
- Partner Care – offering information, explanation, and demonstration of labor support techniques

Consideration for the individual needs of the pregnant woman, her partner, and her family is important when working within the context of the obstetrics unit. Judgments should be avoided, and respect for the family's desires and needs is essential when developing treatment strategies, interaction, and engagement. Principles of family-centered maternity care, implementation of labor support behaviors, and the unique aspects of the individual pregnancy and its impact on the family unit are critical. In addition, consideration for the learning environment of the pregnant woman informs clinical practice and treatment strategies.

Theories of Adult Learning in the Context of Pregnancy

In addition to understanding and integrating the concepts of family-centered maternity care and labor support behaviors, theories and models of adult learning are relevant for appropriate and meaningful music therapy intervention strategies during this stage of life. There are a number of theories related to adult learning that can be useful when designing and implementing interventions during pregnancy. These theories may help the physician, nurse, social worker, psychologist, therapeutic recreation specialist, or music therapist shape the learning environment to have more meaning for the adult under their care. Theories that will be discussed in the context of this chapter address women's psychological and cognitive development as well as how the educator, or music therapist in this case, structures the environment to make the most of an individual's personal experience.

Learning in Adulthood: A Comprehensive Guide (Merriam & Caffarella, 1999) provides an overview of theories and models for adult learning. Theories of psychological and cognitive development are particularly relevant to pregnancy and childbirth. Key psychological theories of adult development are the Sequential Model of Development, Life Events and Transitions model, and Relational Models of Development (Merriam & Caffarella, 1999). Pregnancy is a natural time for learning. The Cognitive Apprenticeship Process (Brandt, Farmer, & Buckmaster, as cited in Merriam & Caffarella, 1999) outlines a five-phase model that describes how instructors of adults can structure the learning process to be more meaningful in the everyday practice of adult activity and social interaction. Specific to women's cognitive development is the construct referred to as the Women's Way of Knowing (Belenky, Clinchy, Goldberger, & Tarule, 1997).

Adult Psychological Development

Sequential Models of Development describes life as a series of developmental stages that occur in a set pattern of stability and transition based on chronological age (Levinson et al., as cited in Merriam & Caffarella, 1999). An individual's psychological development is molded during stages of stability and redefined during stages of transitions, commonly referred to as "teachable moments" (Havighurst, as cited in Merriam & Caffarella, 1999). The "teachable moments" that are most important to the development of one's character are marriage and family, career, social relationships and roles, views on politics and religion, and involvement in leisure and recreation activities (Merriam & Caffarella, 1999). Gender differences can affect the outcome of developmental construct. When working with women and their partners during pregnancy, the therapist must consider how the pregnancy and birth fit into each individual's life stage. Considerations should be made for their social, cultural and family roles, the influences of their age during pregnancy, and past experiences that have contributed to the development and idea of themselves as individuals. These issues will impact the perception of pregnancy and how the couple internalizes this new "teachable moment" into their lives.

Another theory of psychological development is summarized as Life Events and Transitions (Merriam & Caffarella, 1999). While closely related to the Sequential Model of Development, it is based on life experiences rather than chronological age. Life Events and Transitions contends that psychological development is based on the experiences that shape or direct an individual's life. Life events can be either cultural or individual. Cultural events are occurrences in history and society that influence an individual's development. Cultural events that may influence pregnancy are current societal views of pregnant women, acceptance of methods of inception (e.g., in-vitro fertilization), expectations on the role of mother and partner, and feeding practices for infants. Individual life events are unique to the person and may include marriage, birth, death, and divorce (Merriam & Caffarella, 1999). Pregnancy and the impending birth are major life events and significant transitions in the lives of the parents. High-risk pregnancy that requires hospitalization further complicates this transition.

Transitions are an ongoing form of development that become orienting factors to the direction of individual development. Adult transitions may be unexpected or planned and may affect each individual's life differently based on what the transition is, how it occurs, and what changes it will create (Bridges, as cited in Merriam & Caffarella, 1999). Seven stages of coping with a transition have been identified: immobilization, reaction, minimization, letting go, testing, searching for meaning, and integration. These seven stages correspond to the emotional characteristics that may be experienced during pregnancy (Sugarman, as cited in Merriam & Caffarella, 1999).

For example, after a woman learns she is pregnant, she may initially feel immobilized or powerless at the idea of pregnancy and motherhood. Reactions may vary from feelings of joy to feelings of frustration, helplessness, and fear. By the middle of the pregnancy, she may have minimized her feelings, coming to terms with the idea of pregnancy. As the woman forms a relationship with the fetus, she may reexamine past relationships with her parents and other maternal role models, perhaps releasing past feelings. Testing of the new environment and role of motherhood occurs as the woman prepares for the birth of the baby (e.g., painting the room, buying clothes, arranging for medical care and care providers) (Wohlreich, 1986). For some women, this stage of testing may evolve after the birth of the baby, extending the transition stage into the postpartum period. Most women search for meaning as they come to understand and accept the pregnancy as the birth approaches; however, the search for meaning and integration of the change may take weeks or months to occur following the birth of the baby.

Fathers also experience similar stages in the transition to parenthood. Four primary tasks have been identified during expectant fatherhood: (1) developing an attachment to the fetus beginning mid-pregnancy and continuing into the postnatal period; (2) adjusting to the additional family member and its impact on the dynamics of the couple and other children in the family; (3) transitioning and conceptualizing himself as a father, influenced by the man's level of maturity, coping, and adjustment to the new infant; and (4) determining the type of father he would like to become, either defined by personal role models or influenced by personal reflection and discussion (Condon, 2006).

Coping with this transition will depend on the assessment of the situation (i.e., the amount of perceived control), concept of self, the type of support network that has been developed, and the coping strategies (Schlossberg et al., as cited in Merriam & Caffarella, 1999). A high-risk pregnancy that requires hospitalization becomes a life event and transition stacked on top of one another, stretching even the most capable woman and her family in their ability to cope. For this family, the stages of transition may be lengthened, exaggerated, or even revisited. Some speculate that adult learning occurs during life events and transition as a coping tool (Merriam & Caffarella, 1999). The music therapist can have a role in the learning environment by encouraging coping skills during this transition.

A third view of psychological development in adulthood is the Relational Model of Development (Merriam & Caffarella, 1999). The key to this model is the relationship between the learner and the teacher. This applies to care providers because the interactions between the learner (the pregnant woman and partner) and the teacher (care provider) are interconnected in the learning process. This theory is based on women's development; however, it has application to men as well because people find value and growth within understanding the relationships of which they are a part. Therefore, the care provider should strive to create an environment that takes into consideration four key points to structuring the learning relationship. First, learning should be a collaborative effort between the caregiver and pregnant woman and her partner. Second, the learning environment should provide supportive encouragement. Third, communication should encourage cooperation; and fourth, the recognition of feelings is important to building relationships in this learning experience (Caffarella, as citied in Merriam & Caffarella, 1999).

Women's Cognitive Development

Understanding how adults think is important to the music therapist so that interventions can encourage and accept all patterns of thinking and processing of new information. One theory, Women's Way of Knowing (Belenky et al., 1997), specifically addresses female cognitive development. This theory defines women's thought processes as "knowing" and places their cognitive development into five categories. The first category is *silence*. In this category, a woman's self-identity is defined by the opinions of others. The woman may be passive and experience feelings of incompetence. The second category is *received knowledge*. A woman in this category is more concrete and literal. She is able to receive knowledge from others and can even reproduce it; however, she is unable to create her own knowledge. When a woman begins to have her own unique sense of knowledge or "voice," she is categorized as holding *subjective knowledge*, the third category. She may value intuition, truth, and knowledge, but feel that they are personal and private constructs. *Procedural knowledge*, the fourth category, is characterized when the woman displays a desire to learn and is objective in obtaining and communicating her knowledge. Finally, *constructed knowledge* is demonstrated when a women values subjective and objective knowing and is able to create her own knowledge as an expression of her authentic voice.

Understanding what categories of "knowing" characterize a woman will inform the therapist on how to adapt his or her approach to information sharing and interventions. Music therapists should encourage an interaction that is comfortable for the individual and allows for as much freedom and control of the interventions that the individual can handle. For example, a woman who is within the category of silence may find the emotional and physical experiences of pregnancy frightening, particularly if she is not given support that nurtures these normal changes due to pregnancy. In addition, if she finds herself in a high-risk pregnancy, particularly one that requires hospitalization, her feelings of incompetence may intensify and she may shut down her mechanisms to cope with the situation. In that situation, the music therapist must carefully structure the introduction of music therapy services and ensuing interventions to be sensitive to that individual's cognitive processing style.

Structuring the learning situation

Once the therapist understands how knowledge develops and how one thinks about knowledge, decisions must be made concerning the approach to the learning environment. Women will naturally learn during pregnancy; the life event itself creates a learning curve. Some women, based on their construct of knowledge, will gather and integrate more knowledge than other women. The role of the therapist in the hospital setting is to guide the patient to see the connection between past experiences and the current situation and how new knowledge applies to the future (Merriam & Caffarella, 1999).

To learn from experience, individuals must be willing to become involved in a new learning situation and be able to view their situation from a variety of perspectives. Integrating the new knowledge into their constructs of knowledge and being able to use this knowledge to problem solve and make decisions in real-life situations is key to adult learning (Merriam & Caffarella, 1999). The developmental processes for learning and coping may be impaired for women who are hospitalized during pregnancy. For example, a woman could be immobilized in the transition to hospitalization and be unable to synthesize any more information related to her situation. It may fall upon the caregiver to guide her through this process, evaluating the therapeutic process as it evolves, and adapting to the woman's needs to help her gain the most benefit from the hospital learning environment. Providing a structure to learning, which can help the process become more clear, may be one way the music therapist designs interventions for the hospitalized pregnant woman.

Cognitive apprenticeship models structure experiential learning. The Cognitive Apprenticeship Process (Brandt, Farmer, & Buckmaster, as cited in Merriam & Caffarella, 1999) is a five-phase model that uses the instructor (therapist) as a model to coach the learner (pregnant patient). The goal of this model is to help the learner internalize the new information so that it can be used by the individual alone, and to generalize the information in order to apply it in other situations. Table 1 outlines the Cognitive Apprenticeship Process model, addressing the practical applications of music therapy within its context. This model could be particularly helpful in structuring the learning environment and the therapist–client interaction in an antepartum hospital setting.

Table 1

Cognitive Apprenticeship Phases in Music Therapy Application During Hospitalized Pregnancy

	Role of Therapist	Role of Patient	Key Concepts	Music Therapy Application
Phase 1: Modeling	Models real-life activity that learner wants to perform, e.g., MT talks through concept and how it applies to situation	Observer of activity Develops a mental idea of activity	Articulation Domain-specific	Introduction of MT technique and description of intervention, e.g., demonstrates sample of music choices
Phase 2: Approximating	Provides coaching to patient Provides support as needed	Practices the techniques in a simulated situation, e.g., as a coping skill or during labor and delivery	Scaffolding Coaching	Begins practice of techniques (e.g., relaxation and music therapy assisted childbirth, adapting as necessary. Increase difficulty of task as appropriate
Phase 3: Fading	Decreases coaching and scaffolding	Continues to practice with therapist and individually	Fading	Provides access to music for self-practice and measurement tools for evaluation
Phase 4: Self-directed learning	Provides assistance when requested	Practices interventions on own	Self-directed learning	Provides patient with MT contact information. May check on occasionally, depending on individual
Phase 5: Generalizing	Discusses the use of interventions in future stages of pregnancy, birth, and motherhood	Discusses how interventions can be used in future stages of pregnancy, birth, and motherhood	Generalizability	Provides written literature for future references. Follow-up evaluation on effectiveness and usefulness of interventions

Adaptation of Cognitive Apprenticeship Phases (Merriam & Caffarella, 1999, p. 244)

Special Considerations for the Pregnant Teen

Historically, youth pregnancy was a normal feature of social life, a developmental milestone in harmony with the cultural traditions of a pre-industrial era (SmithBattle, 2000b). As the United States became an industrialized nation, the youth of the dominant culture began to prepare for the responsibilities of adulthood through formal education and the exploration of a wider range of professional and personal opportunities. It is during this time that the shift from childhood to adulthood became known as "adolescence" (SmithBattle, 2000b). As a result of this historical shift, the dominant social culture no longer views early pregnancy as an expected cultural norm, but rather as an incident that could jeopardize a successful trajectory from childhood to adulthood (SmithBattle, 2000b).

The terms *teen pregnancy* and *pregnant teen* are often used when speaking of adolescents who become pregnant between the ages of 15 and 19; however, females as young as age 10 and up to age 20 may also be referred to as "pregnant teens" (Bacon, 2000). Despite a decrease in teen pregnancy from 1991 to 2005, the United States has recently shown a slight increase in births for 15- to 19-year-old females (Martin et al., 2009). In fact, the United States continues to have higher teen birth rates than any other developed country (Elfenbein & Felice, 2003; Martin et al., 2009; SmithBattle, 2000b). The incidence of teen pregnancy and parenting is greatest within minority cultures, many of whom live in a very different environmental, social, and economic context than the dominant culture (Elfenbein & Felice, 2003; Gallup-Black & Weitzman, 2004; Gold, Kennedy, Connell, & Kawachi, 2002; Kirby, 2002; Martin et al., 2009; Spear & Lock, 2003).

Pregnant and parenting teenagers are found across socioeconomic levels, educational environments, and ethnically and religiously diverse backgrounds. For the young mother and her child, focus is often on the negative consequences of teenage pregnancy, such as an emphasis on prepregnancy loss history (e.g., abuse, poverty, limited education) and future loss due to early childbearing (Finkel, 1995; Geronimus, 2003; Logsdon, Birkimer, Ratterman, Cahill, & Cahill, 2002; Shaller, 2001). However, some cultural subgroups view teen pregnancy as an alternative life course (Finkel, 1995; Geronimus, 2003; SmithBattle, 2000a; Spear & Lock, 2003). Regardless, pregnant teens are faced with a developmental dilemma that requires them to attend to the changes of pregnancy and tasks of parenting often before they have completed the developmental milestones and tasks of adolescence (Hudson, Elek, & Campbell-Grossman, 2000). Although teenage pregnancy and parenting can contribute to negative outcomes for the teen and her child, pregnancy can also bring purpose and direction to a young woman's life and thus serve as a catalyst for change and the making of positive life choices (Finkel, 1995; Lesser, Koniak-Griffin, & Anderson, 1999; Montgomery, 2003; Rentschler, 2003; SmithBattle, 2000b; Spear, 2004). Music therapists, health professionals, and teachers working with these young women must be familiar with several factors that inform communication style, therapeutic interactions, and the structure of clinical interventions. These factors include typical milestones and considerations of adolescent development and complex external and internal risk and protective factors.

A Personal Reflection on an Experience with a Teen Mother

by Jessica Shaller, Winter 2004

I use the daily commute to practice my observation skills. Last night, I was riding the bus, when I found myself watching a young woman and her child. The young mother impressed me immediately. She spoke to her child in a calm manner, using "Please" and "Thank you," and modeling positive behaviors. The child asked multiple questions; the mother respectfully answered them all. When the child informed her mother that she wanted candy instead of her granola bar, the mother replied, "We do not eat candy before dinner. This is called a healthy snack." Munching on her granola bar she tried to say granola: "grbola." The young mother corrected her through teaching: "Repeat after me: gra nol ah."

The mother and I started to talk and she immediately spoke of the multiple negative comments and glares she receives from others on her daily commute with her child. She spoke openly of her life experience. As a foster child, she was moved from home to home and began using drugs and alcohol at a very young age, "...on a road to self-destruction". She became pregnant at fifteen and her life changed dramatically. Her desire to raise her child in a loving and stable home motivated her to stop using drugs and alcohol, stay in school, graduate on time and continue on with higher education. She is now nineteen years old and independently providing for her child while working and attending college. They live in a one-bedroom apartment that costs $725 a month. Her child appears healthy, happy, clean, developmentally appropriate, and socially adept. She is not on welfare. I spoke with her about how I have used music therapy with pregnant and parenting teens. As she expressed interest, we discussed how the criticism she received affected her and what supports would have helped her and her young child the most. Before we parted, I complimented her on the positive choices she has made in her life. For this young woman, becoming a mother at the age of fifteen was the catalyst for positive change and healing.

The young mother's story described above is similar to the stories of many pregnant and parenting teens to whom the authors have provided music therapy over the years. Their stories often take place within an environmental context characterized by disadvantage, disorganization, and dysfunction that sets the stage for chronic experiences of loss, abuse, and neglect. Risk factors such as growing up in poverty, poor attachment to school, and sexual abuse are directly related to an increased incidence of risk-taking behaviors correlated with teenage pregnancy, such as reduced use of contraception and earlier initiation of sexual activity (Martin et al., 2009; Osborne & Rhodes, 2001). Either the stress and loss associated with teenage pregnancy can be exacerbated by these risk factors and contribute to further poor outcomes for these teens and their children, or the teen can courageously break through the confines of the environment to provide a more positive life experience for the child. This latter outcome is more likely to occur when pregnant and parenting teens are provided with personalized support, education, and opportunities for emotional, cognitive, and behavioral change. Music therapy, a unique mediating stimulus, can both facilitate the patient-centered changes desired in overcoming the adversity associated with teen pregnancy, and empower these young mothers to make choices that are in the best interest of their unborn/infant child and themselves.

Adolescent Development Concepts

Adolescence begins with the onset of puberty most easily identified by the vast physical changes associated with adult mature bodies. In addition, adolescence affects major changes in cognitive and social-emotional development. Adolescence is commonly divided into three phases: early (approximately ages 10–14 years); middle (approximately ages 15–17 years); and late (approximately ages 18–20+) (Bacon, 2000; Montgomery, 2003). Teens in the early phase of adolescence are present-time oriented and self-focused. They are often dependent on their family for emotional and physical support and need assistance in health care decisions (Montgomery, 2003). During this phase, it is important to place the emphasis on how the teen's behaviors will affect her health and that of her baby in the present-time context, rather than future implications. This is particularly important if the teen is participating in harmful behaviors (Lesser & Escoto-Lloyd, 1999). The use of simple language and visual aids is helpful for clear communication of information (Koniak-Griffin & Turner-Pluta, 2001). During the early phase of adolescence, teens are not typically initiating sexual activity. If pregnant at this phase, there is an increased likelihood that the teen has been the victim of abuse or coercion and, therefore, an assessment for a past history of sexual abuse is strongly suggested (Montgomery, 2003; Osborne & Rhodes, 2001).

The middle phase of adolescence is characterized by the development of abstract thinking and emerging understanding of later consequences related to current behaviors. Cognitively, teens between the ages of 15 and 17 are developing operational thought processes and often have difficulty with abstract concepts and thinking (Martin, Hill, & Welsh, 1998). For example, if a teen cannot actually see the sperm and the egg joining and the egg becoming fertilized, then he or she does not believe it is happening. So, when a young pregnant teen says, "I didn't think it could happen to me," she is telling the truth, as is consistent with the stage of her cognitive development. Another characteristic of the concrete stage of cognitive development is the inability to plan (Martin et al., 1998). Teen pregnancy is often the result of a lack of planning in terms of implementing birth control methods. These factors of cognitive development contribute to unplanned and unwanted pregnancy. A worldwide research study by Blanc, Tsui, Croft, and Trevit (2009) finds that sexually active 15- to 19-year-olds are more likely to inconsistently use contraception than their 20- to 49-year-old counterparts and to experience a greater rate of contraceptive failure by 25% on average.

Additionally, during this developmental stage, teens tend to feel insecure regarding their communication abilities and, because of this feeling, often shy away from asking questions. It is important that health care providers of pregnant and parenting teens promote an environment of open and concrete communication, trust, acceptance, and support as they encourage these young mothers to ask questions and express their concerns (Montgomery, 2003).

During the late stage of adolescent development, abstract thinking is more fully developed and teens can begin to predict the consequences associated with their decisions. Teens in this phase of development are capable of engaging as an active participant in their health care decisions (Harner, Burgess, & Asher, 2001; Montgomery, 2003). In most states, teenagers over the age of thirteen who are pregnant/parenting, living apart from their parents or living financially independent from their parents are considered medically emancipated (Harner, Burgess, & Asher, 2001). These teenagers may legally consent to a wide variety of medical and psychosocial services provided to them in the hospital setting. However, they may be forced to act on the health care decisions made for them by their parent, guardian, or partner/significant other. It is important for caregivers to determine the motivation behind health care choices made by these teens during such a vulnerable and overwhelming time (Jacoby, Gorenflo, Black, Wunderlich, & Eyler, 1999). This is especially important if the teen is in a suspected or reported abusive relationship.

While pregnant teens are still in need of parental attention and guidance, they develop an increased dependence on their peer group for support and identity formation. The type and quality of a teen's social interactions have great influence on her behavioral, emotional, and spiritual development. A teen's peer group can offer experiences in social competence, emotional support, and a sense of identity and belonging; conversely, it can also create and reinforce a sense of social ineptitude, loneliness, and a lack of acceptance. There are five polarities related to an adolescent's social development that can contribute to conflict with parents and other significant adults. These polarities are rebellion of adult control/need for direction, wish for closeness/fear of intimacy, pushing and testing of limits/viewing limits as a sign of caring, thoughts of the future/orientation to the present, and sexually mature/cognitively not ready to experience sexuality (Kees, 2000). These polarities contribute to the pregnant teen's overall psychosocial development, decision-making process, and use of coping mechanisms.

Coping mechanisms are still developing during adolescence (Passino et al., 1993), thus pregnant and parenting teens may be limited in their internal resources to cope with stress. Teens most frequently employ coping mechanisms that involve problem solving, wishful thinking, focus on the positive aspects of a situation, avoidance, and denial (Byrne, 2000). Females more often employ emotion-based strategies of coping in comparison to male teens (Byrne, 2000). Emotion-based strategies of coping require an emotional outlet and strong social support network of friends that stresses the importance of intimate relationships (Byrne, 2000). While the teen is developing psychosocial competence through her social interactions, she is also developing strategies for coping. Social support networks are critical for the developing adolescent, especially the pregnant teen, who may be more dependent on others for emotional support than her non-pregnant peers. Adversely, pregnant teens often experience changes in their social situation over the course of their pregnancy and into parenthood. They may lose friendships, their social role(s), or the ability to participate in group activities such as sports or shopping. In the case of hospitalization, pregnant teens become even more socially isolated and disconnected. Lack of a social support network during teen pregnancy/parenting can contribute to experiences of depression, stress, loneliness, poor-self-esteem, social isolation and poor coping overall (Hudson et al., 2000; Logsdon et al., 2002).

There are five core issues of adolescent development that are affected by the complex environmental, socioeconomic, and personal issues that correlate with teen pregnancy. These core issues include trusting in the predictability of events, gaining a sense of mastery and control, forging relationships marked by belonging, believing the world is fair and just, and developing a confident self-image (Balk & Corr, 2001). Additional developmental tasks of adolescence include obtaining a sense of individuality, psychological separation from the family of origin, developing a consistent identity, developing a peer-group identity, attaining a sexual identity, developing a personal value system, and developing life goals (Kees, 2000; Martin et al., 1998). The inherent challenges and characteristics of adolescent development combine with the unique experiences and beliefs of childhood to influence the risk of teen pregnancy.

External and Internal Risk and Protective Factors Associated with Teen Pregnancy

Within the hospital setting, pregnant teens are provided with medical services in the same place as adult pregnant women. Consideration for the patient's age and complexity of issues/needs is essential to successfully create and implement experiences of learning, coping, and stability throughout pregnancy. A variety of external and internal factors influence a teen's risk for pregnancy during adolescence. While also relevant to the adult pregnant woman, these factors are of greater consequence to the teen because the age at which pregnancy occurs influences her cognitive, emotional, physical, and social responses to the pregnancy as well as to her own development. An awareness of these complex issues and the developmental needs related to teen pregnancy may better prepare music therapists to assist these teens in reaching their greatest potential as women and mothers.

External risk and protective factors associated with teen pregnancy involve the environmental, cultural, and socioeconomic context of the teen at the state, community, school, family, and peer levels. External risk factors contribute great limitations, challenges, and threats that teens experience every day. For example, teens that have experienced physical abuse or sexual victimization are at a greater risk for sexual exploitation, particularly by older men (Elfenbein & Felice, 2003; Harner et al., 2001; Jacoby et al., 1999). In fact, in a study by Osborne and Rhodes (2001), 17.7% of pregnant/parenting minority teens report a history of sexual abuse/victimization. In 72.3% of these cases, the victimization was in the form of unwanted sexual intercourse and most often occurred before the age of 11 (Osborne & Rhodes, 2001). Even more disturbing are the facts that the men involved were on average 12.77 years older than their female victims at the time of the victimization and that 23.4% of these perpetrators were considered boyfriends or ex-boyfriends at the time (Osborne & Rhodes, 2001). Emotional responses to sexual victimization are related to risk-taking behaviors such as earlier initiation of sexual intercourse, reduced use of contraception, multiple sex partners, and greater sexual activity (Osborne & Rhodes, 2001). These behaviors may be a coping strategy for the teen, a way to regain a sense of mastery and personal control by acting as the master instead of the victim (Martin et al., 1998). Knowledge of the external risk and protective factors of pregnant teens can influence the perspective of the situation and clinical approach in an effort to promote positive experiences for the teen, her child, and her health care providers.

It is important to view the case of each pregnant and parenting teen in the true context of her everyday lived experience, rather than from the assumptions projected by the dominant culture that teen pregnancy and parenting automatically lead to poverty, jeopardize development, and create huge public costs (SmithBattle, 2000b). External protective factors are viewed within the state, community, school, family, and peer context of the teen. Family members and peers strongly influence adolescent decision making and are often role models. As such, these individuals have the potential to be a strong protective factor against the occurrence of teen pregnancy. However, negative and limiting beliefs taught to the teen by external sources such as parents, teachers, or siblings can negatively influence the way in which the teen perceives herself and her life, especially in relation to experiences of trauma, loss, and abuse. For example, the teen who is taught that she "can never do anything right" may feel she is to blame for abuse received and may stay in an unhealthy relationship. Personal belief systems, inherent emotional responses, and individual psychosocial traits create internal risk and protective factors (Kirby, 2002).

Internal risk factors related to teen pregnancy and parenting are influenced by the teen's relationship with her family, school, peers, and partners, as well as by her own behaviors, emotional well-being, beliefs, and loss history. How a teen copes with and perceives personal experiences of physical abuse or general maltreatment and neglect by her family or other adults is a contributing risk factor of teenage pregnancy (Spear & Lock, 2003). The teen's experiences and views of school also influence her level of risk for pregnancy (Kirby, 2002). Teenagers who experience a compromised emotional well-being related to psychiatric disorder(s), depression or anxiety, low self-esteem, a lost sense of personal control over their lives and decisions, unresolved or complicated grief reactions, or developmental delays are at greater risk for pregnancy (Spear & Lock, 2003).

Personal beliefs held by a teenager also influence the likelihood that she will become pregnant during adolescence, as does the meaning she assigns to having a child. Teenagers who come from troubled homes and have experienced significant losses throughout their life often seek out intimate relationships in order to fill a void from their childhood (Martin et al., 1998; Shaller, 2001). Many have been given messages that they are unlovable, inept, powerless, and alone, or that they are a failure. Many pregnant and parenting teens in school and hospital music therapy groups have made statements such as "My baby will love me for forever," "I want to love someone and be loved in return," and "I can be a good mom; that's something I'll be good at" (Shaller, 2001; Stevens-Simon & Lowy, 1995). These statements exemplify the teenager's desire to be loved, love another, have a lasting relationship, create secure attachment bonds, and feel a positive sense of self. They also illustrate how the pregnant teenager may be trying to compensate for a significant sense of loss and hurt in her life. Strong internal protective factors, such as the teen's relationship with her family, school, and peers, as well as her emotional well-being and positive beliefs about herself, can mitigate the risks for teen pregnancy (Kirby, 2002). Table 2 outlines the external and internal risk and protective factors related to teen pregnancy.

Table 2

Risk and Protective Factors for Teen Pregnancy

	Risk Factors	Protective Factors
Environmental		
State/Community	Restrictive state laws that reduce access and education to reproduction and birth options Decreased state educational spending Lower overall socioeconomic status High unemployment	Coordinated, comprehensive state programs and policies that address the multifaceted issues of teen pregnancy Spending on comprehensive education Low unemployment High socioeconomic status
School	Higher school dropout rates Vandalism within the school setting Poor school performance Limited support or lack of plans for higher education	Sense of attachment to their school Academic success Value placed on education Support and plans for higher education
Cultural		
Family	Higher rates of divorce, domestic violence, single-parent households Incidence of sibling pregnancy and early childbearing norms within the family Family role models of destructive behaviors Multiple home placements Absent father figure Teen serving as the babysitter for younger siblings Sexual victimization and physical abuse as a child or adolescent	Higher parental levels of education Responsible parental figures in the home Higher income level Parental disapproval of teen sex and risk-taking behaviors Sense of connection to, respect, and support from, parents Open communication about dating, sex, and risk-taking behaviors Appropriate parental supervision Parents model healthy behaviors and decisions

	Risk Factors	Protective Factors
Peer	Friends engaged in higher rates of sexual intercourse, substance use, risk-taking behaviors Poor grades and school dropouts Pregnant friends Gang involvement Older male partners acceptable within peer group Experiences of social isolation, rejection, and mistreatment	Friends engaged in few risk-taking behaviors Good grades with a sense of attachment to school Supportive of delayed sexual intercourse and use of contraceptives Positive social experiences that create a sense of belonging Participation in extracurricular activities
Individual Traits/ Characteristics		
Psychosocial	Superficial peer relationships Engaged in aggressive and risk-taking behaviors such as alcohol use, substance use, unprotected sex, delinquency, and gang involvement Disadvantage, disorganization, and dysfunction within the daily context Experiences of social isolation	Strong, significant peer relationships Limited or absent aggressive and risk-taking behaviors Organized and safe daily context Sense of belonging in relationships
Inherent emotional and belief systems	Unrealistic expectations of home responsibilities Perceived lack of control Limited opportunities for decision-making and future-oriented opportunities Beliefs that parenthood provides the best means of escape from an intolerable home or living situation; someone to love Beliefs that friends are engaging in sexual intercourse and do not support use of contraception	Personal goals related to education (success in school, higher education) Positive attitude towards school Sense of a future direction and life purpose Sense of positive personal beliefs, behaviors, and attitudes Beliefs that friends are engaging in similar behaviors and attitudes

(Elfenbein & Felice, 2003; Harner et al., 2001; Jacoby et al., 1999; Kirby, 2002; Lesser, Koniak-Griffin, & Anderson, 1999; Martin et al., 1998; Osborne & Rhodes, 2001; SmithBattle, 2000b; Soto, n.d.; Spear & Lock, 2003; Stevens-Simon & Lowy, 1995)

Many pregnant teens live in impoverished urban settings where themes of disadvantage, disorganization, and dysfunction are common and can be seen throughout the external and internal influences on the teens' life experience (Elfenbein & Felice, 2003; SmithBattle, 2000b). While these external and internal risk and protective factors discussed here are associated with teen pregnancy, their presence does not determine whether a young woman will or will not become pregnant during adolescence. Just as in the case of adult pregnancy, the pregnant teen will also experience juxtaposing emotions such as happiness/sadness, excitement/fear, relief/anxiety, and joy/anger (Shaller, 2001).

One of the most significant losses the pregnant teen experiences is that of her independence as the result of having to care for another being (Martin et al., 1998). This loss of independence is so significant because adolescence is the time during which a child transitions into becoming independent and autonomous. In addition to a loss of independence, pregnant teens often experience a loss of self-identity, especially as defined in relation to their peer group (Hechtman, 1989). The teen's previously held definition of her self must change in order to incorporate additional identities associated with multiple new roles. A pregnant teen may take on new roles including that of mother, father, provider, educator, wife, single parent, and partner in addition to her preexisting roles of child, sibling, student, dependent, and friend. The addition of these new roles, loss of old roles, and creation of a new self-identity may be experienced as multiple losses and significant stress for the inexperienced, unprepared teen mother (Shaller, 2001).

During pregnancy, teens experience multiple relationship changes that can be considered significant losses. Changes within family dynamics may occur as the family tries to adjust to the exchange of roles within the household. Shaller (2001) describes:

> For example, the child becomes a mother who herself is still in need of being mothered. The adult mother becomes a grandmother, often gaining greater responsibility for the rearing of another child just when her own child, the pregnant teen, may have been reaching a point of independence. (p. 9)

These changes in the family dynamics can be experienced as a loss for multiple family members. For the pregnant teen, the change in family dynamics often creates conflict and struggle as she continues to strive for separation from the family and a sense of autonomy despite her increased level of dependence. Such family conflicts may cause significant stress for the majority of pregnant teens who continue to live with their family of origin (Martin et al., 1998).

Another significant relationship loss may be that of close friends. Pregnant teens often become alienated from their friends due to different levels of independence, responsibilities, priorities, life views, experiences, and self-isolation (Shaller, 2001). Many pregnant and parenting teens who have participated in music therapy sessions report that they have lost their close friends because they were at either school or work, or were caring for their child. The loss of multiple friends may contribute to the teen having a poor sense of adequacy, self-worth, and self-esteem (Hechtman, 1989). As the pregnant teen acquires many new responsibilities, she may find that she does not have the time to "hang out" with friends or to engage in dating. This life experience of the pregnant teen is often very different from that of her peers and can result in a sense of isolation and estrangement (Hechtman, 1989).

The numerous changes and losses associated with teen pregnancy and parenting can make it challenging to forge relationships and achieve a sense of belonging. As a result, these young mothers may have difficulty getting along with others and may find themselves in conflict with their friends and family members. Once a teen becomes pregnant, she may lose her partner and the accompanying sense of being loved, supported, and protected. Promises of financial, emotional, and social support from the partner are often broken, and the teen mother may experience a great sense of abandonment and fear (Shaller, 2001).

Despite the oppressive environmental and socioeconomic context many of these teens live in, and the multiple traumatic and abusive experiences they may experience, pregnant and parenting teens are resilient. They are survivors with personal strengths such as perseverance, determination, optimism, and hope (Spear & Lock, 2003). Clinicians and health care providers have the privileged opportunity to foster these strengths. With optimism and hope for a new future, pregnant teens often view parenthood as a means of escape from a limited, intolerable living situation (Rentschler, 2003; Spear & Lock, 2003; Stevens-Simon & Lowy, 1995). They view parenthood as a "rite of passage to adulthood" (SmithBattle, 2000a). For these teens, the attainment of a maternal role is achieved through responsibility, respect, and reparation (Lesser, Koniak-Griffin, & Anderson, 1999; Spear & Lock, 2003).

Responsibility in the context of teen pregnancy necessitates the attainment of new roles and behavioral changes that promote the health and well-being of both the teen and her child (Lesser et al., 1999). With responsibility also comes a sense of obligation to her friends, partner, and family. *Respect* is achieved as an extension of responsibility experienced as a reciprocal give-and-take of honor, solidarity, and loyalty (Lesser et al., 1999; Spear & Lock, 2003) that is received from others as a by-product of motherhood. *Reparation* is defined as the positive qualities of a good mother that pregnant and parenting teens desperately seek to achieve in order to become the ideal mother they may not have had (Lesser et al., 1999). Within the context of these beliefs, teenage pregnancy and parenting offer the opportunity to heal the wounds of the past and move forward into a more positive future.

A woman's external and internal risk and protective factors must be viewed along a continuum of severity. The severity and degree to which the risk factors outweigh the protective factors can mitigate for or against positive outcomes and resilience. Many teens and adult women experience a combination of risk factors. The individual history of disadvantage, disorganization, and dysfunction can be complex. To fully understand the impact of the risk factors and the role they play in the lives of pregnant women, these factors must be placed within the context of the developmental milestones of adolescence and adulthood.

Pregnancy is a life transition, during which understanding the woman's developmental context, as it relates to her personal history and the characteristics of the medical condition, informs treatment interventions. Music therapy during pregnancy is unique in the hospital setting in that these women are typically considered "well." With some exceptions, the medical necessity for hospitalization is directly related to the pregnancy and will cease to exist for the woman following the delivery of the infant. With that in mind, the remainder of this chapter will describe the characteristics of pregnancy and music therapy for two contexts of hospitalization during pregnancy: labor and delivery and antepartum. Intervention strategies described can be adapted for short-term treatment or consultation within the obstetrics clinic.

Characteristics of Pregnancy

During the 40 weeks of gestation, the pregnant woman will experience a variety of physical as well as psychological and emotional issues. Some of these changes may be minor or non-existent for some women and more extreme for others. The changes may last for a short time or for the duration of the pregnancy. Just as individuals are unique, so is each pregnancy; however, there are some commonalties that are typical to pregnancy that provide the woman with an idea of what she can expect in the ensuing months.

Physical Changes

The first symptoms of pregnancy that a woman may notice are most likely physical changes. For many women, the absence of a menstruation cycle may send them to the store seeking a home pregnancy test. According to the authors of the book *What to Expect When You're Expecting* (Murkoff & Mazel, 2008), common physical symptoms of the first trimester include fatigue, sleepiness, and nausea, commonly known as "morning sickness," which may occur with or without vomiting. Breasts often become sensitive due to changes that may include feelings of fullness or heaviness, tenderness, and darkening of the area surrounding the nipple (areola). Specific desires for and aversion to certain foods can be more pronounced during pregnancy. For some women, heartburn, indigestion, flatulence, and bloating are also common physical discomforts. As the first trimester progresses, constipation, headaches, dizziness, and clothing tightness may be experienced as well as a desire for frequent urination (Murkoff & Mazel, 2008).

The majority of physical symptoms from the first trimester continue into the second trimester, except that there may be a less frequent need to urinate, and most women will experience a decrease in nausea that is often replaced with an increase in appetite. At this point, women may also experience nasal congestion, ear stuffiness, bleeding or sensitive gums, and mild swelling of ankles, feet, and sometimes the face and hands. Additional physical changes in the second trimester include the beginnings of fetal movement, achiness in the back and lower abdomen (sometimes accompanied by itchiness), varicose veins, hemorrhoids, and leg cramps (Murkoff & Mazel, 2008).

The final trimester brings stronger and more frequent fetal activity as the baby continues to grow and develop. The physical stress of the steady weight gain makes for an overall feeling of discomfort and difficulty sleeping. Many of the physical changes experienced in the first and second trimester continue. In addition, women begin to experience Braxton Hicks, which is a tightening of the uterus, beginning sometime around the 20th week of pregnancy and becoming more frequent and intense as the pregnancy progresses. These are often described as practice contractions for real labor. Breathing is more difficult as the growing uterus crowds the lungs; however, this eases as the baby's position lowers in preparation for birth toward the end of the third trimester. The need to urinate increases as the baby's lowered position puts pressure on the bladder (Murkoff & Mazel, 2008).

Emotional Changes

In addition to the physical characteristics of pregnancy, there are unique emotional issues. Pregnancy creates a variety of feelings and emotional situations that a woman may have never experienced, or may have experienced for only short or isolated instances. There is a sequence of emotional alterations during the normal pregnancy that follow a pattern of predictability. In the first trimester, a heightened emotional expressiveness often leads to episodes of crying, feeling irritable or irrational, and mood swings (Murkoff & Mazel, 2008). Emotional irregularity can occasionally lead to mild depression that usually dissipates after the first 3 months (Wohlreich, 1986).

In addition to emotional instability, pregnant women may also experience feelings that swing among doubts about the pregnancy, fear of the unknown, and overwhelming joy (Murkoff & Mazel, 2008) as she develops a relationship to her fetus. This relationship evolves throughout pregnancy, beginning with acceptance of the fetus as part of her self and then later differentiation of the fetus as a separate being that she will nurture and care for outside of her physical body (Wohlreich, 1986).

As the fetus grows and movement begins, the woman may start fantasizing about the baby. She may also evaluate her relationship with her parents and other maternal figures in an effort to form her own framework for motherhood (Wohlreich, 1986). The second trimester continues with mixed forms of emotional expression ranging from acceptance of the pregnancy to frustration with the changes happening to her body. Also, women may begin experiencing a sensation of absentmindedness, such as forgetfulness and difficulty concentrating on everyday tasks (Murkoff & Mazel, 2008).

The final trimester of pregnancy also tends to be a mixture of emotions from one end of the spectrum to the other. Excitement for the impending birth is contradicted with fear for the baby's health and the event of labor and delivery and motherhood. In the final month, the feelings of excitement, anxiety, apprehension, and forgetfulness intensify, as do impatience, restlessness, irritability, and oversensitivity (Murkoff & Mazel, 2008). In addition to the emotional reactions the woman may experience due to pregnancy, the relationship between her partner and other family members and her obstetrical care provider can also affect her emotional well-being (Wohlreich, 1986).

Labor and Delivery

The birthing process has been divided into three stages: labor, delivery of the infant, and delivery of the placenta. The first stage, labor, includes Phase 1, dilation or early labor; Phase 2, active labor; and Phase 3, transition. During early labor, the cervix begins to thin and dilate to approximately 3 centimeters. Contractions begin, but can range in their frequency from 5 to 20 minutes apart. For first time mothers (primaprivarou), early contractions can last several hours to days. The first phase may occur more quickly for multiprivours mothers (second or more births). Positive signs that labor is impending include consistent frequency and duration of contractions for a significant amount of time (e.g., 3–5 minutes apart for 1 hour); the breaking of the membranes, commonly referred to as the water breaking; an increased desire to urinate; menstrual-like cramping or backache; and nausea or vomiting (Mayo Clinic Staff, 2007; Merck, 2003; Murkoff & Mazel, 2008; Parrott, n.d.).

Phase 2, active labor, continues with increased intensity of the contractions (e.g., 3–5 minutes for 45–60 seconds). The cervix dilates from 4–7 centimeters and is almost completely **effaced**. The duration of this stage is typically between 2–4 hours, but depends on the progression of the labor and the individual woman. During this stage, the woman may experience pressure and discomfort in her pelvis, legs, and back as the baby moves down the birth canal. She may physically react to the contractions with increased heart rate, restlessness, crying, or holding her breath. She also starts to become more tired and may start to verbalize her inability to continue (Mayo Clinic Staff, 2007; Merck, 2003; Murkoff & Mazel, 2008; Parrott, n.d.).

Phase 3 is referred to as transition. This is the hardest part of labor when the contractions are constant, coming 2 to 3 minutes apart and lasting approximately 60–90 seconds. There is very little time to rest between contractions. The cervix is now dilated from 8–10 centimeters and is completely effaced. The woman may have an extreme urge to push and struggle with the energy and emotional drive to continue. During transition, the woman may be extremely agitated, have difficulty with rational thought and conversation, and be challenged in remembering and using her birthing strategies. It is at this point that the caregivers and birth partner need to be extremely patient, calm, supportive, and reassuring (Mayo Clinic Staff, 2007; Merck, 2003; Murkoff & Mazel, 2008; Parrott, n.d.).

Throughout labor it is important that the medical caregivers are aware of the birth partner's coping strategies and overall physical and emotional state. In the face of the woman's anxiety and exhaustion, the birth partner may also experience similar physical and emotional challenges. He or she may have a hard time staying calm and relaxed, and may require supportive services from the caregivers in order to best be available for the birthing woman. If the mother-to-be has been using a variety of physical labor support behaviors, she may be moving throughout the contractions. It is during transition that the medical caregivers will assist her return to the bed in preparation for delivery (Mayo Clinic Staff, 2007; Merck, 2003; Murkoff & Mazel, 2008; Parrott, n.d.).

Stage Two is delivery. Contractions continue, coming 2 to 5 minutes apart and lasting about 60 seconds. The woman is now able to fulfill her urge to push and does so with each contraction. Like each phase within Stage One, the duration of this stage varies from woman to woman and birth to birth. This stage continues to be physically challenging, but for many women there is renewed excitement and enthusiasm as the birth of the baby is imminent. The delivery can be prolonged for a variety of reasons. If medications for pain management or progression of labor (e.g., **Pitocin**) are used, delivery may be longer. Other reasons may be that pushing is ineffective in moving the baby through the birth canal, the size of the baby is large, the position of the baby is complicated, or fetal distress is present. Any of these situations can result in an emergency cesarean section (Mayo Clinic Staff, 2007; Merck, 2003; Murkoff & Mazel, 2008; Parrott, n.d.).

The final stage of the birthing process is the delivery of the **placenta**. Following the birth of the baby, contractions will resume so that the woman can deliver the placenta, also commonly known as the afterbirth. This generally happens within 2 to 30 minutes after the delivery. The woman will also have the urge to push as the placenta detaches from the uterus wall. During this time the woman may or may not experience pain similar to delivery.

Some hospitals practice kangaroo care, a technique in which the baby is immediately placed on the mother's naked chest and covered with warm blankets. The baby and the mother's concentration on him or her can be a cognitive focus that often serves to reduce the perception of pain related to the delivery of the placenta. Following the delivery of the placenta, the woman and room will be cleaned. Depending on the hospital setting, the new family may reside in the birthing room for the duration of their hospitalization or may be relocated to a family friendly room on the postpartum unit (Mayo Clinic Staff, 2007; Merck, 2003; Murkoff & Mazel, 2008; Parrott, n.d.).

At times a vaginal birth is not possible due to a variety of medical reasons, in which case the pregnant woman may have a cesarean section, also called a C-section. Some situations in which a scheduled C-section is planned include when the baby is in a **breech** position, there are problems with the placenta, the baby is too big to pass safely through the birth canal, the pregnant woman has an infection (e.g., HIV or herpes) or serious medical condition (e.g., high blood pressure or diabetes), there are multiple babies to birth, the baby has a certain type of birth defect making a C-section a safer option for delivery, or previous births were delivered by cesarean section (March of Dimes, 2008).

There are also times during a vaginal delivery when a C-section may be necessary. Reasons for an emergency C-section include when the baby is **transverse**, the labor is not progressing (i.e., too slow or stops), the umbilical cord slips in the birth canal where it could be squeezed or flattened during birth (umbilical cord prolapse), or the infant is demonstrating behaviors that show it is under stress (fetal distress) (March of Dimes, 2008). A cesarean section is considered major surgery in which the doctor makes an incision in the abdomen and uterus (womb) and removes the baby. The recovery time for a C-section is typically longer than a vaginal birth. Average post-delivery hospitalization is 3 to 4 days, with 4 to 6 weeks for a full recovery. C-sections also put the woman at risk for complications due to the anesthesia or the surgery itself (March of Dimes, 2008).

Music Therapy Assisted Childbirth

The majority of births in the United States take place in the hospital setting. Unfortunately, not all hospitals employ a music therapist. Of those hospitals that have a music therapy program, many do not provide services to obstetrics. One way that music therapists can provide Music Therapy Assisted Childbirth (MTACB) services to labor and delivery is through a contractual or private practice (Clark, 1986; DiCamillo, 2008; May et al., 1996). One such program, *Sound Birthing,* is a private music therapy agency that specializes in prenatal music sessions, Music Therapy Assisted Childbirth, labor doula services, and postpartum support. In addition to client-based services, *Sound Birthing* also provides training for music therapists interested in such services (DiCamillo, 2008).

Using music during labor and delivery has a long history primarily linked to the use of music as an audioanalgesia in pain management and relaxation (Allison, 1991; Browning, 2000, 2001; Clark et al., 1981; Durham & Collins, 1986; Geden et al., 1989; Hanser et al., 1983; Hunter & Hunter, 1994; May et al., 1996; Phumdoung & Good, 2003). Music Therapy Assisted Childbirth (MTACB) refers to a prescribed music-based program that is used in conjunction with childbirth techniques. It is not a replacement for childbirth classes, but a complement to the presented techniques. MTACB offers another tool to empower the birthing couple through the process. The prescribed use of music during childbirth is differentiated from the general use of music as an environmental stimulus. It complements the practice of family-centered maternity care and fits into the model of labor support behaviors used by **intrapartum** nurses.

In consultation with the couple, music is programmed for the stages of childbirth in a manner that matches the musical elements with the physical and emotional needs of the birthing partners, taking into account their preferences. Music therapists assist the birthing partners (pregnant woman and her birth partner, e.g., a spouse, close friend, or doula) in the careful selection of the music. The selection of music is followed by opportunities to practice techniques of music-assisted relaxation in conjunction with traditional childbirth techniques prior to the birth (Clark, 1986). The practice sessions are meant to result in a trained relaxation response and serve as a motivator and energizer for the birthing woman, with the music acting as the cue for the response. The programmed music corresponds with the stages of labor and delivery, culminating with a birth tape that is a celebratory recognition of the new infant.

The potential benefits of music therapy during labor and delivery address both physical and emotional needs. These are the two primary areas addressed by nurses in labor support behaviors. In addition, the benefits of MTACB extend beyond the birthing woman and include benefits to the labor partner. Physical benefits include pain reduction, tension reduction, structure for movement, and general physical comfort. Pain reduction outcomes include stimulating the release of **endorphin**, decreasing the need for medication, providing a distraction from pain, and functioning as a focal point during contractions. Tension reduction benefits may be seen in decreased blood pressure and heart rate, and the relaxation of muscles due to a trained physiological response to the music (Browning, 2001; Clark et al., 1981; May et al., 1996).

A variety of movement strategies is encouraged during labor and delivery. Walking, squatting, sitting, and rocking are often recommended to birthing woman, particularly as the labor progresses to the active labor and transition stages (Adams & Bianchi, 2008). Movement stimulates a neuromuscular response and provides a rhythm to focus on and a more socially accepted avenue for organized movement (Browning, 2001; Clark et al., 1981; May et al., 1996). For example, couples can be encouraged to dance during labor. The close contact supports the woman physically and emotionally. Couple-specific music selections may elicit positive memories that can function to regenerate energy, shift waning attitudes to a more positive place, and empower the birth partner with a positive strategy. It is important to keep the birthing woman in physical comfort so that she conserves energy and is fully invested throughout the birth process. The pairing of selected music to complement the physical stages and events of labor provides a source of physical comfort.

Music as a Physical and Emotional Support During Labor and Delivery
(Browning, 2001; Clark, McCorkle, & Williams, 1981; May, Young, & Conant, 1996)

Physical Needs:

Pain reduction – stimulates endorphin release, decreasing need for medication; provides distraction from pain; functions as a focal point during contractions.

Tension reduction – decreases muscle tension through trained response to music; may contribute to decreased blood pressure and heart rate.

Movement – stimulates a neuromuscular response; provides a rhythm to focus on and a more socially accepted avenue for "organized" movement.

Physical comfort – musical elements of selections complement the physical events and stages of labor and delivery.

Emotional Needs:

Sense of security – use of familiar, preferred music gives the couple a comfort zone of familiarity in an unfamiliar environment.

Anxiety/fear reduction – practice of relaxation exercises paired with music provides an entrained response to the music; serves as a tool to provide central focus and empowerment.

Mental focus – structures visualization, imagery, and focusing techniques.

Emotional comfort – music is individualized to match desired emotional associations identified by the couple prior to labor and delivery and matched to the emotional needs at the different stages of labor and delivery. Careful selection of music is critical to avoid any negative connotations or associations with the played music for the birthing couple.

Cognitive focus – preferred music provides a perceived feeling of control and positive cognitive messages; additional support tool that provides a focus of control (e.g., whether to play, change in selection).

Bonding – creates a sound environment that connects all people involved in the birth; connects partners through personal messages and feelings expressed through the chosen music.

Emotional support can also be enhanced with the use of couple-specific familiar, preferred music. The music can create a sense of security by providing a feeling of comfort in the context of an unfamiliar environment. Relaxation exercises paired with music may reduce anxiety and fear that can develop during labor and delivery. The music provides a mental focal point that can distract and calm the birthing couple. At times during labor, the woman may need emotional support to give her a sense of positive control. The individualized selection of music can create a cognitive focus that reinforces the woman's feelings of control by using her and her partner's judgment in how it is used in the birth process. The music also creates a mental focus by pairing it with **visualization**, imagery, and focusing techniques (Browning, 2001; Clark et al., 1981; May et al., 1996).

Listening to music can create strong emotional responses. Emotional comfort is created through the music via emotional associations desired by the couple during labor and delivery. It is very important that the therapist ensures that neither the birthing mother nor the partner have any negative emotional associations or responses to a specific piece of music. While it is desirable to select music primarily based on the needs and wishes of the woman, a family-centered maternity care approach ensures that the partner also has positive associations with the various musical selections. Thus, the partner can be more invested in supporting the woman in the manner that she requires. The connection created with the music creates a nurturing sound environment. This sound environment can connect all the people involved in the birth, but most importantly, it can connect the birthing couple through the personal messages created by their shared musical selections (Browning, 2001; Clark et al., 1981; May et al., 1996).

Music Therapy Assisted Childbirth Case Study

Daniel and Lisa used music during the birth of their first child and were looking forward to using music therapy assisted childbirth for the birth of their second child. The recordings of their desired music were carefully organized for the various stages and phases of labor and delivery. As part of the birth plan, Lisa had selected a specific song, "I Think I Love You," performed by the Partridge Family, a favorite song from her childhood that had positive associations. She wanted this song to be played when she felt like she was having a hard time. Daniel thought the song was a funny choice, but looked forward to using it at the right opportunities. As Lisa was moving from Stage 2, active labor, to Stage 3, transition, she was starting to lose her cognitive attention and energy. When Lisa asked for "I Think I Love You" to be played, it changed the energy and associated feelings in the room. Daniel, the attending nurse-midwife, the intrapartum nurse, and a medical student started laughing. Lisa joined in and began moving rhythmically through her contractions in a more engaged and focused manner. It provided the boost she needed to proceed through the final stages of labor and delivery. In addition, the laughter and positive feelings emulating from the labor room attracted other nurses and staff from the labor and delivery suite. Everyone was curious as to what the laughter and good times were all about; this was a different experience than what was typical for most laboring women brought to the unit.

There are several ways in which the music therapist can provide MTACB. One way is for MTACB to be integrated into a group childbirth class (Clark, 1986). Hospitals may choose to offer a fully integrated MTACB course co-taught by the childbirth instructor and the music therapist. The music therapist's role is to guide the families in the use of music and help them structure a personalized music selection for their birth experience. Other programs may find that interested couples prefer to have small group or individualized MTACB instruction coordinated with the childbirth courses (e.g., meeting for 30–45 minutes following the childbirth courses). This type of integration is more efficient for courses that meet in consecutive weeks rather than in one day. Costs of the childbirth courses would reflect the addition of MTACB.

Another option is to offer MTACB courses individually as a service of the obstetrics unit. Referrals can result from the contact made by interested couples with the therapist or from the obstetrics staff. Fee structures would be determined prior to offering the service. Private pay is one option. A flat fee is the most likely fee structure for a contractual therapist (Clark, 1986). A sliding scale could be considered in order to offer the service to a variety of socioeconomic levels. Another pay option is to tie MTACB into the fee structure of labor and delivery. This is a viable option for music therapists who are employed by the hospital and are not required to direct bill for their services (Clark, 1986).

The process of MTACB will be described in the following section based on individual sessions. For the music therapist working within the context of the childbirth class, these concepts can be modified to accommodate the structure of the group and class format. The music therapist works with the couples to design a compilation of recordings (CDs or mp3 playlists) of preferred, appropriate music to correspond to the stages of labor.

The music therapist should consider several things when designing the MTACB sessions. First, the music therapist in the hospital setting frequently may work with patients who are hospitalized due to an illness. The needs of the expectant couple are addressed within the context of a wellness model of care in which the couples are seekers of information. Assessment procedures should reflect this philosophy and include determination of the learning styles of the woman and her birth partner, birth plan desires, medical contraindications, name of the obstetrician or midwife providing prenatal care, childbirth education classes, and prior pregnancy and birth history. The assessment should also investigate the couple's level of self-directed behaviors, as their efforts are critical to the beneficial outcomes of the MTACB experience. Knowledge of adult learning theories, childbirth education, family-centered maternity care, and labor support behaviors will assist the music therapist in designing sessions that fit the various needs of the birthing partners. It is also helpful for the music therapist to be familiar with the therapeutic functions of music (e.g., how the various musical elements influence physiological, psychological, neurological, and biological changes).

Typically, MTACB training involves four sessions with the pregnant woman and her birth partner. The birth partner may not always be able to attend. In some cases, the pregnant woman may attend MTACB training on her own and share the information with her birth partner. For example, if someone lives in a rural area and comes to the hospital or obstetrics clinic for prenatal care, the music therapist may coordinate the MTACB sessions with the obstetrics clinic visits. It is wise for the music therapist to provide written materials to the pregnant woman and couples during MTACB sessions as a reference for the information covered in sessions and their weekly homework. The music therapist can create handouts outlining the needs of the hospital, music therapy program, and session format (e.g., individual, integration into a childbirth education course, or implementation by nursing staff).

The initial session may be the first opportunity for the therapist to meet the birth couple, although sometimes the music therapist can meet the pregnant woman and the birth partner in the obstetric clinic prior to the first session. Sample session outlines for four consecutive birthing couple MTACB sessions are provided below. The music therapist should adapt these session formats as appropriate for his or her own style, hospital setting, and clientele. High-speed recording/copying/editing equipment is recommended for efficient music compilation.

Hospital-Based Music Therapy Assisted Childbirth (MTACB)
Session Outlines (approximately 1 hour)
(adapted from May, Young, & Conant, 1996)

Session One

1. Complete intake assessment form. Mail or email prior to first session or complete in consultation with music therapist. Review as part of introductory conversation and rapport-building.

2. Educate to MTACB process
   – prerequisites of childbirth classes
   – review physical and emotional benefits of MTACB (handout on physical and emotional benefits)
   – review concept of compilation formation (handout on stage of labor corresponding to recorded music)
   – method of playback at home and in hospital
   – review copyright regulations regarding recorded music
   – signed copy of agreement for compliance of copyright law

3. Determination of music preferences
   Couples listen to recorded selections from a variety of musical styles and independently complete assessment on level of stimulation, liking, thoughts and associations, feelings and emotions, and body reaction. The recorded selections can be provided by the couple, or samples from the music therapist's collection can be utilized. A personal music preference form can be given to the couples to help categorize and organize their personal music selections.

4. Practice breathing, and **progressive** or **autogenic relaxation** exercises
   Provide couples with a recording of scripted progressive and autogenic music-based relaxation (tightening and relaxing of body parts) techniques to take home for practice (simulating the type of music used during early and active labor).

Couples Homework:

Practice progressive and/or autogenic relaxation nightly with training tape. Begin listening to own music for positive associations and appropriateness to the various stages of labor. Start the categorization process. Bring selected recordings (if they want the music therapist to compile the labor and delivery recordings) and the couple's personal music preference forms to the next session.

Therapist Homework:

Assess preference list for compatible styles and associations for the couple and follow up with the couple before the next session. Gather possible music selections for use during various stages of labor that were indicated as "high need" (e.g., relaxation, movement music) to supplement the couple's personal collections. Comply with copyright restrictions. Prepare for Session Two.

Session Two

1. Discuss concerns, thoughts, feelings from previous week's practice and listening/compiling exercises.

2. Discuss formation of early labor and active labor compilations and how best to proceed (i.e., therapist- or couple-directed compiling). Provide couple with supplemental recordings if indicated.

3. Instruct the couple that you will be practicing autogenic relaxation using their preferred music and will transition into a visualization exercise. Pick a visualization exercise—e.g., autumn day, comfortable place, pine forest, rainy city, sailing, seashore, spring day, winter day, summer day—and begin the autogenic relaxation and visualization exercise.

4. Provide the couple with a sample music and visualization exercise recording to practice at home.

5. Discuss the role of music during transition and delivery. Play appropriate examples and discuss some potential selections based on the personal music preference forms.

6. Determine a mutually convenient time for the couple to pick up the early and active labor compilations if the therapist will be doing the compilations.

Couples Homework:

Practice autogenic and visualization relaxation for at least 30 minutes daily. Transition practice to utilize the labor tapes as they are completed in order to begin training the body to respond to the music. Listen and select music for transition and delivery. Begin compilation process or bring selections to next session if the music therapist is making the compilations.

Therapist Homework:

Make compilations as needed. Evaluate supplemental music selections as indicated. Prepare for Session Three.

Session Three

1. Discuss concerns, thoughts, feelings from previous week's practice and listening/compiling exercises.

2. Discuss progress and use of early, active, transition, and delivery compilation recordings. Determine how the therapist can assist/support the process/formation of the labor and delivery compilations. Provide couple with supplemental recordings if indicated.

3. Evaluate couple's practice with relaxation and visualization techniques. If needed, and/or requested, practice at this time.

4. Evaluate the couple's knowledge and comfort level of various labor support behaviors (LSB), particularly those useful during active labor and transition. Practice LSB using the couple's selected music (if ready) or with appropriate musical examples from the music therapist's collection.

5. Discuss the role of the birth music and its use during pregnancy, at the birth, and post-birth. Play example birth compilations. Facilitate a discussion on the type of songs and/or messages they want to convey to their newborn.

6. Determine a mutually convenient time for the couple to drop off and/or pick up musical selections for the compilations if the therapist will be doing them. Encourage continued practice with each of the compilations.

Couples Homework:

Complete compilations or deliver selected music to the therapist. Continue daily practice of progressive/autogenic relaxation and visualization exercises. Practice other more active strategies that can be transferred into labor, e.g., dancing and gentle stretches. Finish any compilations not completed. Make changes to anything that evokes any negative associations or feelings for either partner. Begin making selections for birth compilation. Bring anything to Session Four that requires the assistance of the music therapist.

Therapist Homework:

Complete any compilations necessary. Evaluate any supplemental selections as necessary. Touch base with the couple to determine if they require any special assistance/support prior to next session. Prepare for Session Four.

Session Four

1. Discuss concerns, thoughts, feelings from previous week's practice and listening/compiling exercises.

2. If needed and/or requested, practice any music-based strategies at this time.

3. Discuss birth tape. Provide guidance and suggestions if necessary.

4. Discuss the value and use of music at home (music and development; infant-directed singing; music and play; music to support transitions, e.g., sleep patterns for both baby and parents, bath time, diaper changes, and feeding).

Creating the Music Compilations

The music selections for each of the various phases and stages of labor and delivery should be organized into compilation CDs and color-coded and labeled for quick identification during labor and delivery. It may also be helpful to provide a quick reference or tip sheet to be used by the birth partner or other labor support caregivers. This will ensure the most beneficial use of the music during the various stages of labor and delivery. The compilations can be organized to best fit the couple by the stages of labor and delivery (May et al., 1996) or by the desired outcomes (e.g., relaxation, movement) (DiCamillo, 2008).

During early labor, the role of music is to help store energy, decrease anxiety, and promote relaxation and sleep, if possible. This music should consist of selections that have been indicated to be most relaxing to the couple. These selections will have little variation in dynamics or style and may range in tempo from 60–90 beats per minute. Music may be instrumental or with non-obtrusive lyrics (DiCamillo, 2008; May et al., 1996).

As the woman moves into more active labor, the intensity of the music should also shift. The music selections during this stage will be more energetic, yet still calming and relaxing. Anything that is too intense may cause the woman to tense her muscles; a more relaxed muscle state eases the pain of the contractions. The music is moderately paced (90–108 beats per minute) with more dynamic and stylistic changes. The energy of the music should encourage movement, rocking, swaying, and other physical labor support behaviors (DiCamillo, 2008; May et al., 1996). At this point, couples may choose to dance or hold each other while swaying. Imagery or visualization may also be supported by the music to assist in coping with the intensity of the contractions as the birth process moves to the transition phase. For some, birth imagery scripts may provide additional support as a cognitive support. Birth imagery scripts contain descriptors that help the woman, with each contraction, to visualize the cervix softening and opening, the baby moving down the birth canal, and the body working to support the birth. In one experience, visualization of the cervix dilating to a specific number gave the birthing mother a cognitive focus during active labor and transition.

Case Study Example of a MTACB Training Program

Darla had been experiencing early labor symptoms for over a week. At her last appointment, her nurse-midwife had cautioned her that she was demonstrating emerging symptoms of hypertension, and she recommended bed rest. At the next clinic visit, it was determined that an **induction** was necessary due to the increasing hypertension. Darla and her partner scheduled the induction for 3 days later, her father's 60th birthday. After settling into the labor and delivery room, the nurse-midwife broke her membranes. Darla was dilated only to 1 centimeter and had a minimally effaced cervix. The nurse-midwife had to return to the clinic and warned Darla that if she did not progress (i.e., dilate and efface), then Pitocin, a synthetic hormone used to start contractions, would be administered to help the labor progress. Darla strongly desired a natural childbirth and decided to use visualization during her contractions.

Darla and her partner had worked with the music therapist and had organized their music selections in preparation for labor and delivery. They had also practiced visualization techniques as part of their MTACB training program. Darla selected the music that they had used in their home practice for visualization to assist her now. As the music played, Darla visualized the number 4 and with each contraction focused on her cervix. She and her partner were surprised when the nurse-midwife returned 45 minutes later and found Darla dilated to 4 centimeters.

Throughout active labor, attended by her partner, the nurse-midwife and a medical student, Darla continued to use the music to support her visualization of the number 7. Darla utilized the music and visualization so effectively that those in attendance joked that they should have brought some games to play, as they felt unnecessary to the process. As Darla moved into transition, the nurse-midwife again checked her cervix; it had dilated to 7 centimeters. Pleased with the progress, Darla quickly began to focus on the number 10 (the dilation necessary to ready the cervix for delivery). In 10 minutes, she was on the bed and pushing.

Transition is the hardest part of labor. At this point, many women begin to tire and the contractions come closer together and are more intense. At this time, the couple needs to be supported musically by selections that are designed to engage the attention of the mother, increase endorphin release, and assist the couple with rhythmic movement, cognitive focus, and breathing. The music should support very intense imagery, or fast, strong, rhythmic movement with little effort from the couple. It is important to keep in mind that the music does not have to be fast, but that it should be high in energy. Additionally, some women may require a return to slower relaxation and calming music to reduce anxiety and exhaustion, and increase coping strategies (DiCamillo, 2008; May et al., 1996). Mothers may not recall the presence of the music during this time, so it is important for the birthing partner or other labor support caregivers (**intrapartum** nurses, music therapist, doula) to be aware of her needs and adjust the music appropriately.

Music to support delivery should function as a focal point with selections having the highest level of energy. With each contraction, the woman will be pushing. This music should have a strong rhythmic focus that may serve to help the couple count beats while pushing. The musical phrases of the song or piece can also help focus the pushing; for example, the birth partner can instruct the mother to push through a particular phrase in the song, or the partner can support the pushing by singing the phrase or providing intense imagery.

At the moment of birth, or shortly thereafter, the intensity of the music should lessen to create a calm, relaxed, and welcoming environment. Returning to the music used during early labor, or music with similar characteristics, will support the delivery of the placenta and a return to a calm and nurturing environment. Once the family is alone together, special birth music can be played that represents messages of special meaning from the family to the new infant. The music selected should be significant to the parents and any older siblings. It should be a compilation of music deemed important by each family member in welcoming the new baby. Some examples include children's music, lullabies, or songs from the couple's wedding or special events (DiCamillo, 2008; May et al., 1996). Some birthing couples may choose to use the music selected for early labor, followed by a birth music compilation. Others may choose to integrate the two types: a song or two of special meaning at the birth, paired with relaxation music, and then followed by the significant birth music. The most important consideration is for the music therapist to personalize the experience for the couple's greatest usefulness and benefit.

Music Selection Organized by Stages of Labor and Delivery
(May, Young, & Conant, 1996)

Music CDs for use during labor and delivery are set up in five different categories to correspond with the various levels of intensity during labor and delivery. It is recommended that the CDs be color-coded and labeled for easy and quick reference. Use of mp3 players is highly encouraged.

Early labor – music is used to help store energy, decrease anxiety, and promote sleep if possible/necessary. It has been indicated to be most relaxing to the couple.

Active labor – music is moderately paced to encourage slow, smooth movement, but to maintain relaxation. Music has more stylistic changes and energy than during early labor.

Transition – music is fast and energizing, designed to engage the attention of the mother, increase endorphin release, and assist the couple with rhythmic movement, cognitive focus, and breathing.

Delivery/Pushing – highest energy music with a strong rhythmic focus that is used as a focal point. Couples can push through a sung phrase, count beats, or use very intense imagery.

Birth – following the birth, music promotes an atmosphere of special meaning from the parents to the infant. Music is significant to the parents/siblings and can be followed by relaxation music to assist the mother in post-birth procedures. The music can be anything that has a special meaning for the couple and conveys a positive message.

When creating the compilation CDs, there should be little space between selections, and few style, instrumentation, timbre, or dynamic changes. Multiple CDs for each phase/ stage of labor will ensure that there is enough variety and time to avoid the end of a song or CD in the middle of a contraction. The use of mp3 players (e.g., iPod) is an easy and convenient way for the music to be organized, to provide access to alternative music (if needed, particularly during the postpartum recovery), and for easy transport to the hospital. Some hospitals may provide playback equipment, but in most cases the birthing couple will have to provide their own portable playback equipment (e.g., boombox or docking station).

It is important for the music therapist to follow copyright laws and to ensure that the couple owns the original source of the music contained on the personalized labor and delivery and birth compilations (May et al., 1996). The music therapist can also provide preselected music for labor and delivery to the obstetrics unit. Inservice presentations to train the nursing staff on its appropriate use could be beneficial for those couples who did not participate in MTACB training but would like to have music or could benefit from additional forms of labor support behaviors.

Music Selection Organized by Desired Benefit
The Sound Birthing Music Categories
(reprinted with permission from *Sound Birthing*, DiCamillo, 2008)

Positive Focus: These programs are used during the early stage or at any time the birth mother needs music for emotional support (rather than physical support). It should not be played during transition, however, because the level of physical support is generally much greater and this music is not appropriate for that stage. It may have vocals and may be andante or moderato in tempo. This music may be effective in helping the mother to psychologically turn her birth process in a good direction by giving her emotional support, helping her to let go, and giving her renewal and confidence.

Meditation: These programs are used during any stage while the birth mother is in a reclining position or in the tub. Tempo is about 60–72 beats per minute.

Relaxation: 72–90 beats per minute, relaxing music is used typically during early and active tage.

Movement: These programs are used usually during the active stage while the birth mother is about 4–7 centimeters dilated. The music supports movement in any position—on the ball or upright. Selections are about 90–120 beats per minute. This music can be used well for Lamaze breathing or movement.

Imagery: These programs are usually used during the transition stage while the mother is 8–10 centimeters dilated. The music has a very relaxing quality yet is increasing in intensity with a tension-release feel; it is instrumental only and full in texture. The music is evocative of imagery and it can support the imagery techniques to be utilized by the birth mother. Selections are about 60–72 beats per minute.

Breathing Baby Down: These programs are used when the mother is breathing the baby down and pushing the baby after dilating completely. Instrumental music that is gentle yet has a supportive feel and steady beat is used. The music is about 72–120 beats per minute.

Birth Music: Played at the moment of birth, it is celebratory in naturo, followed by gentle birth songs with vocals.

Lullabies: These programs are played after the birth. Gentle lullabies are included on this CD. Selections are mellow in intensity, have text that is gentle and loving, and are about 72–100 beats per minute.

Following the delivery, the typical hospital stay for a vaginal birth is 2 to 3 days, followed by several weeks for a full recovery. As part of the MTACB consultation, the music therapist can share information with the couples on the significance of music on early development. There is a wide body of literature on infant-directed singing that can be useful in guiding parents as to the messages carried in infant play songs and lullabies and how singing to a baby supports developmental milestones (de l'Etoile, 2006a, 2006b; Trainor, 1996; Trehub, 1993, 2001, 2003; Trehub, Bull, & Thorpe, 1984; Trehub, Hill, & Kamenetsky, 1997; Trehub & Schellenberg, 1995; Trehub, Schellenberg, & Hill, 1997; Trehub & Trainor, 1998; Trehub, Unyk, & Trainor, 1993; Trevarthen & Aitken, 2001). For couples participating in MTACB, the music therapist can provide a home-based follow-up within the first 12 weeks to provide this information in greater depth than what was discussed during the final MTACB session. Some families may benefit from postpartum referrals to music therapy to address issues related to a difficult delivery, postpartum depression, health concerns of the newborn, or other high-risk situations (e.g., adolescent parenthood, unsupportive family environment), as well as stress and anxiety in general related to becoming a parent. Interventions should be based on the identified need, but some suggestions include appropriate postpartum environmental music (i.e., to support a calm, organized, and restful environment); stress reduction and relaxation strategies for the parents, infant, and siblings; and music-based parenting skills.

Considerations for MTACB and Cesarean Section

If a cesarean section delivery is necessary, the use of music will have to be altered to support this surgical procedure. Typically, a C-section is performed under regional anesthesia so the woman is awake and alert for the procedure. Listening to music may reduce anxiety and improve the satisfaction with regards to the procedure (Clark, 1986). Outcomes from a few studies have demonstrated reduced anxiety for women who listened to carefully selected recorded music with the patient selecting preference by style (Chang & Chen, 2005; Stein, 1991). One study predetermined the music; this music was culturally unfamiliar to the patients and the results did not indicate a significant reduction in anxiety (Reza, Ali, Saeed, Abul-Qasim, & Reza, 2007). The use of music listening by women during C-section has indicated greater satisfaction with the procedure and less anxiety than without music listening (Chang & Chen, 2005), as well as reduced perception of pain and use of pain medication (Ebneshahidi & Mohseni, 2008). These results suggest that music can be therapeutic during a cesarean section, but further research is warranted. Future research should reflect outcomes on both the mother's and infant's health, with diverse populations and strong methodology (Laopaiboon, Lumbiganon, Martis, Vatanasapt, & Somjaivong, 2009).

MTACB may also be beneficial for emergency delivery situations. In a documented case study, the patient and her husband had started training in music assisted childbirth when it was determined that an emergency induction was necessary due to pregnancy-induced hypertension. Due to her medical condition, the patient was not able to have an epidural for pain relief. The patient was able to use music throughout this critical, high-risk situation to manage her pain, stay relaxed and calm, and have a cognitive focus on something else. The medical staff also found the environment calm and relaxed due to the music (DiCamillo, 2000). This case study illustrates how music therapy can assist the birthing couple, even during an emergency situation. The following case study illustrates how a mother used music to create a desired environment for the birth of her child.

Case Study Example

Sarah and Max were scheduled for a cesarean section because their baby was in the breech position. For the last month prior to the C-section, Sarah had been listening daily to a prescribed music and meditation recording to assist her in relaxation exercises. Upon arrival at the hospital, Sarah was prepared for surgery and Max was instructed on how to gown and glove. As Sarah was wheeled into the surgery room, she noticed that the room was brightly lit and the sounds were loud and harsh. This was not the environment she had envisioned for the birth of her baby. Thinking quickly, she asked the obstetrician if she could bring her mp3 player with her into surgery. The obstetrician commented that she had never had such a request, but she did not think it would be a problem and consented. Max went back to the hospital room and brought the mp3 player to Sarah. As the preparation for surgery continued, Sarah placed the headphones into her ears, closed her eyes, and began to listen to her music and meditation recording. Due to her regular practice, Sarah was able to focus her attention on being relaxed and calm. The music and meditation recording helped make the transition to motherhood a more pleasant and positive experience for Sarah.

Hospitalization of Women During Pregnancy

Pregnancy can be described as a major life event that involves a multifaceted and extensive transition. Personal motivation, past experiences, self-identity, age, and level of education may be indicators of how a woman handles this situation. A high-risk pregnancy that requires hospitalization intensifies this life event and transition, creating opportunities for supportive services such as music therapy. When designing interventions for this population, the music therapist should consider three variables. First, the learning environment for the hospitalized pregnant woman is vastly different than for a woman experiencing a normal pregnancy. Second, the therapist should understand the woman's role in the hospital environment and how that affects her interactions, feelings, and relationships. Third, the therapist must know how to balance the woman's individual needs and desires with the medical requirements for her and her unborn child.

Hospitalization can complicate the emotional and physical changes a woman is already experiencing related to her pregnancy. In the literature there is little attention to the needs of hospitalized pregnant women (Kramer, Coustan, Krzeminski, Broudy, & Martin, 1986; Maloni, Chance, Zhang, Cohen, Betts, & Gange, 1993); however, based on the literature (Kramer et al., 1986; Loos & Julius, 1989; Maloni et al., 1993; White & Ritchie, 1984; Wohlreich, 1986) and clinical experience, there are trends in the physical and psychological well-being of the woman during the antepartum period.

Physical Characteristics

A range of physical characteristics can affect the antepartum woman in addition to those already present as a result of normal pregnancy. A common treatment for high-risk pregnancy is bed rest, defined as confinement to the bed for the complete day or a portion of the day (Maloni et al., 1993). During extended hospital bed rest, women have reported that they feel lethargic and restless. They also report that they sleep excessively, have difficulties breathing and getting comfortable, and experience nausea and dry mouth side effects from medication (e.g., magnesium sulfate).

Women on complete or partial bed rest have demonstrated more shortness of breath following exertion after the baby is born and more deep muscle soreness than postpartum women with normal pregnancies. Bed rest women have also reported difficulty going up and down stairs 1 week following delivery, as well as requiring support to walk or sit, and experiencing knee buckling and hesitation before walking (Maloni et al., 1993).

Grip strength and range of motion for bed rest women appear to remain normal. However, reoxygenation of muscle tissue for women on complete bed rest takes significantly more time to recover. This is particularly likely as the duration of bed rest is increased. Women on partial bed rest also experienced an increase in time to reoxygenate muscle tissue, although the results of one study were not significant (Maloni et al., 1993). Decreased overall weight gain for bed rest women, as well as decreased birth weight and estimated gestational age for the infants of these women, has also been noted (Maloni et al., 1993). Changes in her physical condition complicate matters for the hospitalized pregnant woman. However, the psychological and emotional issues may be more damaging to her copings skills, attachment to her baby, and postpartum recovery (Maloni et al., 1993).

Emotional Issues

Women may experience a variety of reactions to the diagnosis of a high-risk pregnancy. Due to the nature of the pregnancy, the doctor–patient relationship is intensified with more frequent visits. Confidence may decrease with feelings of incompetence and self-blame related to the shift from the ideal pregnancy to one with complications. The woman may be angry at herself or at the fetus, and feelings of guilt may complicate the anger. Anxiety is increased, related to the health of the fetus, possible negative outcomes, and other issues concerning the diagnosis of a high-risk pregnancy (Wohlreich, 1986). Such issues may include financial concerns due to lack of income or extra help required for childcare of other children (Maloni et al., 1993), as well as a strain on family relationships. Isolation is also a feeling associated with high-risk pregnancy, as bed rest is often prescribed whether it is at home or in the hospital (Wohlreich, 1986). Women hospitalized during pregnancy must cope with the emotional, physiological, and social changes associated with pregnancy, while also dealing with the stress of hospitalization (White & Ritchie, 1984). The complications of hospitalization may lead to unique emotional issues for these women.

Specific feelings identified by hospitalized antepartum women are indicative of loneliness, boredom, and powerlessness (Loos & Julius, 1989). Pregnancy and hospitalization are independently stressful; the combination of the two may elicit unique reactions to stress. The Antepartum Hospital Stressors Inventory (AHSI) (White, as cited in White & Ritchie, 1984) allows women to assign a degree of stress to possible situations from seven categories of stress specific to antepartum hospitalization: separation, environment, health status, self-image, emotions, family status, and communication with health professionals.

Based on the AHSI, women rated emotions and separation from home and family as causing the highest level of stress. Changing family circumstances, health concerns, and the women's self-image were rated as being somewhat stressful. The factors of stress remained the same for women who had extended hospitalizations (greater than 2 weeks); however, they experienced a significant increase in the intensity of the stress (White & Ritchie, 1984). A follow-up study found similar results with an additional indication that financial burdens from prolonged hospitalization contributed to their stress (Maloni et al., 1993).

Antepartum physical and psychosocial symptoms can be assessed using the Antepartum/Postpartum Symptoms Checklist (APSC) (Maloni et al., 1993). Women can indicate their level of severity (mild, moderate, severe, very severe) to 35 possible symptoms related to pregnancy and bed rest. Results from one study indicated a significant decrease in the number of symptoms experienced 1 week postpartum for women who had a normal pregnancy, but not for those who were on partial or complete bed rest. Also, the severity of the symptoms did not significantly decrease for those on bed rest. Moreover, these women also indicated more severe boredom during pregnancy than did women with a normal pregnancy (Maloni et al., 1993).

The length of hospitalization can also adversely affect women's level of compliance with medical care. Negative reactions to hospitalization can include removal of self from the hospital despite medical concerns for the safety of herself and/or the baby, refusal of medical attention, noncompliance with bed rest, symptoms of depression, and extended anger and frustration (Kramer et al., 1986). During a long hospitalization, a woman may develop feelings of attachment to the hospital staff and a level of comfort to her new environment. For some women, the prospect of caring for themselves and their new infant may be overwhelming (Wohlreich, 1986), despite the anticipated transition to motherhood and a return to their home environment. Intervention programs geared specifically for high-risk hospitalized pregnancies may be especially important (Kramer et al., 1986). Programs that address some of the unique concerns related to this difficult time in a woman's life could offer special support to women hospitalized for an extended amount of time.

Structuring supportive programs for the hospitalized antepartum woman may require a unique perspective from the typical hospital program and childbirth preparation education. In many cases, the hospitalized pregnant woman does not feel sick and may not feel as if she is the patient. Instead, it is the fetus that is compromised, receiving the majority of the medical attention (Wohlreich, 1986). Therefore, it is particularly important that the supportive service programs address these women in a manner that will help them understand the present and future value of participation.

High-Risk Teen Pregnancy

Pregnant teens experience multiple changes beyond those of typical adolescent development. In addition to adapting to the hormonal and bodily changes of puberty, the pregnant teen must also adapt to the additional hormonal and bodily changes associated with pregnancy (Shaller, 2001). The fear and anxiety associated with these changes, in addition to the chronic stress of the teen's life, may place the young woman and her baby at risk. In teens under 16 years of age, there may be an increased risk for life-threatening conditions such as **toxemia**, hypertension, anemia, nutritional deficiencies, **abruptio placenta**, and prolonged labor (Hechtman, 1989).

Experiences of sexual victimization and domestic violence appear to correlate with substance use. For the pregnant teen, these experiences can result in a lack of, or late entry into, prenatal care; lower weight gain during pregnancy; lower infant birth weight; and poor health and psychological outcomes for the infant (Kirby, 2002; Renker, 2002; Soto, n.d.). If the teen does not receive adequate prenatal health care, she and her baby are at greater risk for perinatal mortality, neonatal mortality, or infant prematurity (Martin et al., 1998). These threatening conditions may be the result of the increased anxiety and psychological stress that pregnant teens experience (Winslow, 1986).

Higher levels of anxiety, stress, and depression are found among pregnant women who are young in age, financially insecure, minimally educated, and lacking in social support (Winslow, 1986). This is especially true in teens that have a history of sexual abuse and victimization (Osborne & Rhodes, 2001). Difficulty in expressing, communicating, and releasing stress and anxiety have been found to lead to prolonged labor, an increase in obstetric complications, and poorer infant conditions at the time of birth and immediately after (McKinney, 1990). These health risks can exasperate the teen's sense of fear, anxiety, and insecurity regarding pregnancy and childbirth.

Health risks and inadequate prenatal care put the pregnant adolescent at greater risk for experiencing significant trauma and the possible loss of her child. Fifty-four percent of pregnant teens experience early perinatal loss either in the form of miscarriage or abortion (Wheeler & Austin, 2000). As a result, these young women experience a sense of loss, guilt, sadness, and confusion, as well as a yearning for the infant, feelings of anger and despair, **hypochondria**, self-destructive behavior, and long-term denial (Wheeler & Austin, 2000). There is often little recognition and socioemotional support provided to the teen regarding this traumatic loss experience. Family members and friends may feel relieved concerning the loss and be unable to emotionally empathize with the grieving teen. A bereaved teen often finds that her peers are unable or unwilling to talk about her grief experience. As a result, the bereaved teen lacks the necessary emotional and social support of her peers when she needs it the most.

The lack of support in relation to teen perinatal loss can lead to an intense sense of loneliness and emptiness that generates a heightened desire to become pregnant again. Approximately 30–35% of previously pregnant teens will experience a repeat pregnancy within 1 year, while 40–50% will become pregnant for a second time within the second year (Coard, Nitz, & Felice, 2000). Bereaved teens also tend to have greater levels of anxiety and fear over time (Balk & Corr, 2001). The combination of bereavement and pregnancy during adolescence may leave the teen more prone to psychosomatic symptoms, contribute to poorer mother and child outcomes, and exacerbate feelings of depression.

Depression is common among the pregnant and parenting teen high-risk population. Present in more than 50% of pregnant teens, depression is a significant concern for both the young mother and her child, the majority of whom are not formally diagnosed or recipients of professional treatment (Hudson et al., 2000; Martin et al., 1998). Physiological markers of depression in teen mothers include chronic accelerated heart rates, greater relative right frontal EEG activity, elevated cortisol and catecholamine levels, and lower vagal tone (Field et al., 2000). Depression within the teen mother commonly results in emotional unavailability and increased self-preoccupation. These young mothers often display flat affect, an irritable mood, and depressed mood state, and are less vocal with and responsive to their infants (Field et al., 2000).

Age is a significant factor in the severity of depressive symptomology. Young pregnant teens have greater symptoms of depression (Hudson et al., 2000; Martin et al., 1998). They feel more self-conscious than older teens about their condition, particularly with their peers (Balk & Corr, 2001). The fear of being different or misunderstood prevents younger teens from seeking the emotional and social support they need from their peers during pregnancy. As a result, they may not receive the supports needed the most while experiencing a significant life change such as pregnancy.

It is common for teens who experience multiple, significant external and internal risk factors during childhood and adolescence to experience depression, particularly if the loss experience is recent (Wheeler & Austin, 2000). Pregnant teens experience greater levels of depression and higher levels of social and physical grief when a significant loss occurs within 2 years of their pregnancy (Wheeler & Austin, 2000). In the teen pregnancy population, depression correlates with other emotional factors of well-being, such as low self-esteem, loneliness, and lack of social support. When the pregnant teen has positive social support, she has more positive self-esteem, reduced feelings of loneliness, and lower levels of depression (Hudson et al., 2000). Self-esteem for the pregnant teen is also related to her ability to parent effectively and the extent of her knowledge about parenting and child development (Hudson et al., 2000).

Therapeutic interventions to reduce depression provide pregnant women, regardless of age, with a stronger internal resource to cope with the daily external stressors they encounter. Music therapy during pregnancy can provide social support to remediate the negative indicators of depression. The systematic application of music interventions can also effectively modify affective responses, promote the development of coping mechanisms, and support social functioning. The music therapist can also teach the teen parent(s) and other caregivers how to use music to interact with, stimulate, and calm the infant in developmentally appropriate ways.

The Associative Network Theory (Bower, 1981) proposes that thoughts and memories are associated with a particular mood and are stored together in the brain. According to this model, when an individual is in a particular mood state (e.g., sad), thoughts and memories previously associated with that mood state will be more readily available in the brain. Due to this association, it is more difficult to access memories and thoughts when they are of a different mood state than the one currently felt (Bower, 1981). A reciprocal relationship between negative thinking and depression may exist in that the accessibility to negative thoughts increases with depression and thus produces more negative thoughts (Teasdale, 1983). In addition, mood state can affect the level of executive functioning within the brain. Depression has been found to cause impairments in executive functioning tasks such as problem solving, strategic processing, planning and complex behaviors, and continuous revision of strategies and behavior based on environmental changes (Elliott, 1998). Depression and the resulting impairments in executive cognitive functioning often lead to a compromise in social functioning (Elliott, 1998). For the pregnant teen, depression can compound the social isolation she may already be experiencing and can contribute to a decreased sense of competence associated with the planning and preparation aspects of pregnancy. Addressing depression in the pregnant teen is of great importance, not only for her own well-being but also for that of her infant. Infants born to depressed teen mothers have higher heart rates and cortisol, norepinephrine, epinephrine, and dopamine levels that signify greater infant stress and depression (Field, Pickens, Fox, Nawrocki, & Gonzalez, 1995; Field et al., 2000).

The application of therapeutic interventions within a social context, particularly a group setting, provides pregnant and parenting teens with opportunities to learn and practice healthy behaviors, positive social interactions, and experiences in social competence (Yalom, 1995). Music can be used to enhance the social microcosm and alter mood states, both of which are beneficial outcomes for the pregnant or parenting teen. Music experiences are structured to require the use of fundamental social skills such as establishing eye contact, turn taking, leading, following, and problem-solving. Pregnant or parenting teen members are actively involved in the therapeutic medium, creating and changing the music in ways that allows negative feelings and their associated behaviors to be explored in the process of creating meaningful and positive desired mood states and thus behaviors. The function of the music in this context follows a classical conditioning paradigm (de l'Etoile, n.d.). Since participation in music experiences results in desirable positive emotional responses, teen group members are able to improve their attitude, disposition, and perception. Pregnant and parenting teens are simultaneously engaging in the music, experiencing positive emotions, and interacting appropriately with others teen parents/mothers and their health care providers. In accordance with the classical conditioning paradigm, after repeated pairings the positive emotions become associated with the social interaction instead of the music. Social interactions may then become a valued behavior, which transfers outside of the therapy group. Within this model the unifying component is the music, which helps group members to explore relationships, experience emotions, understand their problems, and achieve changes in attitude and behavior (Bright, 1995). Given that social behavior is governed by emotional experiences and cognitive processes, improvements in social adjustment through music therapy interventions may be revealed by an increase in problem solving and consequential thinking (Ulfarsdottir & Erwin, 1999). For the pregnant or parenting teen, these emotional, social, and cognitive changes can lead to more positive outcomes overall in terms of teen parent and infant well-being.

Systematically applied music therapy interventions can also facilitate interaction between affect and cognition. The concept commonly used by music therapists to alter mood states is known as the **iso principle** (Shantin, 1970). The iso principle is a technique in which the characteristics of the music are initially matched to the patient's mood state, thus validating his or her current emotion. The musical characteristics are then altered to support a change in mood state in the direction of the desired therapeutic goal. Music-based affect modification is built on evidence that music evokes affective-mood reactions, including emotional peak experiences, and can alter a listener's mood. In addition, affective-mood responses to music are accompanied by physiological changes in the individual. Consideration for the patient's existing mood, musical preference, cultural expectations, and arousal needs also to play a role in determining affective-mood responses to a given musical stimulus (Thaut, 1989). For individuals with depression, music mood induction techniques have been found to be wholly effective in modifying affect (Clark, 1983; Field et al., 2000). Moreover, music has been shown to increase emotional state toward greater positivity and promote greater levels of arousal and present-mindedness (Sloboda, 1999).

Applying the iso principle to a pregnant and parenting teen is beneficial to both the teen and the infant. For example, when a young infant wakes multiple times during the night, the inexperienced teen mother can easily become exasperated, as do many new mothers regardless of their age. With the knowledge that teens often have an underdeveloped coping mechanism and heightened levels of stress, we can understand how a teen mother could walk into her crying infant's room in a state of great distress and angst. It would be difficult to successfully soothe a crying infant when the soother herself is in a state of distress with pressured/rapid speech and elevated heart and respiration rates. The new teen mother could sing lullabies taught during group music therapy sessions as she walked down the hallway to her infant's room. Humming a familiar and soothing lullaby, the teen mother can change her own mood and physiological state so that she can then be in a present and calm state of mind for her infant, therefore capable of successfully applying the lullaby to soothe her infant.

Music Therapy and Antepartum Hospitalization

Music therapy services implemented on the antepartum hospital unit can address the specific issues related to hospitalization and high-risk pregnancy and provide an avenue for socialization. The music therapist can create a learning environment based on theories of adult learning that are meaningful to the woman and her situation by offering her a choice of interventions and explaining the immediate and long-term benefits relevant to her situation. Understanding the role of the therapist in adult learning can assist the music therapist in structuring the interventions to be interesting, engaging, supportive, independent, and appropriate to the pregnant woman's learning needs. Music therapy may be an appropriate intervention due to its adaptability to the individual, situation, and environment.

Referral

Referrals for music therapy in obstetrics can be made for patients on the outpatient units who are interested in MTACB or have an identified need (e.g., emerging high blood pressure, anxiety, or depression) that could benefit from music therapy services. The referral process is reflective of the requirements and procedures determined by the specific hospital. In some facilities, a doctor's order is required for all referrals, often generated by nursing and medical staff, patients, and families, or other therapists and professional staff (e.g., therapeutic recreation specialist, social worker, or chaplain). However, some specific units have a standing order for music therapy, as the services have been identified as beneficial to the patients on the unit based merely on the diagnosis. This is often the case on the antepartum unit.

A standing order for music therapy means that individual referrals may or may not be given by the unit staff, but that the music therapist is at liberty to offer services to patients and to prioritize the needs of the individuals based on the music therapist's expertise. When a standing order for music therapy exists, strong communication with unit staff and a regular presence on the unit are necessary to ensure consistent provision of services and the continued recognition by hospital staff of the efficacy and viability of the services.

A successful music therapy program on the antepartum unit can be facilitated by scheduling regular days and times to offer services on the unit. At one hospital, the part-time music therapist allocates two afternoons a week to visit the unit to offer services to patients. Nursing staff know when to expect the music therapist and often make suggestions as to which patients can most benefit or be receptive to music therapy services. Prior to arriving on the unit, or immediately upon arrival, the music therapist obtains a unit census to learn of any new admissions, discharges, or transfers to other units (e.g., the birth of a baby requires the transfer of the mother to the postpartum or maternal care unit, or, in the case of a premature birth, the potential discharge of the patient and the admittance of the baby on the Neonatal Intensive Care Unit).

Consultation with nursing staff is a prerequisite to visiting any patients. Priority is given to patients already on the music therapist's caseload, followed by recommendations for additional patients. Patient status can change quickly on the antepartum unit, and it is important for the music therapist to be aware of such changes. The nursing staff can also alert the music therapist to the patients who may be sleeping, who have requested not to be disturbed, or who would be inappropriate to visit on a particular day. In addition to consulting with the nursing staff, it can be beneficial to quickly review the patient's chart prior to making a visit.

Approach to the Patient

The style of approach used by the music therapist can be indicative of the acceptance or dismissal of the music therapist and potential services. Music therapy on the antepartum unit most often are individual sessions conducted in the comfort of the patient's room. Frequently the patient's door is closed. Consideration for the patient's privacy and autonomy, as well as respect for the patient, is of the utmost importance. The music therapist should not enter the patient's room without permission. Etiquette requires a soft but audible knock on the door to draw the patient's attention, but not loud enough to awaken the patient if she should be sleeping. When the patient has responded to the knock, the music therapist can open the door, introduce him or herself, and ask permission to enter the patient's room.

During the initial interaction, the patient may invite the therapist in or may ask for more information regarding the service. Patients are frequently interrupted in their room and some may find additional interruptions bothersome or unnecessary. Introductions facilitated by the nursing staff may be helpful, particularly if a patient has previously indicated resistance to recommended interventions or services. If the patient does not understand or have knowledge about music therapy, he or she may be skeptical and may hesitate to consider or accept music therapy services. To alleviate some of these concerns, following the initial introductions, the music therapist briefly describes the types of services available and the potential benefits of participating in music therapy, allowing opportunities for the patient to ask questions. If the patient is receptive, the music therapist can proceed with a session. If the patient is not receptive, the music therapist can leave contact information and written information about music therapy, and offer to return at a later date.

Written information specific to the antepartum unit is helpful in making patients aware of the benefits of music therapy during their hospitalization and provides more detail than what can be described in the initial contact. Such information can be given to the patient to independently review. References to research, specifics regarding intervention strategies, and outcomes can be described. Many hospitals have wireless Internet service, and some patients have their own laptop computers available. Information can refer to websites (including the hospital's website) for those individuals who are interested in pursuing indepth knowledge of music therapy. A flyer can be left for patients who are not in their rooms or are unavailable when the therapist attempts to visit. In addition, a brochure could be provided in the hospital information packet that some hospitals give to patients upon admission. One hospital music therapy program created a tabletop placard that was left in the antepartum rooms so patients had some familiarity of music therapy services prior to the music therapist's first visit.

The receptiveness to music therapy services and the desire for knowledge may be related to cultural aspects of the patient, such as age, education, socioeconomic status, and ethnicity. Moreover, the medical condition, **prognosis**, and length of hospitalization can impact a patient's openness to music therapy. Most patients admitted on the antepartum unit are high functioning individuals who feel relatively healthy other than the risks associated with their pregnancy. Consideration for the patient's cultural aspects will allow the music therapist to appropriately modify his or her initial approach. For example, adolescent antepartum patients may be sensitive and distrustful of adults in the medical setting and may feel uncomfortable and overwhelmed in the environment. The music therapist who is sensitive to the adolescent antepartum patient will modify the initial approach to be relative to the patient's age, speaking to her without judging her situation, and building initial rapport that may not at first involve information about intervention strategies.

On the other end of the spectrum, some patients may ask questions that demonstrate a desire for supplementary information. For example, one patient was a doctor from a Middle Eastern country whose husband was doing a residency in the United States. While she was not practicing in the United States, she was quite knowledgeable about her situation and was interested in the more technical aspects of music therapy in the medical setting. The initial approach with this patient involved an indepth conversation about research and areas of practice in music therapy and how it would be viewed in the woman's home country. This discussion led to a beneficial therapeutic relationship for the duration of her hospitalization.

A Music Therapy Program with At-Risk Pregnant Teens

The Perinatal Family Support Center of the Department of Obstetrics/Gynecology and Pediatrics of Evanston Northwestern Healthcare established the *Connections for Pregnant and Parenting Teens Program* to provide pregnant and parenting teens with support services. The Connections Program was established in 1998 to promote patient wellness and self-care by reducing socio-emotional and environmental obstacles to health care (Cardone, Soto, & Altfeld, n.d.). The program was supported by a generous grant from the Auxiliary of Evanston Northwestern Healthcare and continues to this day.

The Connections Program offers various modalities of support including prenatal care, education on neonatal development, labor and delivery, nutrition, infant care and normal development, community resources, mentoring, and music therapy. As of 2005, the Connections Program served approximately 125 culturally diverse teens each year, comprised of African American (42%), Latina (29%), Caucasian (19%) and multiracial/other (9%) adolescents. Approximately 35% of these teens have been referred for psychotherapeutic services in previous years (Soto, n.d.).

A bilingual social worker in the Perinatal Family Support Center of the Department of Obstetrics/Gynecology and Pediatrics of Evanston Northwestern Healthcare completes a psychosocial assessment for every pregnant teen or new teen mother under the age of 18 to determine eligibility for the Connections Program. Nurses or physicians of the outpatient clinic, the inpatient antepartum unit, or the level three Infant Special Care Unit (ISCU) can refer teens that they consider high-risk to the Connections Program. A teen's parents, friends, community agency, high school, or the teen herself can also make a referral to the program. Referral criteria for the teen include having an unplanned pregnancy or history of multiple pregnancies; having a suspected history of abuse or trauma, mental illness (e.g., depression), substance use, or loss; exhibiting a developmental delay or other parenting ability concerns; lacking support or experiencing family conflict; demonstrating high anxiety; being homeless, transient, or living in poverty; or exhibiting other risk factors. Services provided by the Connections Program, including music therapy, are free of charge to the patient.

Pregnant teens with three or more psychosocial risk factors are automatically referred to music therapy by the social worker. An individual music therapy assessment session is then scheduled for the patient's next prenatal visit. If the patient is on the antepartum unit or her infant is in the ISCU, the music therapist consults with the teen's medical providers and completes an assessment within 48 hours.

The initial interaction and introduction to music therapy is important in order to establish trust and rapport. Pregnant teens may feel uncomfortable and overwhelmed in the hospital environment, unsure about trusting adults in such a setting. With this understanding, the music therapist approaches each teen with respect, kindness, and honesty. On occasion, it is best for the social worker to facilitate an introduction between the pregnant teen and the music therapist. This can be especially helpful when there is a language barrier, or when the social worker has already had one or two sessions with the patient and established rapport. Pregnant teens are often considered at-risk adolescents in terms of their environmental context, life experience, and psychosocial well-being. Work experience in adolescent psychiatric settings and with high-risk youth can help prepare the music therapist for working with pregnant teens because of several similarities: the environmental context of these youth, their developmentally-based needs, and emotional struggles such as depression and low self-esteem.

Once introductions are made, a room in the outpatient clinic is selected for the music therapy session. If the pregnant teen is a patient on the antepartum unit of the Women's Hospital, the session is provided in the comfort of her room. It is important to ask the pregnant teen whether she would like her door open or closed for the duration of the session. The music therapist provides each patient with a brief introduction to music therapy and the ways in which it could benefit her and her unborn infant. The patient is encouraged to ask questions about music therapy at any time during this conversation. Following the introductory conversation about music therapy, a discussion develops regarding the patient's specific needs and concerns, as she is comfortable sharing. This discussion often includes information about the teen's current living situation, physical condition, emotional state, support system, and desire to parent. The music therapist helps the teen determine her intention and goals for music therapy.

The physical assessment of the pregnant teen includes her due date, gestational week, prior pregnancy history, nutritional intake, current complications or risk factors, symptoms of discomfort or pain, and energy level. Detailed medical information is provided in each patient's medical chart. This information is gathered in addition to the patient's perspective to ensure that medical and physical components of the music therapy assessment are complete and accurate. Consultation with the patient's nurse or physician occurs as needed to inform the music therapist of the patient's current medical situation and needs prior to treatment sessions.

Assessment of the pregnant teen's emotional state includes self-report, clinical observation, and consultation with additional psychosocial service providers within the hospital setting, such as social work, psychiatry, and spiritual care. Both social work and psychiatry complete their own psychosocial assessments and implement additional assessment measures available on the hospital computerized charting system. The emotional state section of the music therapy assessment includes the teen's current mood state and recent mood changes; related thoughts and life perspective; emotions related to her pregnancy; fears/concerns about labor, delivery, and motherhood; and sense of attachment to her baby.

Throughout the assessment interview and session, the music therapist observes the patient's affective state, level of eye contact, body language, repetitive movements, dynamics of speech, and gestures related to her pregnancy overall and in direct relationship to the conversation at any given time. Gestures related to pregnancy include the patient rubbing/holding her belly, gesturing/looking toward the baby in the womb when referring to it, responding to movement of the baby, and speaking directly to her unborn child. Each pregnant teen is asked to describe her current level of involvement with her friends, how this has changed since becoming pregnant, her feelings regarding any friendship changes, and the recreational activities she and her friends participate in.

Individual outpatient and inpatient music therapy treatment goals and objectives are based on a patient-centered approach and are congruent with the patient's needs identified during the assessment. Common music therapy interventions include music-facilitated relaxation (MFR), music combined with therapist-directed imagery, and learning of lullabies and lullaby songwriting. An abuse history can be a contraindication for the use of MFR techniques. Music combined with therapist-directed imagery is used with pregnant teens when appropriate and is designed to promote attachment to the unborn infant or to rehearse for labor/delivery. Lullaby songwriting is done through a "fill-in-the-blank" template and allows the teen to express her wishes and hopes for the unborn infant's immediate and future life experience. In many cases, the wishes/hopes that the teen holds for her unborn child are those things that she never received herself or perhaps desires for herself.

In addition to individual music therapy services, group music therapy sessions are also provided as part of the Connections Program evening educational classes. These classes are designed for pregnant teens, their partners, or their labor and delivery support person. Participants for these groups are recruited by the social worker; groups are open to all pregnant teens that receive prenatal care and supports through the Connections Program. Prior to the first group session, the music therapist consults with the social worker regarding the expected number of attendees and their therapeutic issues and needs. An average of 4 to 10 pregnant teens, all at different stages of pregnancy, attends each group. Sometimes parenting teens attend the group sessions. Group goals are determined by the purpose of the group and common needs of all attendees. Education, coping, and psychosocial support are common needs/goal areas of the pregnant or parenting teen group. Goals are designed based on one of two levels of group therapy interventions in the short-term outpatient and inpatient hospital setting. The level of Supportive, Activities-Oriented Music Therapy includes goals such as improving social interactions and impulse control, and the level of Reeducative, Insight- and Process-Oriented Music Therapy includes goals such as identification and expression of feelings, increased problem solving, and behavioral change (Wheeler, 1983). These goals are achieved through interventions of therapeutic group drumming/instrumental improvisation, lyric analysis, group songwriting, and teaching of developmentally appropriate infant interactions to music.

Assessment

Due to the acute nature of the hospital setting and the changing medical needs of the antepartum patient, hospital assessments are generally brief and may be repeated in some form upon each visit. The music therapist must be aware that the needs and desires of the patient may change from session to session based on the patient's and infant's medical stability and anticipated length of stay, and on who is present at the time of each session. These changes inform the treatment direction and may make a traditional assessment format irrelevant. For example, during the initial visit, the music therapist determines that the patient is feeling isolated and lonely. The music therapist determines that the goal should be to increase social interaction. However, when the therapist arrives for the next session several days later, she discovers that the patient has had visitors for several hours each of the last 2 days. She is no longer showing signs of being lonely, thus the initial assessment is not reflective of current needs. On the third visit, the patient's family is present and the direction of the intervention takes an entirely different perspective.

A formal antepartum music therapy assessment document ought to facilitate gathering of pertinent information that can be generalized to various treatment directions. Pertinent information includes the history of the patient related to the hospitalization, such as admit date, anticipated length of stay, reason for hospitalization, and medications. Additional assessment information relates to other therapies, education (e.g., childbirth training), health and medical concerns of the fetus, family situation, and patient's current psychological state. Assessment information can be gathered from the patient's chart, nursing report, other therapists, and the patient. The assessment should also depict the needs of the individual patient in order to set relevant goals.

Sometimes the assessment will be used as a tool to familiarize the therapist with the preferences and general interests of the patient for music therapy, rather than to set treatment goals. Due to the changing needs, medical stability of the patient, and length of stay, treatment goals may change from session to session. A formal assessment session allows the therapist to build rapport and trust with the patient in order to design intervention strategies that best fit her desires, abilities, and interests.

The assessment can also provide an opportunity to create objective data for outcome measures. Patient outcomes illustrate individual benefits of music therapy, as well as provide cumulative data that can be used in program summary reports. Depending on the acuity of the patients seen on the antepartum unit, the assessment outcomes may be the only objective measures that are consistently tracked. These outcomes can document the effectiveness of short-term interventions (i.e., single session) among multiple patients. Documentation of the assessment summary is frequently integrated into the hospital chart note following the initial visit. An example of an assessment summary is provided in Figure 1.

Music Therapy Assessment
Obstetrics and Gynecology – Antepartum Unit

Patient Name: ______________________ **Patient Number**: ________________

Assessment Date: ______ **Admit Date**:______ **Expected Days in Hospital**: _________

Gestational Age: ______________ **Expected Delivery Date**: _______________

Reason for Hospitalization:
premature labor ________ ruptured membranes ________ pre-eclampsia ___________

placenta previa _______ gestational diabetes ________ demise of pregnancy ________

Diagnosis/Care Requirements: ____
____

Restrictions: ____
____

Medical History: ____
____
____

Personal History: ____
____
____

Family-Friends/Relationship: **Visitation Availability**:

Family-Friends/Relationship	Visitation Availability
________________________	daily 3-4x/wk 1x/wk less
________________________	daily 3-4x/wk 1x/wk less
________________________	daily 3-4x/wk 1x/wk less
________________________	daily 3-4x/wk 1x/wk less
________________________	daily 3-4x/wk 1x/wk less

Identified Concerns:

______ pain ______ lethargic ______ excessive sleep ______ uncomfortable

______ breathing difficulties ______ motor weakness ______ anger

______ guilt ______ decreased confidence ______ isolation

______ anxiety (related to ____)

Stress Scale (White & Ritchie, 1984):

Separation	(low)	1	2	3	4	5 (high)
Environment	(low)	1	2	3	4	5 (high)
Health Status	(low)	1	2	3	4	5 (high)
Self-Image	(low)	1	2	3	4	5 (high)
Emotions	(low)	1	2	3	4	5 (high)
Family Status	(low)	1	2	3	4	5 (high)
Communication w/ Staff	(low)	1	2	3	4	5 (high)
Financial Concerns	(low)	1	2	3	4	5 (high)
Physical	(low)	1	2	3	4	5 (high)

Music Preferences:

1. *Styles of music*:

Country	(low)	1	2	3	4	5 (high)
Pop	(low)	1	2	3	4	5 (high)
Rock	(low)	1	2	3	4	5 (high)
Folk	(low)	1	2	3	4	5 (high)
Jazz	(low)	1	2	3	4	5 (high)
Blues	(low)	1	2	3	4	5 (high)
Rap	(low)	1	2	3	4	5 (high)
New Age	(low)	1	2	3	4	5 (high)
Classical	(low)	1	2	3	4	5 (high)
Gospel	(low)	1	2	3	4	5 (high)
Rhythm & Blues	(low)	1	2	3	4	5 (high)
Inspirational	(low)	1	2	3	4	5 (high)

***Favorite artists/songs*:**

____

____

____

***3. Familiarity w/ infant/children's songs*:**

___ good _______somewhat ______nothing

List: ____

____

***Recommended Music Therapy Goals*:**

____

____

____

Suggested Intervention Strategies:

_ Relaxation Techniques ______ Leisure Activities

_ Music and Rhythm Activities to be shared with baby pre- & post-birth ______ Isolated Movement

_ Music Therapy Assisted Childbirth ______ Birth Tape

Therapist Comments:

____
____
____

Figure 1. Music Therapy Assessment, Obstetrics and Gynecology – Antepartum Unit

Goals and Interventions

Little has been written on appropriate supportive intervention services for the hospitalized antepartum patient. Much of the music therapy literature addressing pregnancy focuses on labor and delivery. One study (Winslow, 1986) discussed music therapy techniques specifically for antepartum hospitalization. Individual sessions were provided three to four times a week to learn and practice relaxation techniques. Group sessions involving antepartum women, as well as postpartum women with their babies, were provided weekly to encourage socialization and support. Case study examples demonstrated that women felt a greater sense of control during music therapy sessions. These women experienced less anxiety and improved mental and physical state, resulting in better compliance with their medical treatment (Winslow, 1986).

Documented music therapy interventions (Winslow, 1986) correspond to the recommendations for nursing (Loos & Julius, 1989), such as forming small groups to encourage expression of feelings and to create a sense of support to reduce the sensation of loneliness, to provide structure to the woman's day to help normalize the environment, and to set realistic individual goals that encourage self-care and autonomy to decrease the sensation of powerlessness. Women hospitalized on bed rest identified seven themes during antepartum support groups: methods they used for coping, concerns they had about family, negative outcomes, relationships with caregivers, psychosocial losses associated with bed rest treatment, side effects of medical treatments, and concerns for their infant's and their own safety (Maloni & Kutil, 2000). Group music therapy sessions may provide women with a chance to discuss their situation, to laugh with one another, to be supportive, even to commiserate with each other. Building a support network between the women themselves will encourage a greater sense of autonomy and control.

Each woman's restrictions must be considered when organizing a group music therapy session on the antepartum inpatient unit. Most patients are limited in the amount of time they can sit up, be out of bed, or be off the unit. Securing a location on or near the antepartum unit is highly recommended to allow for a greater number of patients to attend the session and to ensure quick medical availability should the need arise. Consultation with nursing and medical staff will inform the music therapist as to which patients are appropriate for inclusion. Criteria for inclusion will be determined by the medical staff and/or nurses on duty; however, general considerations include medical stability when following recommended medical protocols, ability to sit up for an extended amount of time (e.g., restrictions for 20–30 minutes of wheelchair time), and individual considerations for emotional stability (e.g., a patient experiencing a demise of pregnancy may need to be individually assessed for her emotional availability to cope with other pregnant individuals).

Collaboration with the nursing staff is important for the successful group music therapy experience on the antepartum unit. Depending on the unit census, group sessions may be a regularly scheduled occurrence or take place only when it is relevant to the individual patients. The music therapist, based on his or her experiences with individual referrals on the unit, may initiate facilitating a group music therapy session. Regardless of the frequency of the group sessions, interdisciplinary collaboration with the nursing and medical staff will be critical to the successful implementation. Prior to contacting any of the patients, the music therapist should consult with nursing staff to ensure that only those who have medical permission to be included are invited to attend. The music therapist should also learn which patients will require nursing assistance to transfer from their room to the group location, and which patients the music therapist can assist. Once the music therapist has a list of potential group participants, he or she can visit each patient and invite her to attend.

The music therapist will have to secure a location on or near the unit that can accommodate the potential number of patients and the medical equipment they require (e.g., wheelchairs and IV poles). The room should be set up prior to bringing in patients. Patients will most likely be brought individually to the session, so the music therapist should plan for this transition time by playing background music, having a co-therapist present to facilitate initial interactions, or collaborating with nursing staff to transport patients to the session location, where the music therapist can greet them.

Techniques that can be incorporated into an antepartum group session include low impact movement (such as range-of-motion exercises), instrument playing, singing, and songwriting. Therapists could facilitate group sessions in which each woman works on her own compilation birth tape. During this process, the women can be directed to use this intervention to make positive associations between the music and the events surrounding the impending birth of their infants and to share these feelings with others in the group. The example below illustrates how songwriting allowed the women to express concerns and thoughts in a humorous and musical manner.

Case Study Example

The holidays were quickly approaching and the antepartum unit was full. The music therapist had been working with four or five women on an individual basis. A frequent topic of discussion was the impending holidays and the impact of their hospitalization on their families and themselves. In discussion with the nursing staff, it was determined that a group session would be appropriate for the inpatients. A group was planned for the next day that the music therapist was available, and a time was secured. It was determined that the session would occur in the unit conference room and that it would be limited to 20–30 minutes, the amount of time allocated for these patients to be up and out of their beds.

On the day of the session, the music therapist arrived on the unit to prepare. She consulted with the nurse on duty to ascertain that the group session was still feasible and which patients would be allowed to attend. Some patients had nursing procedures to be completed prior to attending the group session. The nurse agreed to invite these patients to the music therapy session when she was attending to their needs, and to transport them to the session. While the nurse attended to these patients, the music therapist proceeded to set up the room. Once the room was ready, the music therapist visited the patients and invited them to attend the session. Those patients who were most medically stable and at the lowest level of bed restriction were invited first to ensure that time was available for the session.

Secular holiday music was played as background music while the patients were transported into the conference room. As each patient arrived, she was introduced to the patients already in the room. By the time everyone had been brought to the conference room, the patients had become quite comfortable with one another.

The music therapist had a number of different intervention techniques planned to facilitate the group socialization, but was also aware that the primary focus was to allow for the socialization that these women had so keenly expressed a desire for during their individual music therapy sessions. When a lull in the conversation occurred, the music therapist offered some suggestions as to what they could do. The women were most interested in singing holiday tunes. The music therapist passed out the hospital songbooks and pointed out the holiday section. Singing holiday songs contributed to further discussion of their situations and how they were coping. The discussion created a natural transition to a songwriting activity. The following piggyback song was created, and its performance brought tears of joy and laughter to the group members.

Proud Pregnancy
(to the tune of "Proud Mary")

Left my home for UIHC
Want to go back home every night and day
And I always lose one minute of sleeping
When they wake me up to check my vitals

CHORUS:
Big wheels keep on moving
Everybody here is grooving
Rolling, rolling, rolling on back home

Ate a lot of Jello, both red and green
Wiped a lot of gel off; my tummy's clean
But I am so bored watching cable TV
Highlight of my day is a wheelchair ride

CHORUS

If I went home to my family
Bet I'd find the laundry and dishes all dirty
I don't have to worry 'cause I'm just a-hanging
In my hospital room at UIHC

CHORUS

The session was intended to last between 20–30 minutes. The music therapist was aware of the passing time. As the patients laughed and sang, the nurse visited periodically and gave permission for the session to continue. After 30 minutes, the nurse checked several patients' blood pressure and told us to continue. The session lasted for 45 minutes. One patient commented, "I thought I was the only one on the unit. It was so nice to meet you and realize that I am not alone."

Individual sessions are more typical on the antepartum unit. These are held in the context of the patient's room and can involve a variety of techniques common to medical music therapy and modified for the antepartum patient. Music therapy techniques frequently used with antepartum patients are relaxation with and without visualization, songwriting, improvisation, teaching the patient to play a musical instrument, and facilitating the development of positive parent–newborn music-based interactions.

Relaxation, sometimes paired with guided visualizations, is a common technique used with antepartum patients, similar to those described for MTACB. Sessions involve working with the mother to practice various relaxation techniques paired with music. During the assessment session, the music therapist and patient determine her musical preferences from a wide selection of recorded music. To help the patient differentiate between selections, a Likert scale could be used. Once the patient has determined a style of music she finds appropriate, the music therapist either can provide live music in the same general style or can use a recording selected by the patient.

Music Preference Likert Scales

Hate	Don't Like	It's OK	Like	Love
1	2	3	4	5
Boring	Sleepy	Calm	Exciting	Gives Me a Headache
1	2	3	4	5
Bad	OK	Good		
1	2	3		

Autogenic relaxation is a technique that requires the patient to visualize relaxing the suggested parts of the body. It is the recommended method to guiding the antepartum patient to a more relaxed state. **Progressive muscle relaxation** experiences are contraindicated due to the tightening and loosening of muscles that could be potentially dangerous to the mother and her fetus. The music therapist must carefully observe the patient's respiration rate, heart rate (if monitored), and facial expressions during the relaxation experience and must discontinue if the patient is demonstrating any adverse responses. Once the patient is feeling physically relaxed, with the patient's permission, the music therapist can proceed to a visualization experience. For some patients, this can be accomplished in a single session; for others, it may take several sessions before the patient can successful participate in the relaxation experience.

Guided visualization is recommended only for patients who can successfully reach a relaxed state and maintain a stable heart and respiration rate. Guided visualizations provide specific directions to describe the imagery that creates a mental representation of a positive space. Guided visualizations can be predetermined by the therapist and selected by the patient, or they can be created by the patient and facilitated, if necessary, by the music therapist. Music imagery techniques (e.g., Bonny Method of Guided Imagery and Music) are not recommended without advanced training and purposeful patient goals appropriate for the antepartum patient.

Positive guided visualizations can offer patients on the antepartum unit an opportunity to mentally escape their hospital room. Many hospital rooms are sparingly decorated. During music therapy sessions, many of these women have shared their frustration with staring at the same four walls, the one picture, the television, and the view of the parking lot or roof from their hospital room window. The music therapist can provide a description of a patient-selected image to facilitate the visualization or describe a more standard image. Some women have expressed difficulty imaging a place with only positive associations that is different than their hospital room. Colorful pictures depicting simple scenes, such as a wicker rocker on a porch or a sandy beach, have been helpful in assisting the patient to visualize a different space.

Autogenic relaxation paired with music creates an association of a relaxed physical state and the music. With practice, the desired effect is that the music will initiate the relaxation response in the patient when she is feeling agitated, lethargic, isolated, physically uncomfortable, or when she could otherwise benefit. For one woman, pregnant with sextuplets, the relaxation exercises with the music therapist were so successful that she requested that the music therapist visit when her husband came. One night a week, for several weeks, the music therapist visited the couple on the antepartum unit to provide relaxation and guided visualization instruction. Both found the intervention beneficial, and the husband reported using it at home in the evenings to help him relax.

Measuring changes in the patient before and after the relaxation experience can help her measure changes in her physical and emotional state. Patients have used their relaxation training for pain control when they were getting daily shots (e.g., steroids to help the infant's lungs develop), during childbirth, prior to scheduled C-section, or to remain calm when experiencing contractions due to premature labor. The music therapist can provide the patient with a recording of the music, with and without a relaxation script, so the patient can have this tool available even when the music therapist is not present. The following box is an example of a form a patient would use to document her relaxation experience.

Documentation of the Relaxation Experience

How Do You Feel?

Place a mark on the line to show how you feel at this time for each of the following word pairs.

Relaxed	______________________	Tense
Calm	______________________	Anxious
Good	______________________	Bad
Comfortable	______________________	Uncomfortable
Safe	______________________	At risk

Before relaxation ______
After relaxation ______

Other common intervention techniques for the antepartum patient and her family include songwriting, improvisation, or playing instruments. Family visits can be challenging, particularly if there are young children. Occupying children in a small hospital room is difficult and may increase the stress level of the parents. In their efforts to be close to their mother, children may bump her or climb on her, contributing to discomfort or pain. Family-centered music therapy can facilitate music-based experiences for the children and parents to create a positive and bonding experience.

Music-based techniques can be an effective family-centered intervention to which family members of all ages and abilities can contribute. One family had three small children who regularly visited their mother on the antepartum unit. They lived more than an hour away from the hospital, so their visits usually lasted several hours. Instrument playing, improvisation, and songwriting provided excellent techniques for the family to interact, communicate, and share a positive experience. Families can participate in songwriting experiences that allow them to express their feelings. Music-based techniques create an avenue for family members, including the patient, to express fears, excitement, or frustration related to the patient's hospitalization and the arrival of the baby.

Music can be a mode of communication for the antepartum patient. The music therapist can facilitate and record songwriting experiences for the patient to send to her spouse, partner, or children. Original compositions or piggyback songs are a way to send messages to families. For example, a mother can record herself singing lullaby songs that her children can listen to as they go to sleep. This allows the patient, and her children, to feel connected to the everyday events that are occurring in her home while she is hospitalized. Music can also create a connection with the unborn child.

The music therapist can facilitate music-based activities to promote positive parent–newborn interactions. Some patients have enjoyed creating a compilation recording to be played for the baby. This gives mothers an opportunity to positively associate with the baby as they work with the therapist to compile a series of songs that have a special meaning and positive message that they would like to convey to the baby. This can also incorporate the patient's children and other family members. One mom used the compilation recording as a way to learn traditional songs that she could sing to her baby after he was born. This woman was in her mid-40s, pregnant with her first child. She was hospitalized for placenta previa and was apprehensive about both her own and the baby's health. She had expressed to the music therapist that she did not remember any of the traditional songs. They worked together to create a compilation CD for the patient to listen to while she was restricted to bed rest. This patient found the recording helped her to connect and bond with her baby before his birth and to have more positive associations in the face of her fear for the baby's and her safety. Following the birth of the baby, the patient used the recording in the nursery with her son and felt more confident singing to him with the support of what had become familiar stimuli.

Outcomes and Documentation

Documentation of clinical outcomes is important in any therapeutic environment. In the hospital setting, programs can be retained or eliminated based on the presence or absence of articulate documentation of therapeutic outcomes. Nursing and medical personnel are invested in the overall well-being of their patients on the obstetrics units and clinics. To this end, they may be interested in services that address the medical, emotional, and physical needs of their patients. However, evidence-based intervention strategies that demonstrate objective outcomes will be the ones that are retained and utilized with pregnant women and their families.

Clinical outcomes for individual and group music therapy sessions can be measured by rating forms, surveys, or other standardized measurement tools utilized by the music therapy program and hospital. Non-pharmacological pain and anxiety reduction can be evaluated through pre/post music therapy intervention rating forms. Many hospitals use a computerized charting system to record all patient information and medical treatment provided. Computerized systems maintaining medical records allow clinicians of various disciplines easy access to the reports from other disciplines serving their patient. Documentation of music therapy services in a format accessible to all disciplines provides the music therapist with an opportunity to more widely communicate the efficacy of the service.

Informal reporting of outcomes to nursing staff will further facilitate the dissemination of intervention effectiveness. Additionally, staff inservices and regular reports submitted to unit administrators can enhance awareness of music therapy services and increase referrals. Session outcomes should also be discussed with the patient so she can be informed as to the benefits of the intervention strategies and can share suggestions for adaptations or modifications with the therapist.

Conclusion

Music therapy in obstetrics complements the nursing and family-centered strategies being implemented in hospitals and birthing centers. Growth in clinical practice and research has been limited, but collaboration between music therapists and nursing professionals will enhance the future application of music therapy as an intervention strategy for inpatient obstetrics units and outpatient clinics. Clinical interventions that are supported by theoretical models will integrate medical treatment, nursing protocols, and music therapy techniques. Such evidence-based practices will situate music therapists as an integral part of the obstetrics team and allow for continuity of care from the beginning of a pregnancy to post birth.

Music therapy assisted childbirth and music to support cesarean section delivery have been the most researched to date. Recommendations for future research supporting music therapy assisted childbirth have been made since the 1980s; however, there has been only sporadic progress in the literature. The increasing prevalence of family-centered maternity care and the use of music as a complementary nursing strategy in labor and delivery suggest clinical relevance for MTACB. Suggested areas for future research include the length of labor, the quantity of medication used, emotional responses and level of satisfaction with the birth experience, levels of anxiety during childbirth, and amount and effectiveness of movement during labor (May et al., 1996). In addition, research should examine the therapeutic function of music within the context of labor and delivery to ensure reliable music recommendations based in both science and clinical practice. Through these efforts, MTACB may become an integral part of labor and delivery with more predictable and significant outcomes.

Music therapy with women hospitalized during pregnancy can alleviate the negative psychosocial and physical effects of a high-risk pregnancy, prolonged hospitalization, and postpartum concerns. Applying clinical research to this area will further substantiate music therapy's effectiveness. In addition, positive mother–infant interactions can be developed prior to the birth of the baby and can continue post-birth, possibly easing the transition between the mother and infant's hospitalization and home. Interventions that encourage mother–infant interaction may increase the mother's sensitivity and responsiveness to her infant, as well as her self-efficacy as a mother. Such interventions may also be appropriate for mothers experiencing postpartum depression (de l'Etoile, 2009). Consideration for high-risk outpatient services, such as support services for pregnant teens, is also an area for future development. Little research has been done thus far on the implications and benefits of music therapy for pregnant/parenting teens and their children. Areas of research interest include the influence of music therapy on teen and infant depression/stress levels, compliance with prenatal care (such as attending scheduled visits), perceived parental competence and sense of self, psychosocial well-being, infant developmental outcomes, and infant/child abuse rates.

Music therapy in obstetrics has demonstrated positive trends in both clinical applications and research over the last 25 years. While the research and clinical opportunities have been limited, music therapy for both the typical and high-risk pregnancy continues to show promise as a cost-effective and family-centered intervention strategy. As health care costs continue to rise and patients look for better health care options, intervention strategies that are positive, non-invasive, and beneficial for physical, physiological, and psychosocial health will have prominence in the medical setting. Music therapy is one such intervention strategy. Clinical practice in obstetrics, paired with solid current research, will situate music therapy as an integral component of the pregnancy and labor and delivery process.

References

Adams, E. D., & Bianchi, A. L. (2008). A practical approach to labor support. *Journal of Obstetric, Gynecologic, & Neonatal Nursing, 37*, 106–115.

Allison, D. (1991). Music therapy at childbirth. In K. Bruscia (Ed.), *Case studies in music therapy* (pp. 530–545). Philadelphia: Barcelona.

Bacon, J. L. (2000). Adolescent sexuality and pregnancy. *Current Opinion in Obstetrics and Gynecology, 12*(5), 435–437.

Balk, D. E., & Corr, C. A. (2001). Bereavement during adolescence: A review of research. In M. S. Stroebe, R. O. Hansson, W. Stroebe, & H. Schut (Eds.), *Handbook of bereavement research: Consequences, coping and care* (pp. 119–218). Washington, DC: American Psychological Association.

Belenky, M., Clinchy, B., Goldberger, N., & Tarule, J. (1997). *Women's ways of knowing: The development of self, voice, and mind (10th anniversary ed.)*. New York: Basic Books.

Blanc, A. K., Tsui, A. O., Croft, T. N., & Trevit, J. L. (2009). Patterns and trends in adolescents' contraceptive use and discontinuation in developing countries and comparisons with adult women. *International Perspectives on Sexual and Reproductive Health, 35*(2). Retrieved October 8, 2009, from http://www.guttmacher.org/pubs/journals/3506309.html

Bower, G. H. (1981). Mood and memory. *American Psychologist, 36*, 129–148.

Bright, R. (1995). Music therapy as a facilitator in grief counseling. *The art and science of music therapy: A handbook* (pp. 309–323). Newark, NJ: Harwood Academic.

Browning, C. A. (2000). Using music during childbirth. *Birth, 27*(4), 272–276.

Browning, C. A. (2001). Music therapy in childbirth: Research in practice. *Music Therapy Perspectives, 19*(2), 74–81.

Byrne, B. (2000). Relationships between anxiety, fear, self-esteem, and coping strategies in adolescence. *Adolescence, 35*, 201–215.

Capogna, G., Camorcia, M., & Stirparo, S. (2007). Expectant fathers' experience during labor with or without epidural analgesia. *International Journal of Obstetric Anesthesia, 16*, 110–115.

Cardone, I., Soto, M., & Altfeld, S. (n.d.). *Connections for pregnant and parenting teens: A program of the Perinatal Family Support Center, The Department of Obstetrics/Gynecology and Pediatrics.* Unpublished program summary paper presented at Evanston Hospital In-service, of Evanston Northwestern Healthcare, Evanston, IL.

Chang, S., & Chen, C. (2005). Effects of music therapy on women's physiologic measures, anxiety, and satisfaction during cesarean delivery. *Research in Nursing and Health, 28*(6), 453–461.

Clark, D. M. (1983). On the induction of depressed mood in the laboratory evaluation and comparison of the velten and musical procedures. *Advances in Behaviour Research and Therapy, 5*, 27–49.

Clark, M. E. (1986). Music therapy-assisted childbirth: A practical guide. *Music Therapy Perspectives, 3*, 34–41.

Clark, M. E., McCorkle, R. R., & Williams, S. B. (1981). Music therapy-assisted labor and delivery. *Journal of Music Therapy, 28*(2), 88–100.

Coard, S. I., Nitz, K., & Felice, M. E. (2000). Repeat pregnancy among urban adolescents: Sociodemographic, family, and health factors. *Adolescence, 35*, 193–200.

Condon, J. (2006). What about dad? Psychosocial and mental health issues for new fathers. *Australian Family Physician, 35*(9), 690–692.

de l'Etoile, S. K. (n.d.). *Therapeutic applications of music*. Unpublished handout: Music Therapy Practicum, MU486, Colorado State University, Fort Collins, CO.

de l'Etoile, S. K. (2006a). Infant behavioral responses to infant-directed singing and other maternal interactions. *Infant Behavior and Development, 29*, 456–470.

de l'Etoile, S. K. (2006b). Infant-directed singing: A theory for clinical intervention. *Music Therapy Perspectives, 24*(1), 22–29.

de l'Etoile, S. K. (2009, March). Infants and postpartum depression. Paper presented in S. K. de l'Etoile & D. Hanson-Abromeit, *Infants' Auditory & Vocal Development: Implications for Clinical Practice* Continuing Music Therapy Education workshop at the American Music Therapy Association Great Lakes Region Conference, Minneapolis, MN.

DiCamillo, M. (2000). Music therapy assisted childbirth: A case study of an emergency high-risk pre-term delivery due to pregnancy-induced hypertension. *International Music Society for Prenatal Development Review, 12*(2), 8–13.

DiCamillo, M. (2008). *Sound Birthing program materials*. Rancho Santa Margarita, CA: Sound Birthing.

Durham, L., & Collins, M. (1986). The effect of music as a conditioning aid in prepared childbirth education. *Journal of Obstetrics, Gynecologic, & Neonatal Nursing, 15*(3), 268–270.

Ebneshahidi, A., & Mohseni, M. (2008). The effect of patient-selected music on early postoperative pain, anxiety, and hemodynamic profile in cesarean section surgery. *Journal of Alternative & Complementary Medicine. 14*(7), 827–831.

Ecenroad, D., & Zwelling, E. (2000). A journey to family-centered maternity care. *The American Journal of Maternal/Child Nursing, 2*(4), 178–186.

Elfenbein, D. S., & Felice, M. E. (2003). Adolescent pregnancy. *The Pediatric Clinics of North America, 50*, 781–800.

Elliott, R. (1998). The neuropsychological profile in unipolar depression. *Trends in Cognitive Sciences, 2*, 447–454.

Everett, K. D., Bullock, L., Gage, J. D., Longo, D. R., Geden, E., & Madsen, R. (2006). Health risk behavior of rural low-income expectant fathers. *Public Health Nursing, 23*(4), 297–306.

Federico, G. F., & Whitwell, G. E. (2001). Music therapy and pregnancy. *Journal of Prenatal and Perinatal Psychology and Health, 15*(2), 299–311.

Field, T., Pickens, J., Fox, N. A., Nawrocki, T., & Gonzalez, J. (1995). Vagal tone in infants of depressed mothers. *Development and Psychopathology, 7*, 227–231.

Field, T., Pickens, J., Prodromidis, M., Malphurs, J., Fox, N., Bendell, D., Yando, R., Schanberg, S., & Kuhn, S. (2000). Targeting adolescent mothers with depressive symptoms for early intervention. *Adolescence, 35,* 381–414.

Finkel, M. (1995). Focus on adolescent pregnancy and childbearing: A bit of history and implications for the 21st century. *Bulletin of the New York Academy of Medicine, 72*(2), 500–511.

Gallup-Black, A., & Weitzman, B. C. (2004). Teen pregnancy and urban youth: Competing truths, complacency, and perceptions of the problem. *Journal of Adolescent Health, 34*(5), 366–375.

Geden, E. A., Lower, M., Beattie, S., & Beck, N. (1989). Effects of music and imagery on physiologic and self-report of analogued labor pain. *Nursing Research, 38*(1), 37–41.

Gentz, B. A. (2001). Alternative therapies for the management of pain in labor and delivery. *Clinical Obstetrics & Gynecology, 44*(4), 704–732.

Geronimus, A. T. (2003). Damned if you do: Culture, identity, privilege, and teenage childbearing in the United States. *Social Science & Medicine, 57,* 881–893.

Gold, R., Kennedy, B., Connell, F., & Kawachi, I. (2002). Teen births, income inequality, and social capital: Developing an understanding of the casual pathway. *Health & Place, 8,* 77–83.

Gonzalez, C. E. (1989). The music therapy-assisted childbirth program: A study evaluation. *Pre- and Peri-Natal Psychology Journal, 4*(2), 111–124.

Goroszeniuk, T., & Morgan, B. M. (1984). Music during epidural caesarean section. *Practitioner, 228*(1390), 441–443.

Gramling, L., Hickman, K., & Bennett, S. (2004). What makes a good family-centered partnership between women and their practitioners? A qualitative study. *Birth, 31*(1), 43–48.

Hanser, S. B., Larson, S. C., & O'Connell, A. S. (1983). The effect of music on relaxation of expectant mothers during labor. *Journal of Music Therapy, 20*(2), 50–58.

Harner, H. M., Burgess, A. W., & Asher, J. B. (2001). Caring for pregnant teenagers: Medicolegal issues for nursing. *Journal of Obstetric, Gynecologic, & Neonatal Nursing, 30*(2), 139–147.

Hechtman, L. (1989). Teenage mothers and their children: Risks and problems: A review. *Canadian Journal of Psychiatry, 34,* 569–575.

Hottenstein, S. E. (2005). Continuous labor support: Creating optimal birth experiences through theory-driven nursing care. *Association of Women's Health, Obstetric and Neonatal Nurses Lifelines, 9*(3), 242–247.

Hsieh, Y.-H., Kao, C.-H., & Gau, M.-L. (2006). The lived experience of first-time expectant fathers whose spouses are tocolyzed in hospital. *Journal of Nursing Research, 14*(1), 65–73.

Hudson, D. B., Elek, S. M., & Campbell-Grossman, C. (2000). Depression, self-esteem, loneliness and social support among the adolescent mothers participating in the new parents' project. *Adolescence, 35,* 445–453.

Hunter, L. L., & Hunter, B. C. (1994). *Music therapy-assisted childbirth times two.* Paper presented at the 45th Annual Conference of the National Association for Music Therapy. Orlando, FL.

Jacoby, M., Gorenflo, D., Black, E., Wunderlich, C., & Eyler, E. (1999). Rapid repeat pregnancy and experiences of interpersonal violence among low-income adolescents. *American Journal of Preventive Medicine, 16*(4), 318–321.

Kees, N. (2000). *Group work with adolescents.* Colorado State University Text: Group Guidance and Counseling ERIC Document 651 (93–95). Fort Collins, CO.

Kershner, J., & Schenck, V. (1991). Music therapy-assisted childbirth. *International Journal of Childbirth Education, 6*(3), 32–33.

Kirby, D. (2002). Antecedents of adolescent initiation of sex, contraceptive use, and pregnancy. *American Journal of Health Behavior, 26*(6), 473–485

Koniak-Griffin, D., & Turner-Pluta, C. (2001). Health risks and psychosocial outcomes of early childbearing: A review of the literature. *Journal of Perinatal & Neonatal Nursing, 15*(2), 1–17.

Kramer, P. D., Coustan, D., Krzeminski, J., Broudy, D., & Martin, C. (1986). Hospitalization on the high-risk maternity unit a pilot study. *General Hospital Psychiatry, 8*, 33–39.

Laopaiboon, M., Lumbiganon, P., Martis, R., Vatanasapt, P., & Somjaivong, B. (2009). Music during caesarean section under regional anaesthesia for improving maternal and infant outcomes. *Cochrane Database of Systematic Reviews (2): CD006914.*

Lesser, J., & Escoto-Lloyd, S. (1999). Health-related problems in a vulnerable population: Pregnant teens and adolescent mothers. *Nursing Clinics of North America, 34*(2), 289–299.

Lesser, J., Koniak-Griffin, D., & Anderson, N. L. (1999). Depressed adolescent mothers' perceptions of their own maternal role. *Issues in Mental Health Nursing, 20*, 131–149.

Logsdon, M. C., Birkimer, J. C., Ratterman, A., Cahill, K., & Cahill, N. (2002). Social support in pregnant and parenting adolescents: Research critique, and recommendations. *Journal of Child and Adolescent Psychiatric Nursing, 15*(2), 75–83.

Loos, C., & Julius, L. (1989, January/February). The client's view of hospitalization during pregnancy. *Journal of Obstetrics, Gynecologic, & Neonatal Nursing, 18*(01), 52–56.

Maloni, J. A., Chance, B., Zhang, C., Cohen, A. W., Betts, D., & Gange, S. J. (1993). Physical and psychosocial side effects of antepartum hospital bed rest. *Nursing Research, 42*(4), 197–203.

Maloni, J. A., & Kutil, R. M. (2000). Antepartum support group for women hospitalized on bed rest. *MCN American Journal Maternal/Child Nursing, 25*(4), 204–210.

Maloni, J. A., & Ponder, M. B. (1997). Fathers' experience of their partners' antepartum bed rest. *Image: The Journal of Nursing Scholarship, 29*(2), 183–188.

March of Dimes. (2008). Cesarean birth for medical reasons. Retrieved July 1, 2008, from http://www.marchofdimes.com/pnhec/240_1031.asp

Martin, C. A., Hill, K. K., & Welsh, R. (1998). Adolescent pregnancy, a stressful life event: Cause and consequence. In T. W. Miller (Ed.), *Children of trauma: Stressful life events and their effects on children and adolescents* (pp. 141–160). Madison, CT: International Universities Press.

Martin, J. A., Hamilton, B. E., Sutton, P. D., Ventura, S. J., Menacker, F., Kirmeyer, S., & Mathews, T. J. (2009). Births: Final data for 2006. *National Vital Statistics Reports, 57*(7). Retrieved July 16, 2009, from http://www.cdc.gov/nchs/data/nvsr/nvsr57/nvsr57_07.pdf

Martin, L. T., McNamara, M. J., Milot, A. S., Halle, T., & Hair, E. C. (2007). The effects of father involvement during pregnancy on receipt of prenatal care and maternal smoking. *Maternal and Child Health Journal, 11*, 595–602.

May, K. E., Young, H. E., & Conant, R. P. (1996). *Music therapy assisted childbirth: A manual to accompany CMTE training*. Austin, TX: CCC Music Therapy Center.

Mayo Clinic Staff. (2007, April). *Stages of labor. Baby, it's time!* Retrieved July 2, 2008, from http://www.merck.com/mmhe/sec22/ch260/ch260b.html

McDowell, C. R. (1966). Obstetrical applications of audioanalgesia. *Hospital Topics, 44*, 102–104.

McKinney, C. H. (1990). Music therapy in obstetrics: A review. *Music Therapy Perspectives, 8*, 57–60.

Merck. (2003, February). *Labor.* Retrieved July 2, 2008, from http://www.merck.com/mmhe/sec22/ch260/ch260b.html

Merriam, S. B., & Caffarella, R. S. (1999). *Learning in adulthood* (2nd ed.). San Francisco: Jossey-Bass.

Montgomery, K. S. (2003). Nursing care for pregnant adolescents. *Journal of Obstetric, Gynecologic, & Neonatal Nursing, 32*(2), 249–257.

Murkoff, H. E., & Mazel, S. (2008). *What to expect when you're expecting* (4th ed.). New York: Workman.

The National Women's Health Information Center. (n.d.). Prenatal tests. In *Healthy pregnancy.* Retrieved September 25, 2010, from http://www.womenshealth.gov/pregnancy/you-are-pregnant/prenatal-care-tests.cfm#c

Olson, S. L. (1998). Bedside musical care: Applications in pregnancy, childbirth, and neonatal care. *Journal of Obstetrics, Gynecologic, & Neonatal Nursing, 27*(5), 569–575.

Osborne, L. N., & Rhodes, J. E. (2001). The role of life stress and social support in the adjustment of sexually victimized pregnant and parenting minority adolescents. *American Journal of Community Psychology, 29*(6), 833–849.

Parrott, F. G. (n.d.) *Music Therapy Assisted Childbirth: Birthing on a good note.* Unpublished manuscript from Broadlawns Medical Center, Des Moines, IA.

Passino, A. W., Whitman, T. L., Borkowski, J. G., Schellenbach, C. J., Maxwell, S. E., Keogh, D., & Rellinger, E. (1993). Personal adjustment during pregnancy and adolescent parenting. *Adolescence, 28*, 97–122.

Phillips, C. (2003a). *Family-centered maternity care.* Sudsbury, MA: Jones and Bartlett.

Phillips, C. (2003b). *Phillips + Fenwick, The Women's Healthcare Company, Vision, Mission, Philosophy.* Retrieved September 23, 2010, from http://www.pandf.com/website/vision.htm

Phumdoung, S., & Good, M. (2003). Music reduces sensation and distress of labor pain. *Pain Management Nursing, 4*(2), 54–61.

Renker, P. R. (2002). Keeping safe: Teenagers' strategies for dealing with perinatal violence. *Journal of Obstetrics, Gynecologic, & Neonatal Nursing, 32*(1), 58–67.

Rentschler, D. D. (2003). Pregnant adolescents' perspectives of pregnancy. *The American Journal of Maternal/Child Nursing, 28*(6), 377–383.

Reza, N., Ali, S. M., Saeed, K., Abul-Qasim, A., & Reza, T. H. (2007). The impact of music on postoperative pain and anxiety following cesarean section. Middle East Journal of Anesthesiology, 19(3), 573–586.

Robinson, A. (2002). Music therapy and effects on laboring women. *Kentucky Nurse, 50*(2), 7.

Sammons, L. N. (1984). The use of music by women during childbirth. *Midwifery, 29*(4), 266–270.

Sauls, D. J. (2004). The labor support questionnaire: Development and psychometric analysis. *Journal of Nursing Measurement, 12*(2), 123–132.

Sauls, D. J. (2006). Dimensions of professional labor support for intrapartum practice. *Journal of Nursing Scholarship, 38*, 36–41.

Shaller, J. L. (2001) *Adolescent pregnant and parenting: A phenomenon in need of exploration and therapeutic intervention.* Unpublished paper for Colorado State University. Ft. Collins, CO.

Shantin, L. (1970). Alteration of mood via music: A study of the vectoring effect. *Journal of Psychology, 75*, 81–86.

Sloboda, J. (1999). Music—where cognition and emotion meet. *The Psychologist, 12*, 450–455.

SmithBattle, L. (2000a). Developing a caregiving tradition in opposition to one's past: Lessons from a longitudinal study of teenage mothers. *Public Health Nursing, 17*(2), 85–93.

SmithBattle, L. (2000b). The vulnerabilities of teenage mothers: Challenging prevailing assumptions. *Advances in Nursing Science, 23*(1), 29–40.

Soto, M. (n.d.) *The face of the Latina pregnant teen.* Unpublished handout for presentation at Evanston Hospital In-service, of Evanston Northwestern Healthcare, Evanston, IL.

Spear, H. J. (2004). A follow-up case study on teenage pregnancy: "Havin' a baby isn't a nightmare, but it's really hard." *Pediatric Nursing, 30*(2), 120–125.

Spear, H. J., & Lock, S. (2003). Qualitative research on adolescent pregnancy: A descriptive review and analysis. *Journal of Pediatric Nursing, 18*(6), 397–408.

Stein, A. M. (1991). Music to reduce anxiety during cesarean birth. In C. Dileo, (Ed.), *Applications of music in medicine* (pp. 179–190). Washington DC: National Association for Music Therapy.

Stevens-Simon, C., & Lowy, R. (1995). Teenage childbearing: An adaptive strategy for the socioeconomically disadvantaged or a strategy for adapting to socioeconomic disadvantage? *Archives of Pediatric & Adolescent Medicine, 149*, 912–915.

Teasdale, J. D. (1983). Negative thinking in depression: Cause, effect, or reciprocal relationship? *Advances in Behaviour, Research, and Therapy, 5*, 3–25.

Thaut, M. H. (1989). Music therapy, affect modification, and therapeutic change: Towards an integrative model. *Music Therapy Perspectives, 7*, 55–62.

Trainor, L. J. (1996). Infant preferences for infant-directed versus non-infant directed playsongs and lullabies. *Infant Behavior and Development, 19*, 83–92.

Trehub, S. E. (1993). The music listening skills of infants and young children. In T. J. Tighe & W. J. Dowling (Eds.), *Psychology and music: The understanding of melody and rhythm* (pp. 161–176). Hillsdale, NJ: Lawrence Erlbaum Associates.

Trehub, S. E. (2001). Musical predispositions in infancy. In R. J. Zatorre & I. Peretz (Eds.), *The biological foundations of music. Annals of the New York Academy of Sciences, 930*, 1–16. New York: New York Academy of Sciences.

Trehub, S. E. (2003). The developmental origins of musicality. *Nature Neuroscience, 6*, 669–673.

Trehub, S. E., Bull, D., & Thorpe, L. A. (1984). Infants' perception of melodies: The role of melodic contour. *Child Development, 55*, 821–830.

Trehub, S. E., Hill, D. S., & Kamenetsky, S. B. (1997). Parents sung performance for infants. *Canadian Journal of Experimental Psychology, 51*, 385–396.

Trehub, S. E., & Schellenberg, G. (1995). Music: Its relevance to infants. In R. Vasta (Ed.), *Annals of Child Development, 11*, 1–24. New York: Jessica Kingsley.

Trehub, S. E., Schellenberg, G., & Hill, D. (1997). The origins of music perception and cognition: A developmental perspective. In I. Deliege, & J. Sloboda (Eds.), *Perception and cognition of music* (pp. 103–128). Hove, United Kingdom: Psychology Press.

Trehub, S. E., & Trainor, L. J. (1998). Singing to infants: Lullabies and play songs. In C. Rovee-Collier, L. P. Lippsitt, & H. Hayne (Eds.), *Advances in infancy research, 12*, 43–77. Stamford, CT: Ablex.

Trehub, S. E., Unyk, A. M., & Trainor, L. J. (1993). Adults identify infant-directed music across cultures. *Infant Behavior and Development, 16*, 193–211.

Trevarthen, C., & Aitken, K. J. (2001). Infant intersubjectivity: Research, theory, and clinical applications. *Journal of Child Psychology Psychiatry, 42*(1), 3–48.

Ulfarsdottir, L. O., & Erwin, P. G. (1999). The influence of music on social cognitive skills. *The Arts in Psychotherapy, 26*, 81–84.

Wheeler, B. (1983). A psychotherapeutic classification of music therapy practices: A continuum of procedures. *Music Therapy Perspectives, 1*(2), 8–16.

Wheeler, S. R., & Austin, J. (2000). The loss response list: A tool for measuring adolescent grief responses. *Death Studies, 24*, 21–34.

White, M., & Ritchie, J. (1984). Psychological stressors in antepartum hospitalization: Reports from pregnant women. *Maternal-Child Nursing Journal, 13*(01), 47–56.

Wielgos, M., Jarosz, K., Szymusik, I., Myszewska, A., Kaminski, P., Ziolkowska, K., & Przybos, A. (2007). Family delivery from the standpoint of fathers—Can stereotypes of participant or non-participant father be fully justified? *European Journal of Obstetrics & Gynecology and Reproductive Biology, 132*, 40–45.

Winslow, G. A. (1986). Music therapy in the treatment of anxiety in hospitalized high-risk mothers. *Music Therapy Perspectives, 3*, 29–33.

Wohlreich, M. W. (1986). Psychiatric aspects of high-risk pregnancy. *Psychiatric Clinics of North America, 10*(1), 53–68.

Yalom, I. D. (1995). *Interpersonal learning. Theory and practice of group psychotherapy.* New York: Basic Books.

Zwelling, E., Johnson, K., & Allen, J. (2006). How to implement complementary therapies for laboring women. *American Journal of Maternal Child Nursing, 31*(6), 364–370.

Zwelling, E., & Phillips, C. R. (2001). Family-centered maternity care in the new millennium: Is it real or is it imagined? *Journal of Perinatal and Neonatal Nursing, 15*(3), 1–12.

CHAPTER 3

Intensive Care Unit (ICU)

Jessica Shaller Gerweck
Xueli Tan

The Intensive Care Unit (ICU) is a dynamic tapestry of sounds, sights, smells, and sensations. These sensory experiences in the ICU are often noxious and stress-inducing for the patient, the family, and the highly specialized, interdisciplinary medical team dedicated to providing care. Many hospital administrators and medical staff concerned with ICU outcomes acknowledge and accept that noxious environmental stimuli (Almerud & Petersson, 2003; Bonny 2002a, 2002b), stress (Lee, Chung, Chan, & Chan, 2005; Medina, 2005), and inadequate communication (Dowling & Wang, 2005; Gentling, Grady, & Mattox, 2005; Lederer, Goode, & Dowling, 2005; Medina, 2005) negatively impact outcomes for ICU patients.

Studies investigating the environmental, communicative, and psychosocial needs of family members in adult ICU settings reveal emerging themes related to the experience of family members awaiting the outcome for their loved one. The incidence of a critical illness has a profound effect on family members, threatening their stability, resources, and coping abilities (Abott, Sago, & Breen, 2001; Lopez-Fagin, 1995; Medina, 2005). Recent research findings support the hypothesis of a reciprocal relationship between family satisfaction and patient outcomes (Lam & Beaulieu, 2004; Medina, 2005).

Efforts in the ICU setting that increase communication, improve support systems, and create friendlier environments result in greater patient and family satisfaction and a reduced sense of frustration (Dowling & Wang, 2005; Lederer et al., 2005). For example, implementation of the Critical Care Family Assistance Program (CCFAP), created to address the needs of family members in ICU settings, resulted in reduced family stress levels at an equal, inverse ratio to the percentage that communication increased (Dowling & Wang, 2005). Furthermore, the CCFAP demonstrates that interdisciplinary models focused on providing support, promoting communication, and reducing stress levels of families in ICU settings result in positive patient outcomes (Gentling et al., 2005; Medina 2005). Administrators and ICU staff of the hospitals where the CCFAP studies took place agreed that care of the patient is improved by a family-focused, interdisciplinary approach in ICU settings (Gentling et al., 2005; Guntupalli, McCaffree, Vender, Clary, & LoCicero, 2005; Lederer et al., 2005).

Recent literature estimates 80% of Americans will experience an ICU event in their lifetime, either as the patient, a family member, or a friend (Dowling & Wang, 2005). Both nurses and music therapists, for decades, have championed the use of music in the ICU to address patient and family needs. In fact, initial investigations on the therapeutic uses of music for critically ill patients were grounded in many of the same theories and anecdotal findings in medical settings. Furthermore, initial research studies conducted by ICU nurses investigating the effects of music on ICU patients used taped music listening programs designed by a professional music therapist as the independent variable of their studies. Helen L. Bonny, PhD, CMT, creator of the Bonny Method of Guided Imagery and Music (BMGIM), conducted one of the first research studies on the use of music listening in the critical care setting. The study investigated the effects of taped music listening programs designed by Bonny on ICU patients. Bonny refined these taped programs and expanded them with guidelines for use by nurses and physicians in medical settings. These tapes were marketed as *Music Rx* (Bonny, 1983b) and utilized by critical care nurses as the independent variable in at least seven research studies between 1989 and 2007.

Co-existence of differing nurse- and music therapist-directed applications of music in ICU settings necessitates that roles, interventions, and ethical considerations are defined and discussed. This chapter presents a comprehensive review of the art and science of therapeutically applied music in intensive care settings over the past three decades with the aims of:

- providing a historical account of the development and growth of music as a non-pharmacologic agent in ICU settings;
- defining (a) the roles of music in ICU settings, and (b) the roles of professional nurses and music therapists who employ music to promote positive patient outcomes;
- discussing music therapy within the context of a family-centered, interdisciplinary approach to care;
- providing a comprehensive explanation of the benefits of music therapy for ICU patients and their families in accordance with the American Music Therapy Association's (AMTA) definition of music therapy and established standards of professional practice;
- recommending future clinical and research directions for professional music therapists in adult ICU settings.

The foundation of this chapter is knowledge gained from an extensive literature review of the past 30 years, combined with the clinical training and experience of the authors, professional music therapists whose specialties include pediatric and adult intensive care and end-of-life settings. Clinical examples of music therapy approaches and interventions are integrated throughout the chapter, demonstrating through empirical evidence that music therapy improves the care of adult ICU patients and their families.

Uses of Music in the ICU: An Historical Account of the Past Three Decades

Staff attending to the needs of patients and families in the ICU setting are now researching and implementing non-pharmacologic interventions to reduce noxious environmental stimuli and promote patient comfort. Physicians, nurses, and professional music therapists have applied music for therapeutic purposes in the ICU setting for over 30 years. A thorough search of the research literature with the search criteria *music therapy, music listening, music intervention, music protocol*, or *music* and *intensive care, critical care, mechanical ventilation*, or *ICU* settings reveals interesting clinical outcomes, trends, and practices.

Our search of the music therapy research literature included the *Journal of Music Therapy*, years 1964–2007; *Music Therapy*, years 1981–1996; *Music Therapy Perspectives*, years 1982–1984, 1986–2009; and Clinicaltrials.gov (last searched April 1, 2008). Three published, related research studies were identified. There are currently two unpublished research studies involving music therapists that are in process. The same search criteria were used to identify medical research studies through the database OVID Medline, Clinicaltrials.gov, and medscape.com through April 1, 2008. Forty published articles in the medical literature were identified as relevant and were reviewed. All articles identified in accordance with these search engine parameters were read by the primary author, arranged chronologically, and dissected for categorization.

There are several limitations to the literature review presented here. The terms *cardiac intensive care unit, CICU*, and *coronary care unit* were not included in the literature review in preparation for this chapter. Also, terms referring to specific life-threatening illnesses or traumatic events, such as *acute myocardial infarction, burn*, or *traumatic brain injury* were not used. Several of the articles reviewed for this chapter refer to studies outside our search parameters defined above. These studies were gathered and reviewed as well, and those deemed relevant were added to our literature review. Additional articles relevant to the uses of music in ICU settings may exist outside our search parameters or may be published in international medical or music therapy journals.

Of the total 45 articles deemed relevant (43 published, 2 unpublished), the primary author of this chapter categorized 25 as *research* (quantitative and qualitative), 12 as *literature reviews* (three of which contain protocols; one contains a survey), 4 as *related to families* (music therapy secondary), 3 as *discussions*, and 1 as a *survey*. Board-certified music therapists participated in 9 of these articles, while nurses and physicians specializing in critical and intensive care participated in 41. Of the 9 articles involving music therapists, 1 is published in a music therapy journal, 2 are published in complementary journals, 4 in critical care medical journals, and 2 remain works in progress. All other articles included in this review were published in medical journals.

The findings of our literature review demonstrate an imbalance of research inquiry and dissemination of information between the disciplines of nursing and music therapy on the uses of music in ICU settings. Our search also reveals an interdependent relationship between these two disciplines in regard to the implementation of music in ICU settings. The first author created *The ICU Music Tree of Knowledge: A Symbolic Diagram of Research Roots and Development* to accurately and concisely communicate this synthesis of the articles deemed relevant to the topic, and their relationship to one another. The purpose of the diagram in Figure 2 is to serve as a visual aid to increase understanding of this written historical account and the dynamics of the complex and interdependent research efforts of critical care nurses, physicians, and music therapists presented.

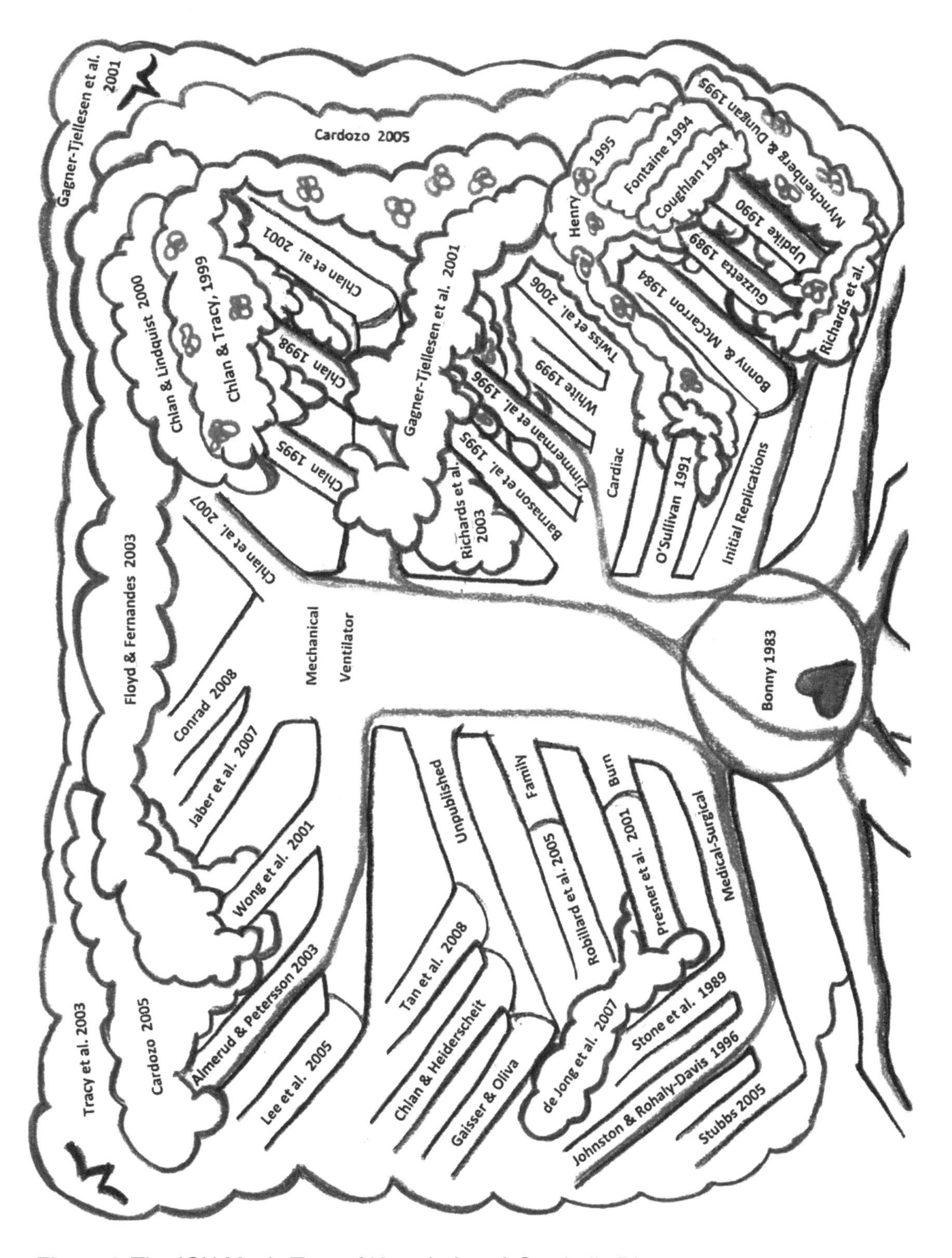

Figure 2. The ICU Music Tree of Knowledge: A Symbolic Diagram of Research Roots and Development (J. Shaller Gerweck)

The ICU Music Tree of Knowledge: A Symbolic Diagram of Research Roots and Development portrays the growth of music as a non-pharmacologic intervention in ICU settings. The interface of line and symbol within the diagram represents the efforts of nurses and music therapists in their championing of music for ICU patients, and how these efforts interdependently relate. The symbol of a ***heart-shaped seed*** at the base of the tree represents Bonny's personal cardiac ICU experience that inspired the creation of the *Music Rx* tapes (Bonny, 1983b). Well-established ***roots*** nourish the heart-shaped seed with knowledge imparted through theoretical foundations established in medicine, psychology, and music therapy. Located around the heart-shaped seed, a ***mandala*** (a circle, representational of the self in Jungian psychology) portrays the emergence of this seed from its grounded place, a metaphor for Bonny's 1983 unprecedented research study investigating the effects of her *Music Rx* tapes for ICU patients. This seed grows and changes over time, developing into individual branches, leaves, and flowers.

The ***large branches*** of the diagram depict the categorization of the 26 research studies into seven subcategories (initial replications, medical-surgical ICU, Cardiac Intensive Care Unit, burn ICU, family, mechanical ventilator, and unpublished studies) related to the ICU. The ***small branches*** spanning outward from the large branches represent individual studies placed in that category. The small branches are arranged longitudinally within each large branch according to the study's date of publication. An arch between the subcategory and the study indicates involvement of professional music therapists. The only exception is the branch labeled O'Sullivan, which represents an early literature review that did not include any of the articles we identified, though it is referred to in later publications. Rising up from the mandala are ***lines*** that flow into some of the branches. The branches that these lines flow into are the nine research studies that utilized Bonny's *Music Rx* tapes as their independent variable. Branches without these lines are studies with a different independent variable than the *Music Rx* tapes. The ***billowing leaves*** that surround the tree's branches represent different literature reviews and the studies they each include. The ***flowers*** depict articles that include protocols and the ***birds*** represent surveys. The ***outermost billowing*** of leaves portrays the synthesis of all the articles reviewed and the continuation of research efforts by nurses and music therapists in ICU settings.

Initial Investigations of Music's Benefits for ICU Patients (Symbols: heart, roots, mandala)

Helen L. Bonny, PhD, CMT, co-author of the book *Music and Your Mind* (Bonny & Savary, 1973), was an expert in the purposeful design of music listening programs and implementation methodology for their therapeutic use. Published in 1983, Bonny's study "Music Listening for Intensive Coronary Care Units: A Pilot Project" was designed to test the effectiveness of her music listening programs as a stress reduction treatment approach for ICU nurses in the care of their patients. The study developed in part as a result of Bonny's personal experience as a patient with cardiac illness and her use of music during critical care hospitalizations in 1980 (Bonny, 2002a). Bonny reflected:

> Frequent hospitalizations made me aware of the values music can bring to areas of acute care where the patient is subject to an alien environment: over stimulation of and assault of the senses, unfamiliar procedures, absence of the usual day-night sequence, physical discomfort of the disease, lack of privacy, illness and death of other patients. (Bonny, 2002a, p. 15)

Based on her personal experience as a patient in Cardiac Intensive Care Unit (CICU) settings and professional knowledge and training as a music therapist, Bonny selected music specifically intended for use by patients "in a depleted energy state" (p. 239) who are compromised due to life-threatening illness/injury (Bonny, 2002b). Classical music selections of a sedative nature, described as having few dramatic changes in dynamics, a simple melody line, regular and predictable rhythms, consonant harmony, and recognized instrumental and vocal timbre (Bonny, 1983a, 2002c) were purposefully complied and arranged by Bonny into three listening programs, 25 to 35 minutes each (Bonny, 2002c). The music chosen was primarily of the romantic music era and was selected for its sedative qualities and ability to evoke positive mood states (Bonny, 1983a, 2002c).

Research investigating the effects of music on patients on intensive/critical care units was scarce and there was a lot to explore. Thus, one hypothesis of Bonny's 1983 pilot study was that the use of music on the Intensive Coronary Care Unit (ICCU) would decrease environmental stress responses in patients. Anticipated outcomes included lowered blood pressure and heart rate and a reduced desire for pain medication (Bonny, 1983a, 2002a, 2002c). Bonny (2002c) also hypothesized that listening to a purposefully designed music listening program would reduce critical coronary patients' anxiety, depression, isolation, and pain experiences and improve their medical management. Furthermore, Bonny proposed that the music listening would positively affect ease of patient care and environmental conditions for nursing staff.

Twenty-six patients in Coronary Intensive Care Units participated in the pre/posttest pilot study and chose from the three classical music listening programs (Bonny, 2002c). Part way through the study, one of the programs was altered and a fourth was added in response to requests from nurses and patients. The fourth program consisted of 25 to 35 minutes of non-classical styles (popular folk, country-western, jazz, and swing) that would appeal to the 50-year and older age group at the time of the study (early 1980s) (Bonny, 2002a, 2002c).

Nurses were educated on the purposes of the study and trained in how to administer the music listening tapes and collect data. The tapes were offered when deemed appropriate for patients by the nursing staff or when requested by patients. Bonny designed the individual tapes and program with a systematic succession and advised nurses to (a) ask the patient's permission, (b) assist the patient in selecting from the classical or popular music programs, and (c) play Program I before proceeding to additional programs (Bonny, 2002c). It was also recommended that nurses (d) administer only two music listening programs a day with critically ill patients, and (e) wait at least 15 minutes before administering the second music program. Pre- and posttest measures of heart rate, blood pressure, pain medication, mood state, and behavioral observations were collected and analyzed. Findings from this pilot study demonstrated a significant reduction in patient heart rate, anxiety, and depression with an increased tolerance for pain and suffering (Bonny, 2002c).

Replication Studies: 1984–1990 (Symbols: large and small branches, lines rising from mandala)

The results of Bonny's pilot study (1983a) caught the attention of the hospital's anesthesiologist who requested that Bonny develop music programs for the specific needs of surgical patients. In response to this request, the effects of purposefully designed music listening programs on surgical patients undergoing short-term anesthesia and spinal block were investigated (Bonny & McCarron, 1984). While this study is not specific to the ICU setting, it was integral to the development of Bonny's taped music programs for medical settings and is thus included in the literature review. In this pilot study, patients selected and listened to one of two 90-minute preselected music programs for 12 minutes preoperatively and 24 minutes postoperatively. Significant decreases in pain, anxiety, and required anesthesia were found (Bonny & McCarron, 1984). Publication of these research findings resulted in an increased interest in music listening programs for patients in hospitals.

In response to the growing interest in music's benefits for critical care patients and desire for appropriate music listening programs, Bonny created *Music Rx,* a music listening toolkit comprised of six cassette tapes, directions for their use, a research report, and list of the music selections (Bonny, 2002a). Two of the music tapes were designed for the ICU, one for use in operating rooms, and one for postoperative recovery. In addition, one tape consisted of popular adult music of the time, and the last contained verbal instructions to medical personnel administering the *Music Rx* tapes (Bonny, 2002a).

Guzzetta (1989) and Updike (1990) modified Bonny's pilot study design, incorporating her recommendations for replication, and conducted research in critical care settings utilizing the *Music Rx* program. The authors of these two initial replication studies examined the effects of Bonny's *Music Rx* program on critical care patients through outcome measures of heart rate, blood pressure, peripheral temperature, cardiovascular complications, anxiety, and pain. Positive outcomes were achieved for all measures, resulting in recommendations that nurses learn and utilize music therapy techniques in order to assist the psychophysiologic recovery of their patients (Guzzetta, 1989). Information regarding pricing and ordering of the *Music Rx* program is provided in Updike's article (Updike, 1990).

The positive findings of these early replication studies inspired critical care nurses to continue their research efforts utilizing Bonny's *Music Rx* program, administration protocol, goals, and recommended evaluation and documentation procedures (Almerud & Petersson, 2003; Chlan, 1995, 1998; Chlan, Engeland, Anthony, & Guttormson, 2007; Guzzetta, 1989; Johnston & Rohaly-Davis, 1996; Updike, 1990; Zimmerman, Nieveen, Barnason, & Schmaderer, 1996). These studies all demonstrate positive effects of Bonny's *Music Rx* taped listening programs on critical care patients' physiologic markers related to homeostasis and stress, mood states, and perception of pain. The protocol established by Bonny for implementation of her *Music Rx* listening programs and the design of these programs themselves are an integral component of the research that directly impacts clinical outcomes for ICU patients. This important consideration of the research design is neither recognized nor discussed in these replication studies.

Review of the Literature: 1990–1995

Between 1990 and 1995, no research studies were published on the use of music in ICU settings in accordance with the defined parameters of our search. However, critical care nurses published five literature review studies on the uses of music in the ICU setting during this time. Similar trends exist among these five literature review studies:

- All five literature reviews discussed the use of music for ICU patients in the context of recorded music listening.
- None of the studies identified Bonny as creator of the *Music Rx* program utilized as the independent variable in several of the studies reviewed. Instead they cited the nurse researchers who utilized Bonny's *Music Rx* taped programs.
- Biomedical theories pertinent to the therapeutic use of music for ICU patients were identified and included the Gate Control Theory of pain (Henry, 1995; O'Sullivan, 1991) and music's effects on the brain including the limbic system, reticular activating system (RAS), and sympathetic nervous system (SNS) (Fontaine, 1994; Henry, 1995; Mynchenberg & Dungan, 1995; O'Sullivan, 1991).

O'Sullivan (1991) stated there are no music studies specific to the ICU setting prior to 1991, though our literature search revealed four music and ICU-related articles. Though O'Sullivan reviewed publications authored by music therapists, the qualifications of music therapists were inaccurately portrayed (e.g., music therapists' training is 18 months). Literature review studies authored by Coughlan (1994) and Fontaine (1994) included the studies identified in our search and extrapolated that ICU nurses can employ music therapy to regulate the noxious stimuli of the environment. Fontaine recommended that future research efforts investigate the benefits of music listening for patients on mechanical ventilators. A literature review by Henry (1995) included the studies by Guzzetta (1989) and Updike (1990), as well as those conducted in cardiac care and post-surgical units. However, the original two pilot studies conducted by Bonny (1983a) and Bonny and McCarron (1984) are omitted from Henry's review. Henry stated that the critical care nurse can use music as a non-pharmacologic distraction intervention to promote comfort. Further recommendations encourage ICU nurses to facilitate uninterrupted music listening time for their patients, create libraries of recorded music on their units, and purchase the *Music Rx* program. Mynchenberg and Dungan's (1995) review of the literature presented the Dungan Model of Dynamic Integration, a holistic model that incorporates relaxation approaches of music therapy and therapeutic touch.

Research Studies on the Use of Music in ICU Settings: 1995–2004

Between 1995 and 2004, eight studies investigated the uses of recorded music listening in ICU settings, and one study investigated the effects of an active music therapy intervention provided by a professional music therapist. Primary authors of all studies were critical care nurses. Four of the studies utilized music from Bonny's *Music RX* program as their independent variable and evaluated both physiologic and emotional changes of ICU patients (Chlan, 1995, 1998; Johnston & Rohaly-Davis, 1996; Zimmerman et al., 1996). The authors of these studies investigated the effects of *Music Rx* on specific ICU patient issues, including **ventilator** dependence, postoperative **Coronary Artery Bypass Grafting** (CABG), and oncological complications. Two studies explored the impact of Bonny's *Music Rx* program for patients on mechanical ventilators and found positive outcomes of reduced respiration rates, heart rates, blood pressure, pain, and anxiety levels (Chlan 1995, 1998). Johnston and Rohaly-Davis investigated the effects of the *Music Rx* program for oncology patients in the ICU setting and positive outcomes again were found for heart rate, pain, and anxiety levels. Postoperative CABG patients responded to *Music Rx* with an overall relaxation response (Zimmerman et al., 1996).

Four studies used recorded music selected from their nursing or family collections. A selection of country-western, instrumental, and New Age music selected by Barnason, Zimmerman, and Nieveen (1995) failed to produce statistically significant results for ICU patients. White (1999) employed investigator-selected recorded music with a tempo of 60 beats per minute and listening for 20 minutes. Positive patient outcomes of decreased respiration rates, blood pressure, oxygen demand, and anxiety levels were found. Researchers investigating the effects of recorded music listening for ICU patients began to incorporate patient preference into their research designs. Ventilator-dependent patients listened to recorded music they chose from a selection of Chinese and Western classical music. Patient's anxiety levels decreased, though no significant changes in respiration rates or blood pressure were found (Wong, Lopez-Nahas, & Molassiotis, 2001). The lack of control concerning the independent variable of music selection and listening is a significant design flaw within these studies and may account for these inconsistent outcomes.

In another study, alert ventilator-dependent patients chose from a collection of recorded music carefully selected by a professional music therapist and self-determined the length of their listening time (Chlan, Tracy, Nelson, & Walker, 2001). The music selected by the music therapist is described in similar terms as that of the *Music Rx* tapes: tempos ranging from 60 bpm to80 bpm, slow and flowing rhythms, restrained dynamics, uniform ascending and descending melodic phrases, and no lyrics. The music therapist consulted with the patient throughout his/her participation in the study and adapted the music listening according to the patient's changing needs and related music preferences. In this study, Chlan et al. referred to the independent variable of the study as "music intervention" and "patient-directed music intervention" and acknowledged the challenges that ICU nurses encounter in their efforts to implement music listening interventions. Furthermore, the authors of this study encouraged critical care nurses to pursue continuing education on the topic of music in the ICU setting to reduce challenges such as selecting appropriate music for critically ill/injured patients and determining patient-specific implementation guidelines.

An innovative pilot study investigated the effects of an active music therapy intervention on the pain and anxiety experiences of 63 burn patients (Prensner, Yowler, Smith, Steele, & Fratianne, 2001). The effects of medical music therapy interventions termed Music-Based Imagery (MBI) and Musical Alternate Engagement (MAE) were investigated during painful procedures. These interventions are described in detail later in this chapter. Positive outcomes for ICU burn patients were indicated due to participation in music therapy interventions that were adapted by the music therapist to the unique needs and changes of each patient.

Literature Reviews and Other Related Articles on the Use of Music in ICU Settings: 1995–2006

Five literature reviews (Chlan, 2006; Chlan & Tracy, 1999; Floyd & Fernandes, 2003; Gagner-Tjellesen, Yurkovich, & Gragert, 2001; Richards, Nagel, Markie, Elwell, & Barone, 2003), one survey study (Tracy et al., 2003), and three discussion papers (Ahmad, Brophy, Grant, & Brandsetter, 1999; White, 2000; Wilkins & Moore, 2004) were published from 1995 through 2004. Of particular interest for music therapists is the article authored by Chlan and Tracy (1999), in which these authors present a music listening assessment tool.

The Music Therapy Assessment and Implementation Tool (MAIT) is designed to assist ICU nurses who incorporate recorded music listening into their patient's plan of care. It includes questions to assess the patient's musical preferences and listening patterns, steps for implementation of recorded music listening, and evaluation questions for nurses to complete (Chlan & Tracy, 1999). The importance of patient preference is stressed, citing publications authored by music therapists. ICU nurses are encouraged to seek out professional music therapists as consultants to create music libraries on their ICU units, or to provide advanced education and training for nurses on the uses of recorded music (Chlan & Tracy, 1999). A description of the theoretical bases of music for relaxation and anxiety reduction, as well as the profession, education, and board certification of music therapists was discussed by Chlan (2006). This article also recommended that ICU nurses consult with professional music therapists to develop recorded music listening libraries. Despite this awareness, the authors continue to advocate music therapy as a non-pharmacologic nursing intervention (Chlan, 2006).

Gagner-Tjellesen et al. (2001) surveyed nurses to determine their use of Independent Therapeutic Nursing Interventions (ITNIs) in acute inpatient settings, their perceived effectiveness of differing ITNIs, frequency of use, reasons for use, and barriers to implementation. Thirty-three ICU nurses participated in the study, with 78.8% reporting they use "music therapy" as an ITNI with their patients. "Music therapy" in this context refers to the use of recorded music listening cassettes or CDs. These nurses report using "music therapy" as an ITNI to reduce stress and anxiety, pain perception, sleep disturbance, depression, and aggression. The nurses' level of comfort and perceived value of "music therapy" influences its use, as do factors of time and access to equipment (Gagner-Tjellesen et al., 2001).

Research Studies on the Use of Music in ICU Settings: 2005–2009

The effects of active music therapy interventions on critical care patients, as provided by a board-certified music therapist, are presented by five studies during this most recent period. Investigation or discussion on the uses and effects of music therapist-created methodologies, other than the *Music Rx* program, in ICU settings were found. In 2005, a series of articles was published on the impact of the Critical Care Family Assistance Program (CCFAP) program on ICU patients and their families. Several of these articles referred to music therapy because two of the pilot sites of this research study provided medical music therapy as part of their CCFAP services offered in the ICU. In the article by Robillard et al. (2005), the role of medical music therapy for ICU patients and their families was presented. Music therapy was accurately defined and the education and training of professional music therapists was described. Common uses for music therapy were identified, as well as examples of family participation in sessions. The CCFAP staff found they had a greater awareness of how the music therapist impacts the ICU environment, in particular the sound environment (Robillard et al., 2005). Researchers of a recently published study investigated the effectiveness of patient-controlled recorded music listening on anxiety self-management for ICU patients receiving mechanical ventilation (Chlan & Heiderscheit, 2009).

The six additional research articles published during this time period were written by nurses or physicians and addressed the use of recorded music listening on ventilator-dependent patients (Chlan et al., 2007; Conrad, 2008; Jaber et al., 2007; Lee et al., 2005; Stubbs, 2005; Twiss, Seaver, & McCaffrey, 2006). Outcomes from several of these studies demonstrated that listening to preferred music considered sedative in nature reduces the experience of stress and anxiety for mechanical ventilator patients (Lee et al., 2005; Twiss et al., 2006) and the need for sedative medications (Conrad, 2008). The authors of these studies suggested that the length of time patients depend on mechanical ventilation can be reduced through music listening and that decreases in related hospital costs and morbidity and mortality rates will result. In addition to these research studies, two literature articles were also published during this time (Cardozo, 2004; de Jong, Middelkoop, Faber, & Van Loey, 2007). These studies continue to interchange the terms *music therapy*, *recorded music listening*, and *music listening* when referring to the application of cassettes or CDs in ICU setting.

Unpublished Articles on the Use of Music in the ICU

Currently, two additional studies are in progress, in which the researchers investigate the effectiveness of active medical music therapy interventions on ICU patients. Tan, Yowler, and Fratianne (2008) investigate the impact of medical music therapy interventions on the coping and adjustment abilities of children visiting adults with severe burns. Another group is currently recruiting subjects to study the effectiveness of an active music therapy improvisation intervention on weaning from mechanical ventilation (Gaisser & Oliva, in progress).

In summary, differences between nurses' and music therapists' professional education, training, and qualifications regarding the purposeful uses of music dictate the ways in which these professionals ethically administer music in critical care settings. The co-existence of varying nurse- and music therapist-directed uses of music in ICU settings necessitates that terminology, roles, interventions, and ethical considerations be discussed and defined.

Table 3 defines and compares the services of *Medical Music Therapy* and *Functional Music* for ICU settings, expanding upon Maranto's (1991) *Classification Model for Music and Medicine*. Maranto identified three subcategories representing the interface between music and medicine: Medical Music Therapy, Functional Music, and Performing Music (Arts) Medicine. The first two subcategories are relevant to the topic of this chapter and serve to compare the differing roles of music therapists and nurses, and their respective uses of music in critical care settings.

Table 3
Defining Medical Music Therapy and Functional Music for ICU Settings

Service Type	Medical Music Therapy	Functional Music
Definition	Music therapy is the clinical and evidence-based use of music interventions to accomplish individualized goals within a therapeutic relationship by a credentialed professional who has completed an approved music therapy program (AMTA, n.d.). Medical music therapy is the use of music therapy strategies in the medical setting to treat illness and maintain health (Maranto, 1991). Music therapy can be defined as a musical experience designed and implemented by the music therapist to effect a systematic process of change with the patient (Bruscia, 1989).	Uses of music in medicine outside the realm of music therapy: listening to recorded music to facilitate physiologic changes, background music, and uses of recorded music by medical personnel (Maranto, 1991)
Profession and Credentials	Board-certified music therapists Certification Board for Music Therapists Credentials – MT-BC, CMT, RMT	Nurses, physicians, surgeons, anesthesiologists State licensure RN exam Credentials – RN, CNS, ACNP, CCRN, MD, PhD
Education	Minimum requirement – BA in Music Therapy Master's and Doctoral degrees available	Minimum requirement – BSN in nursing Optional advanced training and Certified Critical Care Nurse exam (CCRN) Master's and Doctoral degrees available
Training relevant to provision of music	Completion of clinical training internship required. Advanced training may include pain/symptom management, Neurologic Music Therapy (NMT), Bonny Method of Guided Imagery and Music (BMGIM), Hospice and Palliative Care Music Therapy, etc.	No formal training required. Nurses are encouraged to take continuing education courses/classes on the applications of music in ICU medical settings.

Techniques	Music Assisted/Music Facilitated Relaxation, songwriting, lyric analysis, BMGIM, Music-Based Imagery, MAE, NMT techniques	Listening to *Music Rx* tapes Listening to RN-, patient-, or family-selected recorded music
Type of music	Active music provided by board-certified music therapist, tailored to specific needs of patient. Patient preference	Recorded music Patient preference recommended
Role of music	Music as subordinate, equal, or primary role in regards to the therapeutic relationship and dependent upon need(s) of patient/family, level of functioning, and intervention	Sole role Music considered a passive activity
Uses of music in ICU settings	Purposefully designed music therapy interventions to facilitate a wide variety of physical (including stress and pain reduction), neurological, emotional (including anxiety and isolation reduction), and spiritual changes for patient/family	As distraction. To reduce stress, pain, anxiety, and isolation. Promote soothing environment
Role of professional	Function as therapist. Assess patient/family needs, identify goals/objectives, provide patient-directed interventions, observe/evaluate outcomes, communicate with interdisciplinary team. Provide education, training, and listening materials to families regarding use of recorded music	May gather information regarding patient's music preferences and guide patient or family in selection of recorded music
Role of therapeutic relationship	Therapeutic relationship as subordinate, equal, or primary role in regards to the music and dependent upon need(s) of patient/family, level of functioning, and intervention	Use of recorded music in ICU setting may promote positive interactions between medical professionals and their patients/families
Role of patient	Active or receptive participation, patient-preferred music, length of listening. Patient's needs dictate use of music	Passive music listening, may select music and determine length of listening time
Role of family	Active or receptive participation, patient-determined song preferences, involvement of children, receives individualized teaching regarding uses of recorded music in ICU	Possible selection of music for patient

Common Patient Characteristics

Intensive Care Units (ICUs) are medical-surgical adult units specializing in trauma, burn, and postoperative care for patients in critical condition. Patients are admitted to the ICU for numerous medical-surgical reasons, including **cardiothoracic** and **neuro-**

oncology postoperative care, complications related to surgery, antepartum or postpartum complications, or complications related to chronic illness or disease processes. Sudden onset of a critical event such as a stroke, heart attack, brain hemorrhage, or respiratory crisis often leads to ICU admittance. Traumatic burns, brain injuries, and motor vehicle accidents can be life-threatening and necessitate life-sustaining interventions as well. Length of stay in the ICU varies due to these numerous reasons for admittance, spanning 24–48 hours for postoperative patients and up to several months for patients with **co-morbidity**. Fifteen to 20% of ICU patients will die as a result of their life-threatening illness or injury (Heyland et al., 2002).

Physical Experiences

For patients in ICU settings, experiences of a physical nature are related to the cause of their critical condition as well as the life-sustaining medications, interventions, and treatments they receive. The physical experiences of ICU patients discussed below may impede the physical healing process and contribute to emotional and spiritual suffering.

Physical Experiences of the Patient in ICU

- Pain
- Breathing difficulties and associated distress
- Altered states of consciousness (ASC)
- Erratic and unstable physiologic functions of heart rate, respiration rate, blood pressure,and oxygen saturation levels

Pain is a significant concern for ICU patients, since coping with pain is exhausting and patients' tolerance for pain decreases over time. Experienced chronically or acutely, pain is assessed at regular intervals in the ICU setting by all interdisciplinary staff. Pain experiences are often heightened by anxiety (Miller, Hickman, & Lemasters, 1992) and exacerbated by noxious sensory stimuli in the ICU setting. The administration of **analgesics** and **anxiolytics** to ICU patients is the standard care protocol for pain and anxiety management. However, some health care professionals have been noted to under-prescribe analgesics because they overestimate the potential for patients to become addicted to medications such as morphine and codeine (National Institute on Drug Abuse, n.d.). Analgesics alone fail to adequately control pain for 75% of burn patients (Miller et al., 1992). Health care professionals concerned with the issue of finding the right balance between inadequate prescription of narcotics for pain and over-medication seek out non-pharmacologic treatments such as music therapy.

Breathing difficulties and associated distress include irregular, shallow, and labored breathing patterns, **dyspnea**, **apnea,** and respiratory distress. Causes of respiratory failure or reason for **intubation** include congestive heart failure, heart disease, chronic obstructive pulmonary disease, asthma exacerbation, pneumonia, multisystem organ failure, gastrointestinal and liver disease, cancer or leukemia, overdose, **ketoacidosis**, and neurologic emergency. Approximately 30–40% of the total ICU patient population is on mechanical ventilators for either short postoperative support or prolonged support, until their various medical issues can be resolved. These patients may experience difficulties in achieving ventilator synchrony, tolerating breathing trials, and weaning. Prolonged mechanical ventilation occurs for approximately 10% of the ICU patient population. Disproportionately, prolonged mechanical ventilation is associated with the consumption of 50% or more of all ICU resources (Cattapan & Fahey, 2003; McCartney & Boland, 1994; McKinley, Coote, & Stein-Parbury, 2003; Meade, Guyatt, & Cook, 2001; Pochard, Lanore, & Bellivier, 1995).

Altered states of consciousness (ASC) are a common experience for ICU patients and can be due to an acquired brain injury, sedative and analgesic medications, or a medication-induced coma. A coma is defined as an extended period of unconsciousness where the patient exhibits no voluntary movements or behaviors, such as opening eyes or consistently squeezing another's hand when asked (Baker & Tamplin, 2006). Consciousness is characterized by arousal and awareness and is directly related to the functions of the **Reticular Activating System** (Baker & Tamplin, 2006). Disturbances in time perception, sensory stimuli, and thinking commonly occur in ASC. Disorienting factors related to the patient's critical illness or event, analgesic and sedative medications, sleep disturbance/disorder, and the medical environment result in increased confusion, nervousness, distrust, and paranoia. These disturbances and the patient's related disruptive behaviors are referred to as ICU psychosis or ICU syndrome. Up to 60% of ICU patients will experience some form of delusion (Almerud & Petersson, 2003). Music therapy can help ICU patients arouse, orient, and attend to sensory information by providing meaningful stimuli and controlling noxious environmental influences.

Erratic and unstable physiologic functions of heart rate, respiration rate, blood pressure, and oxygen saturation levels are common in ICU patients. Arousal of the **sympathetic nervous system** results in increased production of stress hormones **epinephrine** and **norepinephrine**, causing **arterial** and **venous constriction**, **myocardial** stimulation, broncho-constriction and elevated heart rate (HR), respiration rate (RR), blood pressure (BP), and oxygen demand (Covington, 1998; Johnson & Sexton, 1990; McKinley, Stein-Parbury, Chehelnabi, & Lovas, 2004; Meade et al., 2001; Szokol & Vender, 2001). On the other hand, shock can result in dangerously low blood pressure, lost control of temperature regulation, and irregular breathing. These physiologic reactions increase the patient's risk for complications and prolonged life-support measures. Music therapy interventions often help stabilize and vector the patient's heart rate, respiration rate, blood pressure, and oxygen saturation level in the desired therapeutic directions.

Emotional Experiences

Life-threatening illness and injury produces sudden and abrupt changes within the patient's body and life. A sense of vulnerability and insecurity occurs for ICU patients related to the threat of morbidity and mortality, loss of independence, and lack of control. Feelings of fear, impending doom, dread, apprehension, anxiety, and sense of a paralyzed will are all-pervasive for the ICU patient and can have insidious effects on mind, body, and spirit. These emotional experiences can affect the ICU patient's ability to cope with hospitalization, tolerate routine medical procedures, and recover. Anxiety occurs for 70–87% of ICU patients and is associated with negative physiologic consequences and an inability to tolerate necessary medical procedures (Henry, 1995; Wong et al., 2001). For example, 80% of ventilator-dependent patients demonstrate symptoms of depression, delirium, and anxiety (Lee et al., 2005). Ventilator-dependent patients experience heightened levels of emotional stress due to their inability to communicate pain or discomfort, sleep disorders, and experience of dyspnea (Lee et al., 2005). Ensuing physical manifestations of this emotional stress, such as erratic and unstable heart and respiration rates, irregular blood pressure and oxygen saturation levels, and activation of the sympathetic nervous system, often necessitate increased pharmacologic interventions, prolonging ventilator dependence and thus increasing the patient's risk for morbidity and mortality (Lee et al., 2005; Moser et al., 2003)

Despair, hopelessness, worry, and concern for one's family occur for alert ICU patients and may increase with prolonged lengths of stay. Intense feelings of grief, yearning, and anguish occur for ICU patients who face continued morbidity, physical and psychosocial losses, and a poor or terminal prognosis. Anger, agitation, and a feeling of being stuck can manifest as symptoms of frustration, aggression, and depression. The patient may show overt behavioral signs of distress through:

- repeatedly calling for help, screaming, or crying;
- withdrawal and avoiding eye contact;
- repetitive movements, shaking, or attempts to sit up or get out of bed;
- attempts to pull out tubing or refusal to participate in treatments.

Emotional Experiences of the Patient in ICU

- Sense of vulnerability and insecurity
- Loss of independence and control
- Feelings of fear and dread
- Apprehension
- Anxiety
- Sense of a paralyzed will
- Despair

Hopelessness
Worry and concern
Grief
Anger
Agitation
Aggression
Depression

Spiritual Experiences

The word *spirit* is derived from the Latin word *spiritus*, meaning breath, life force, vigor, animating principle, and otherness (Merriam-Webster Online Dictionary, 2010). The experience of spirit is described as felt both inside and outside of the body and includes an awareness of the metaphysical aspects of life. Spirituality refers to a person's feelings, thoughts, and behaviors related to their experience of the sacred and their search for the Divine (Crowe, 2004). The experience of a life-threatening illness or event and admittance to the ICU can increase patients' awareness of, and focus on, their spiritual needs. Reactions of a spiritual nature include feelings of loss, alienation, abandonment, and anticipatory grief. Patients may question their faith and also search for meaning, comfort, and hope in their suffering. Music therapists often provide their ICU patients and their families with preferred hymns to address spiritual conflicts and increase one's personal sense of spiritual connection or faith. Music therapy sessions are a wonderful form of spiritual support for families who regularly attend church or have a strong religious faith.

Spiritual Experiences of the Patient in the ICU

- Increased awareness of, and focus on, spiritual needs and beliefs
- Questioning of faith
- Feelings of loss, alienation, abandonment, and anticipatory grief
- Search for meaning, comfort, and hope

Hope is important to patients and families in the ICU because it serves as fuel for their *will* to continue on despite their suffering. Like prayer, hope is a positive coping mechanism and provides comfort (Aldridge, 1998). ICU patients and their families experience significant challenges that may hinder their ability to hope. There are three hope-hindering categories: abandonment and isolation, uncontrollable pain or discomfort, and devaluation of personhood (Herth, as cited in Aldridge, 1998). These hope-hindering categories are all experienced by ICU patients. Music therapy interventions are provided to ICU patients and their families to promote and foster hope related to interpersonal connectedness, attainable goals, a spiritual base, personal attributes, light-heartedness, uplifting memories, and affirmation of worth (Herth, as cited in Aldridge, 1998).

End-of-life issues are common in the ICU, since death occurs for 15–20% of this patient population. There are several spiritual tasks ICU patients may seek to accomplish with their families and loved ones in the anticipation of death. Expression and release of a patient's emotional and spiritual suffering can occur through verbal, nonverbal, and energetic means. Patients review their life and accomplishments. Anticipating death, ICU patients grieve their physical, cognitive, and social losses, challenge fears, and search for meaning. Patients begin a process of transcendence, extending beyond their immediate life-threatening situation to achieve new perspectives (Aldridge, 1998). As a result, ICU patients begin to focus on relationship completion and closure, communicating "I love you," "I'm sorry," "I forgive you," "Thank you," and "Good-bye" to family and significant others (Byock, 1997).

This is a particularly vulnerable time for ICU patients and many need additional supports. Nurses, social workers, chaplains, and music therapists all collaborate to meet the complex needs of patients and their families during this time of crisis, grief, and loss. Music therapists may provide sessions during death transitions that occur in the ICU, such as in cases where life support measures of mechanical ventilation and dialysis are withdrawn with the outcome of imminent death.

In summary, the characteristics and experiences of patients in the ICU described above are influenced by the length of time the patient is in the ICU, the amount of sedative and analgesic medications they receive, their age, familial and cultural context, and the severity of their illness. The music therapist may receive referrals for any of these issues in the ICU.

Common Family Member Characteristics

Common Characteristics of the Adult Family Members of ICU Patients

Admission to the ICU often occurs as a result of a sudden and abrupt onset of injury or trauma, catapulting the patient and family into a state of crisis characterized by feelings of shock, fear, confusion, helplessness, and uncertainty (Lam & Beaulieu, 2004). The ICU environment itself can be viewed as threatening and alien, exacerbating fear and stress for patients and their families (Appleyard et al., 2000).

Motler (1979) had 40 family members of ICU patients rank 45 different need statements based on their experience. From their responses, Motler and Leske (1983) developed the Critical Care Family Needs Inventory (CCFNI). Further research studies investigating the experiences of family members of patients in the ICU setting utilizing the CCFNI and Critical Care Family Satisfaction Survey (CCFSS) built upon Motler's work to categorize family needs according to five domain areas: proximity, information, assurance, support, and comfort (Lederer et al., 2005; Motler & Leske, 1983; Wasser, Pasquale, Matchett, Bryan & Pasquale, 2001). These needs are similar to those reported by the spouses of terminally ill or recently deceased ICU patients in a hospital setting (Hampe, 1975). Clinical experience demonstrates that family members most often prioritize the needs of their loved one in the ICU over their own needs of support and comfort. Family members of ICU patients are motivated to be at the bedside, indicated by their related behaviors and coping mechanisms of information-seeking, pitching-in, and fitting-in (Lam & Beaulieu, 2004). The needs of family members of ICU patients (Motler, 1979; Motler & Leske, 1983), their goals for the care of their loved one, and their related behaviors (Lam & Beaulieu, 2004) are integrated in Table 4.

Table 4
Needs of Family Members in the Intensive Care Unit

Domains	Psychosocial and Spiritual Needs and Related Behaviors
Proximity	Maintain a connection with their loved one: visit patient frequently. Attend to the patient's needs: adjust pillows, provide ice chips, place cool rags on the forehead, gentle stroking and massage of patient's extremities, monitor sensory stimulation, oversee visitation, and play recorded music. Be present and helpful to their dying loved one. Serve as liaison between patient, family, and medical staff: function as voice of the patient, clarify information for patient, utilize nonverbal communication tools
Assurance	Ensure patient receives the best care and that necessary tasks are performed appropriately and within a reasonable timeframe. Be assured of the comfort of their dying loved one
Information	Be called at home; know the prognosis; have questions answered honestly; receive information about the patient once a day; have explanations given in understandable terms. Learning about medical equipment, procedures, and the illness itself is a coping mechanism. Be informed about end-of-life care, termination of medical treatments, and life support for dying loved ones in ICU
Support	Feel hospital personnel care about the patient; feel there is hope; emotional expression and release; support between family members; acceptance from health care professionals; consultation with hospital chaplain services
Comfort	Comfort between family members; comfort from health care professionals; search for meaning in the suffering of their loved one or themselves; pray more often or openly, request ICU staff prays for their loved one

Common Characteristics of the Child and Adolescent Family Members of ICU Patients

The presence of children in the families of ICU patients adds another layer of complications. Adult family members may find it difficult to convey the crisis at hand to very young children. Infants and young children are unable to understand why the hospitalized family member cannot be home. They can internalize feelings of guilt and come to irrational conclusions that their behaviors were the cause of the patient's injury and hospitalization.

Children in the family can experience separation anxiety while their adult family member is in the hospital. This characteristic is more profound in ICU settings, as hospital policies may restrict children under a certain age from entering the unit to visit a patient. Restrictions exist to protect both the adult patient and the child. Reasons for restrictions include adverse physiological effects on the patient, disruption or interruption of patient care, uncontrollable children, adverse psychological effects on the child, increased risk of infection, and increased noise levels. While the United States Department of Health, Education and Welfare decreed in 1962 that visits on the ICU should be restricted to 5 minutes per hour, there are huge variations among U.S. hospitals in regard to visitation hours for adults and children (Johnstone, 1994). Decisions regarding visiting hours for children are influenced by individual hospital and unit policies and the nurse in charge, who uses intuition and experience to guide his or her decisions (Johnstone, 1994).

A child's understanding of critical illness and injury influences how one communicates with a child in the ICU patient's family. Piaget's child developmental stage theory can be used to understand the different bonding relationships between children and their parents, and their reactions to a parent's serious illness/injury. During the sensorimotor stage (0–2 years), a child's existence develops in direct relationship to the parents, who symbolize safety and security. Separation disrupts the parent–child bond and can result in grief-like symptoms such as anxiety, increased crying, and rejection of the parent once he or she returns home (Clarke & Harrison, 2001).

The pre-operational stage (2–7 years) can be subdivided into the preconceptual phase (2–4 years) and the phase of intuitive thought (4–7 years). The preconceptual phase is characterized by a child's transition from being egocentric to socially aware, and by the ability to consider others' viewpoints and experience empathy. At this stage, it is important to explore children's understanding of the situation and encourage them to express their feelings and concerns. Children ages 2–4 may perceive parental absence as a punishment and loss of love, and thus they may need reassurance that the illness/injury is not the result of their thinking or behavior. During the intuitive thought phase, children ages 4–7 years are more able to understand explanations. With encouragement, they may express emotions and reveal misconceptions they have (Clarke & Harrison, 2001).

Between the age of 7 and 12, children enter the concrete operational stage and their reasoning becomes more sophisticated and logical. With a tendency to be more literal, children at this stage can have difficulty understanding the invisible and intangible aspects of illness/injury (e.g., internal organs, functions of the body). Children 7–12 years understand that death is irreversible and permanent. For those with a parent, grandparent, or sibling in the ICU, this understanding can cause significant fear and anxiety. They are often reluctant to ask questions for fear of appearing immature. At this stage, it is recommended that children participate in simple aspects of caring for their loved one in the ICU to promote a feeling of being helpful and involved (Clarke & Harrison, 2001).

During the formal operational stage (12–18 years), children begin to think abstractly and are able to perceive the reality and potential for negative outcomes related to their loved one's illness/injury. As children become adolescents, their sense of alarm and anxiety increases, and some cope through denial. At this stage, it is important to find out what adolescents know about their parent's condition. Overly concerned with what others think of them, adolescents may refrain from asking questions in order to appear intelligent (Clarke & Harrison, 2001). Moreover, in households with young children or teenagers, adjusting to illnesses or trauma can be especially difficult due to the pre-existing challenges of childrearing (Armistead, Klein, & Forehand, 1995).

Impact of Critical Illness on Children in the Family

The health and well-being of children is intimately linked to their parents' physical, social, and emotional health (Schor, 2003). Children are very sensitive to changes in routines, parental separation, and parental role-functioning, and they experience significant stress when a parent is admitted to the ICU. There is a tendency to shelter children from the difficult issues related to their parents' trauma (Lewandowski, 1992; Siegel et al., 1992). Well-intentioned adults may inadvertently deny children in the family the opportunity to express their feelings and ask questions because of the frequently held misconception that children are unable to understand what is happening to a critically ill person. Contrary to such beliefs, children are intuitively aware and sensitive to their environment and the feelings of others around them (Lewandowski, 1992).

Children with a critically ill parent not only have to adjust to the absence of their parent and continuous concern for their well-being, but they must also manage the changing role of their well parent (Lewandowski, 1992). The well parent may relinquish some of the parenting role to an alternate caregiver while they spend time on the ICU. A child's sense of abandonment, due to these changes in parental roles, can result in negative emotional and behavioral outcomes for the child (Lewandowski, 1992). Children who have a seriously burned family member may suffer long-term emotional outcomes involving anxiety, depression, and coping difficulties (Wright & Fuwiler, 1974). Even very young children need support (Siegel et al., 1992). Occasionally, serious psychiatric illnesses, such as posttraumatic stress disorder, can develop in children struggling to cope with crisis (Ceranoglu & Stern, 2006).

In summary, family members of patients in the ICU setting experience a wide range of emotions, including worry, fear, apprehension, loss of control, grief, panic, uncertainty, helplessness, anger, resentment, and disillusionment. All of these emotions are experienced along a continuum and can change at any moment in relation to the current situation. The emotional experience and reaction of family members is influenced by the reason their loved one was admitted to the ICU; previous experience in the ICU environment or with death; religious, cultural, and personal values; length of time in the ICU; care and treatment of their loved one in the ICU; care and treatment of themselves; family dynamics; and prognosis. The medical situation of the patient in the ICU setting is often unstable and guarded and can change instantly. Nursing staff, social workers, chaplains, and music therapists all collaborate to meet the complex needs of patients and their family at this time.

Current Treatment Modalities and Approaches Applicable to the ICU

Initial investigations by nurses and music therapists on the therapeutic uses of music for critically ill patients were grounded in many of the same theoretical foundations and anecdotal findings in medical settings. Individual and family medical music therapy sessions in ICU settings are based on a multifaceted framework established by disciplines of psychology, medicine, and music therapy. Theories on music as an anxiolytic and audioanalgesic agent, music's effect on the brain, and familial and ecological systems, provide a framework for both individual and family music therapy approaches and interventions in the ICU setting.

The effects of music as an **anxiolytic** and **audioanalgesia** support music-based interventions in ICU settings. Medical music therapy with ICU patients for anxiety and pain management follows two basic principles: music-assisted relaxation and music as distraction. The term *anxiolytic* refers to the use of music or sound to reduce anxiety (Prensner et al., 2001). *Music-assisted relaxation techniques* encompass the use of live or recorded music paired with common relaxation techniques such as imagery, progressive muscle relaxation, autogenic training, and biofeedback. Music-assisted relaxation sessions are most effective on the ICU when provided at the patient's bedside without any distractions from procedures carried out by medical or nursing staff. The music therapist might recommend music-assisted relaxation sessions for patients to cope with anticipatory anxiety before stress-evoking medical procedures, such as dressing changes, breathing trials, and surgery. Music-assisted relaxation can also be used after medical procedures to help bring the ICU patient's heightened arousal level back down to baseline.

Music's effect on physiological functions is explained in part by the principle of entrainment. **Entrainment** is a phenomenon in which the dominant rhythmic vibrations of one object will cause the less powerful vibrations of another object to oscillate at the rate of the dominant rhythm (Goldman, 1992). For example, two pendulums set to swing at two different rates will eventually synchronize and swing at the same rate. While the influence of music on body rhythms can be unpredictable and inconsistent (Radocy & Boyle, 1997), ICU research studies that utilized Bonny's *Music Rx* music listening program consistently produced comparable changes in physiologic parameters (heart rate, respiration rate, blood pressure, oxygen saturation) of patients in therapeutically desired directions (Almerud & Petersson, 2003; Bonny, 1983a; Bonny & McCarron, 1984; Chlan, 1995, 1998; Chlan et al., 2007; Guzzetta, 1989; Johnston & Rohaly-Davis, 1996; Updike, 1990; Zimmerman et al., 1996). ICU patients often experience wide and erratic fluctuations of their body rhythms, including their heartbeat and respiration rate. Perhaps the significantly large range of fluctuation in these physiologic parameters and the contributing environmental and situational stressors ICU patients experience account for the impact of music listening on ICU patients.

Audioanalgesia is the use of sound or music to reduce pain (Prensner et al., 2001). The **Gate Control Theory of Pain** (Melzack & Wall, 1965) is cited throughout the ICU articles reviewed for this chapter and is identified as an accepted non-pharmacologic theory of pain management. The Gate Control Theory is the more widely accepted theory of pain modulation based on attention-diversion principles (Prensner et al., 2001). According to the Gate Control Theory of Pain, nerve receptors send pain impulses to the spinal cord and through the dorsal horns to the brain. The dorsal horns function as a gate, granting permission for sensory impulses to enter the brain based upon the degree and quality of sensory stimuli (Prensner et al., 2001). The theory states that, because the central nervous system can process only a limited amount of information at one time, the patient's attention can be diverted away from the painful stimuli to an external stimulus such as music. Increasing one's attention on the alternate stimulus of music, such as through humming, singing, or rhythmically moving to the music, can further reduce the brain's awareness of the pain impulses.

The use of varied music therapy attention-diversion techniques follows key principles of pain perception. There are three major psychological dimensions that contribute to one's pain experience: sensory-discriminatory, motivational-affective, and cognitive-evaluative (Prensner et al., 2001). The intensity and quality of a patient's pain experience are influenced by cognitive factors such as anxiety, noxious or competing sensory stimuli, the meaning of their situation, attention and distraction levels, trauma, anticipatory grief, and fear (Prensner et al., 2001). Burn patients, for example, experience the combined effects of noxious auditory, olfactory, and visual stimuli of the ICU environment, in addition to the painful physical stimuli of having their wounds scrubbed and **debrided**. Music therapy attention-diversion techniques that redirect the patient's attention, stimulate emotion centers, and trigger memories can mitigate these factors.

Music therapy approaches that incorporate relaxation and attention-diversion techniques are a viable non-pharmacologic option for ICU patients. In addition to serving as an active focus and distraction from one's pain, music also facilitates a relaxation response, masks noxious auditory stimuli, and is a positive environmental stimulus (Davis, Gfeller, & Thaut, 2008). Medical music therapists purposefully structure interventions so that the various aspects of the ICU patient's pain experience are addressed simultaneously.

Research studies supported by the Kulas Foundation (http://foundationcenter.org/grantmaker/kulas/) employed active medical music therapy interventions of Music-Based Imagery (MBI) and Musical Alternate Engagement (MAE) for burn patients during burn treatment. Through patient self-report, interventions of MBI and MAE have demonstrated significant reductions in patients' perception of pain during the debridement process (Fratianne et al., 2001; Prensner et al., 2001).

Music and Its Effects on the Brain: Implications for ICU Patients and Their Families

The Reticular Activating System (RAS) "forms the core of the brain stem extending upward from the base of the medulla through the pons to the upper border of the midbrain" (Taylor, 1997, p. 37) and includes the reticular formation of the brain stem and the reticular nuclei of the thalamus (Crowe, 2004). The RAS is associated with homeostasis, emotion and attention, wakefulness and sleep, and consciousness in general (Damasio, as cited in Crowe, 2004).

Damage to structures of the RAS can cause a coma. Music can influence functions of the RAS because the auditory nerve has connections to structures of the RAS. Simplified, organized, and predictable rhythmic patterns may also provide an appropriate and necessary form of sensory stimulation accessible to brain-injured ICU patients in a coma, thus promoting cortical recovery (Baker & Tamplin, 2006). Attention processes of the RAS may be influenced by the auditory stimuli of music and may account for the mediating effects of music on pain perception (Taylor, 1997).

The significant trauma and noxious sensory stimuli experiences of ICU patients result in elevated stress levels and activation of the Sympathetic Nervous System (SNS). Increased production and release of **adrenal-medullary** hormones, **noradrenaline,** and **adrenaline** occur with elevated stress and negatively impact physiologic processes (Lee et al., 2005). The process of weaning mechanical ventilation (MV) demonstrates how one's stress reaction to a procedure can negatively impact physiological processes and successful outcomes. Weaning from MV requires the reduction of sedative and analgesic drug combinations used for pain, anxiety, and ventilator synchrony. The experience of **dyspnea**, a difficulty in breathing, causes anxiety and agitation. This can reduce the patient's ability to tolerate necessary treatments, including participation in Spontaneous Breathing Trials (SBT) necessary for MV weaning (Almerud & Petersson, 2003; Blackwood, 2000; Johnson & Sexton, 1990; Wong et al., 2001). Negative psychological outcomes correlated with MV and SBT arouse the sympathetic nervous system (Covington, 1998; Frazier et al., 2002; Johnson & Sexton, 1990; Wong et al., 2001). Physiologic consequences include arterial and venous constriction; myocardial stimulation; broncho-constriction; and elevated heart rate (HR), respiration rate (RR), and blood pressure (BP) (Covington, 1998; Johnson & Sexton, 1990; McKinley et al., 2004; Meade et al., 2001; Szokol & Vender, 2001). The combination of these adverse physiologic and psychological responses prolongs the MV weaning process and places these patients at greater risk for mortality and increased morbidity (Ely et al., 2004; McKinley et al., 2004; Meade et al., 2001; Moser et al., 2003; Sprague & Hopkins, 2003). Clinical experience demonstrates that music therapy is a non-pharmacological method of reducing psychological distress and adverse physiologic outcomes during SBT.

Music and Emotional Response: Implications for the ICU Patient and Their Family

Music is found to have a direct effect on the emotional centers of the brain. Affect modification through music is based on evidence that music evokes affective-mood reactions, alters a listener's mood, and triggers related physiological changes (Thaut, 1989). The patient's affective-mood responses to a given musical stimulus are influenced by the patient's current mood state, musical preference, cultural expectations, and arousal needs (Thaut, 1989).

The **iso principle** explains how music can vector a patient's mood state. The iso principle (Shantin, 1970) is a technique in which the patient's mood state is initially matched within the music. After matching the patient's mood state musically, therefore validating his or her emotional suffering, the music is gradually vectored towards the desired therapeutic goal. The emotional state of the client begins to then vector in the direction of the music. A review of various mood induction techniques (Clark, 1983; Field et al., 2000; Sloboda, 1999) found that musical mood induction techniques vectored emotional states towards greater positivity, increased arousal, and improved present-mindedness. Music's ability to vector mood states positively impacts ICU patients and their families. Therapeutically designed medical music therapy interventions can facilitate a reconnection to lost feelings of hope, joy, and peace when the patient's life-threatening circumstances can cause overwhelming despair and fear.

A Family-Centered Approach to Patient Care in the ICU

Care of the patient's family is an important factor in the patient's experience of illness and recovery. Interventions that support families of ICU patients can positively influence the family's perceptions and expectations, as well as they way they cope and deal with the situation (Appleyard et al., 2000). A family-centered approach to patient care identifies with Family Systems Theory, and nurses, social workers, chaplains, music therapists, and massage therapists in the ICU can provide interventions.

The Family Systems Theory (Broderick & Smith, 1979) states that the family unit is an interdependent and continually interacting whole, greater than the sum of its parts. The model takes into consideration the family's structure and member characteristics, interactional styles, ability to adjust to challenging situations, and life stages the family is cycling through (Turnbull & Turnbull, 1990). A family develops stability by maintaining traditional roles and functions established by family members (Appleyard et al., 2000; Bitter & Corey, 1996). Predictable interactional processes establish patterns of family interrelationship (e.g., how, when, and to whom) (Dykeman & Appleton, 1999). These inherent structures allow for adaptation according to changing internal and external conditions (Appleyard et al., 2000). Therefore, a best practice medical music therapy treatment approach should comprehensively address the needs of the patient and the family.

In the context of a social learning model (Yalom, 1995), music therapy group experiences enhance the social microcosm of families experiencing grief and loss by facilitating honest emotional and behavioral communication patterns. These sessions provide family members opportunities to practice more desirable forms of emotional expression and regulation, social interaction, and behavior that are more conducive to positive family relations (Shaller & Rivera Smith, 2002). When feelings of shock, fear, confusion, helplessness, and uncertainty are overwhelming for ICU patients and their families, music therapy sessions offer experiences of comfort, support, togetherness, and positive coping.

Music therapy initiatives are more readily received and integrated when they are aligned with hospital staff, department, and administrator goals. Implementation of the innovative Critical Care Family Assistance Program (CCFAP), sponsored by the CHEST and Eli Lilly and Company Foundations, began at several ICU pilot sites across the country in 2002. The purpose of the program was to improve patient and family services on the ICU through educational and support resources. Implementation of this program created a wonderful opportunity for interdisciplinary collaboration and music therapy program development. Sponsors of the CCFAP provided funding to include patient and family music therapy services at two of its ICU research sites, Evanston and Highland Park Hospitals of Evanston Northwestern Healthcare in Illinois.

The CCFAP is designed in accordance with five phases: planning and needs assessment, education and information, creation and distribution of comfort care materials, implementation, and evaluation. Music therapy services are briefly discussed in conjunction with these five phases of the project in the assessment, treatment, and outcome sections of this chapter. Detailed information on the CCFAP project is presented in Volume 128 of *Chest* (2005), the journal of the American College of Chest Physicians (see Dowling & Lederer, 2005; Dowling, Vender, Guilianelli, & Wang, 2005; Dowling & Wang, 2005; Gentling, Grady, & Mattox, 2005; Guilianelli, Kelly, & Skelskey, 2005; Guntupalli, McCaffree, Vender, Clary, & LoCicero, 2005; Lederer, Goode, & Dowling, 2005; Medina, 2005; Robillard et al., 2005; Skelskey, Robillard, & Irwin, 2005).

Music Therapy on the Adult ICU

The planning and needs assessment phase of music therapy services focuses on collaboration with research or program development team members, assessment of patient and family needs, and consultation with members of the ICU interdisciplinary team. Education and training must be provided to ICU interdisciplinary team members who often have varied levels of exposure to, and understanding of, music therapy as applied by board-certified music therapists. The ICU staff's accurate understanding of the role and benefits of music therapy, and the reasons for patient and family referrals, is essential to the successful development of a medical music therapy ICU program. As demonstrated in our review of the literature, there are many misconceptions about the role of music and music therapy in critical care settings.

Many patients and families can benefit from medical music therapy services in the ICU. The music therapist considers many issues when triaging patient referrals, such as the patient's level of physical, emotional, and spiritual suffering/distress; need for life support measures (MV or dialysis); level of consciousness; and prognosis. The music therapist also considers family issues, including visitation of young children, concerns and conflicts, lack of support, loss and trauma history, a poor or terminal prognosis, understanding and acceptance of the patient's prognosis, or plan to withdraw life support measures.

Referral Process

All members of the interdisciplinary team make referrals for music therapy, though most commonly they are made by the patient's physician, nurse, or social worker.

Music therapy services, when part of a grant-funded program or the hospital general budget, are free of charge for patients and their families. For example, one music therapy program is dedicated to reducing the pain and anxiety of adult burn patients in the ICU setting. Music therapy on the Comprehensive Burn Care Center at MetroHealth Medical Center is funded through a generous grant from the Kulas Foundation. The Kulas Foundation is well known in Cleveland, Ohio, for their philanthropic efforts toward the promotion of arts, culture, arts education, and music therapy (http://foundationcenter.org/grantmaker/kulas/). Since 1990, the Kulas Foundation has supported music therapy endeavors through research grants. The Kulas Foundation currently provides funding for the MetroHealth Medical Center to hire a research/clinical music therapist from the Cleveland Music School Settlement for its Comprehensive Burn Care Center. The Kulas Foundation, Cleveland Music School Settlement, and MetroHealth Medical Center have continued this collaborative relationship since 1997.

Referrals are made by calling, paging, speaking directly to the music therapist on the unit, or writing an order in the patient's electronic medical chart. ICU patients and their families are referred to music medical therapy for many reasons.

Reasons for ICU Patient and Family Medical Music Therapy Referrals

- Pre- and post-surgical support
- Dangerously erratic physiologic markers of heart rate, respiration rate, blood pressure, etc.
- Procedural support (placement of nasal gastric tube, wound care/debridement, breathing trials and ventilator weaning, extubation)
- Pain and symptom management (breathing difficulties, nausea, sleep disturbance/disorders, ICU psychosis)
- Long-term hospitalization
- Neurologic rehabilitation
- Sensory regulation, integration, appropriate stimulation
- Co-treatment with physical, respiratory, speech, or child life therapies
- Psychosocial and/or spiritual patient and family support
- Reduction of patients' depression, frustration, anxiety, and fear
- End of life, withdrawal of life support measures

Once a referral is made, the music therapist consults with the patient's primary care nurse to assess the patient's situation, gain a broader perspective on the reasons for referral, and gather preliminary information on the family situation. If the referral seems appropriate at this time, the music therapist then speaks with members of the patient's family, as available, to discuss the music therapy referral and gather assessment information.

Assessment Procedure and Approach

Music therapy services are often introduced, explained, and provided to the families of patients in the ICU when they are in a state of shock and crisis themselves. In this context, the music therapist's presence and approach is of great importance. The music therapist modifies her body posture and gesturing, volume level, tone and pacing of voice, use of breath, and eye contact to communicate safety and reassurance. During the initial conversation with the patient's family, the music therapist introduces himself/herself and briefly explains music therapy and the possible benefits to the patient and the family. Patient and family specific questions about music therapy are addressed at this time. When the family is not available for consultation, the music therapist gathers as much information to complete the assessment from the patient (if possible), the medical chart, social worker, referral source, and primary care nurse. Information gathered for the initial ICU patient assessment includes:

- *Physical/Medical:* The patient's current medical diagnosis, situation, and prognosis; significant medical history; current sedative and analgesic medications; physical functioning; current **DNR** status; precautions (contact or droplet), and whether the patient is **intubated** or has a **tracheotomy**.
- *Cognition/Communication:* The patient's level of neurological functioning and consciousness (sedation, coma, significant neurologic damage); nonverbal communication patterns.
- *Psychosocial/Spiritual:* Presence of emotional or spiritual pain and suffering; significant history of mental illness; current emotional or spiritual concerns; needs of the patient's family; coping strategies and abilities.
- *Music:* The patient's past musical experiences, preferences, and uses of music; responses during the initial assessment session.

Music therapy materials are provided to the ICU staff, patients, and their family members to promote comfort and reduce the noxious environmental stimuli of the ICU setting. Comfort care materials on the ICU may include music relaxation tapes and an ICU listening lending library. Patients and families may choose from the library CDs, conscientiously selected by music therapists for the ICU setting, or they can bring their own from home. The library provides portable CD players and disposable headsets. These materials should be stored in a locked closet in an area easily accessible to the family 24 hours a day (e.g., the family consultation room with the key available at the unit secretary's desk or nursing station). Music therapists provide staff and family members caring for ICU patients with education and individualized recommendations for the use of recorded music to promote comfort and reduce stress in the ICU. The music therapist adjusts recommendations for recorded music based on each patient's changing needs, observed responses, and levels of consciousness over the course of his or her ICU stay.

Music therapists at the Metro Health Medical Center (MHMC) in Cleveland, Ohio, currently use the *Metrohealth Medical Center Comprehensive Burn Care Center Music*

Therapy Research Assessment, in the Appendix to this chapter, which was developed by music therapists at the Cleveland Music School Settlement.

Music Therapy Goals for the ICU

Music therapy is provided to meet the varied needs of hospital administrators, program and research funders, interdisciplinary team members, and the patients and their families of various ICU settings. Hospital administrators desire reduced lengths of stay for patients, increased staff retention, decreased legal action, improved coordinated systems of care, and increased professional knowledge about serving the families of critically ill patients (Gentling et al., 2005). Goals of family-focused programs, such as the CCFAP, are addressed by music therapy services. Directors and funders of the CCFAP were concerned with preparing ICU interdisciplinary teams to meet the needs of the families of ICU patients, increasing family satisfaction with the care and treatment of their critically ill family member, and improving the hospital's ability to respond to family needs within a structured feedback model (Dowling, Vender, et al., 2005) The Kulas Foundation provides funds for music therapy services at the MetroHealth Medical Center in Cleveland, Ohio. Promoting music therapy program development, research efforts, and dissemination of knowledge are goal areas of the Kulas Foundation. Clinical research studies on the effectiveness of active/live music therapy interventions for ICU burn patients and their families demonstrate successful attainment of the goals set forth by the Kulas Foundation (Prensner et al., 2001; Tan et al., 2008).

Music therapists provide psychosocial and spiritual support to patients and their family members in ICU settings through individual and family music therapy sessions. The music therapist's primary goal is to holistically support ICU patients and their families throughout their time in the ICU, whether it is a brief 24–48 hour postoperative experience with a good prognosis for recovery, or a long and complicated ICU stay with a poor or terminal prognosis. There are many goals for patients and their adult and child family members. Table 5 below organizes these goals according to three levels of music therapy practice: Supportive, Communicative/Expressive, and Transformative (Dileo & Dneaster, 2005). This serves as a model for music therapy intervention and protocol development along a continuum of care. Applications of music therapy interventions are based on the patient's and family members' needs, as well as the music therapist's level of training and expertise. Goals for critically ill/injured patients in the ICU setting are presented in accordance with these levels of music therapy practice in the Table 5.

Table 5

Levels of Music Therapy Practice and Goals of Care for ICU Patients & Families

Goals for:	Supportive Level of Medical Music Therapy	Communicative/ Expressive Level of Medical Music Therapy	Transformative Level of Medical Music Therapy
ICU patients	*Physical* decreased pain, nausea, breathing difficulties, sleep disturbance, and agitation; increased relaxation and attainment of homeostasis; distraction during invasive or stressful procedures; decreased sedative and analgesic medications *Cognition* decreased/ masked noxious environmental stimuli, increased arousal and orientation; increased appropriate sensory stimulation, regulation, and tolerance; increased nonverbal communication	*Psychosocial* increased nonverbal communication and interaction; increased expression and release of feelings, needs and concerns; improved coping; improved sense of connection with patient; acknowledged fear, anger, sadness, trauma, and loss; acceptance; acknowledgment of limitations and losses; maintained identity; enhanced feelings of control and self esteem; reduced helplessness	*Psychosocial/ Spiritual* resolved fear, anger, and sadness, exploration of grief and loss related to changes/losses; exploration of spiritual/existential issues and concerns; found hope, meaning, and purpose in one's suffering; exploration of new roles and ways of being; experienced success and creativity; explore and address death and dying issues/ conflicts

Adult family members of ICU patients	*Physical/ Environmental* decreased stress and anxiety; reduced noxious environmental stimuli; improved coping; increased use/competence of recorded music to support patient/ alter environment; increased family satisfaction	*Psychosocial* increased sense of connection with loved one; opportunities for nonverbal communication and interaction; emotional expression and release; improved coping	*Psychosocial/ Spiritual* exploration and successful attainment of new role functions, transcendence in time of loss and suffering, experienced peaceful and even beautiful death transitions amidst the barriers of the ICU environment
Child family members of ICU patients	*Environmental* reduced occurrence and severity of traumatic sensory information in the environment; increased sense of comfort and predictability *Cognition* increased understanding of their parents' or grandparents' condition	*Psychosocial* increased communication between critically ill patient and the child; family togetherness; opportunities for the child to play an active role in the patient's care; nonverbal and verbal expression/ release of feelings, fears, and concerns about their parents' or grandparents' health and recovery; sense of control and empowerment; and experiences of creativity, joyfulness, fun, and celebration with family	*Psychosocial/ Spiritual* exploration and discussion of patient's, the well parent's, and child's new roles and changes, experiences of creative success and empowerment, exploration of questions about the meaning of illness and death, increased understanding of death and participation in relationship completion when death of parent, grandparent, or sibling is expected, saying "Thank you, I love you, I'm sorry."

Implementation of Interventions

Adult ICUs are inpatient hospital units where patients with life-threatening illness/ injury receive life-sustaining treatments and interventions. Length of stay on the ICU ranges from 24 hours to 3 months. Environmental influences such as elevated decibel levels, overstimulating light and sensory issues, and cramped spaces impact both ICU patients and their families. Changes in the environment are being implemented to support patients' health and well-being. The United States Environmental Protection Agency (EPA) recommends that noise levels in hospitals should not exceed 40 decibels (dBA) during the day and 30dBA at night (Tijunelis, Fitzsullivan, & Henderson, 2005); however, in one study, researchers found noise levels on the ICU to be between 74dBA and 80dBA (Kahn et al., 1998). Noise pollution on the ICU is not exclusive to hospitals in this country; it is a common phenomenon across the globe (Kahn et al., 1998).

Although noise pollution is frequent, more than 50% of the noise that occurs in intensive care units can be regulated through behavior modification. In a 3-week behavior modification program, ICU staff were asked to place all beepers on vibrate mode, use intercoms for emergencies only, and reduce conversation in patient care areas. They were successful in decreasing noise levels in three out of four time blocks measured throughout the day. The only time block where they found no significant changes in noise levels was the 12 midnight to 6 a.m. block, as these hours are already usually the quietest time of the day (Kahn et al., 1998).

Researchers at Johns Hopkins Hospital studied noise level in their pediatric intensive care unit and its impact on nursing staff (Morrison, Haas, Shaffner, Garrett, & Fackler, 2003). They found that the weighted average sound pressure levels in the PICU were 61.2dBA during the day and 58.8dBA during the night. Both values were more than 20dBA above the recommendations by the Environmental Protection Agency. Since the dBA scale is logarithmic, a small amount of sound increment is perceived as a large increase in noise levels (Kahn et al., 1998).

In support of a calm and quiet environment, critical care nurses and professional music therapists both recommend that ICU patients are provided with uninterrupted time for functional music and medical music therapy. Continued opportunity for rest should follow either of these interventions. Medical music therapy family sessions typically take place in the ICU patient's room, waiting area, or family conference room, allowing for a more controlled influence on the sound environment.

Co-treatment sessions most commonly occur during medical procedures that may increase the patient's pain, anxiety, or stress. The music therapist may work with child life specialists if an older child or adolescent is admitted to the adult ICU, or when children are visiting a parent, grandparent, or sibling in the ICU. Collaborating during physical therapy or occupational therapy sessions can be helpful by increasing a patient's tolerance for rehabilitation activities, thereby facilitating attainment of the goals determined by these disciplines. Music and speech therapy both address goals related to swallowing through tongue and laryngeal strengthening exercises (Rychener, 2005). Social workers and chaplains commonly co-treat with music therapists. In the ICU, co-treatment with these disciplines occurs when the patient's or family member's circumstances are particularly traumatic, when withdrawal of life-support measures is planned, or when inconsolable or conflicted families are negatively impacting patient care.

Music Therapy Intervention Strategies

Anxiolytic and audioanalgesic medical music therapy interventions for ICU patients are common intervention strategies on the ICU. The music therapist facilitates music-assisted relaxation interventions by providing verbal directions to encourage the patient's deep breathing, increase sense of self and body sensations, or increase relaxation and/or imagery. Common instruments used during live music relaxation sessions include the guitar, omnichord/Q-chord, autoharp, and piano/keyboard. The advantage of using live music over recorded music is that the music therapist can immediately adjust the music in response to the patient's outcomes. With live instrumental playing, the music therapist is able to manipulate musical elements such as tempo, dynamics, and meter through the principles of entrainment and the iso principle to facilitate desired outcomes for ICU patients. For example, gradual decreases in the tempo of music have been observed to be highly effective in decreasing respiratory rates in ICU patients. A powerful and instant antagonist to hyperventilation, music regulates and slows elevated and erratic respiration rates frequently observed among patients experiencing pain and anxiety.

One music-assisted relaxation technique is Music-Based Imagery (MBI). MBI is a relaxation technique utilizing music and imagery where the context of the imagery is sung to the patient. During the music therapy assessment, the patient provides the music therapist with a detailed description of a safe and relaxing place. This information is then placed into the context of a song that is sung to the patient during MBI. The melody used in this protocol is the second movement (*Largo*) of Anton Dvorak's *New World Symphony Opus 95.* This melody is also known as an African-American spiritual titled *Going Home.* This particular melody was chosen by music therapists for this intervention due to its simple chord progression, small pitch range, and its alternate ascending and descending musical contours mimicking the patient's inhalation and exhalation of breath. The simplicity and predictability of this melody increases the ICU patient's ability to focus on the words and imagery. The music therapist often accompanies himself/herself on the Q-chord for this protocol.

At the beginning of MBI, the therapist entrains the tempo of the music with the patient's respiratory rate. Patients are encouraged to close their eyes and allow their breaths to slow and deepen as the music therapist gradually slows the music. At this point, the music therapist then sings improvised lyrics describing the patient's safe and relaxing place to the melody of *Going Home.* At the end of the song, patients are encouraged to maintain their deep sense of relaxation as they are guided to gradually bring their awareness back to their body and hospital room.

Common ICU Music Therapy Intervention Strategies

- assisted relaxation supported by therapist instrumental accompaniment
- Music-Based Imagery (MBI)
- Music-based relaxation supported by recorded music
- Music Alternate Engagement (MAE)
- Active music listening
- Therapeutic singing
- Song phrase cued response
- Music with deep breathing exercise
- Therapeutic instrument playing
- Sound of Family Together (S.O.F.T.) Music Program

Medical music therapists also choose to combine personalized verbal directions for relaxation over recorded music. A survey stemming from a multi-stage research study being conducted at MetroHealth Medical Center (MHMC) provides the parameters of the psychophysical properties of music for relaxation (Tan, Yowler, Super, & Fratianne, 2010). Selections of recorded relaxation music recommended by a panel of experts were rated by a group of music therapists and healthy adults. The results from the survey identified the following parameters in defining relaxation music.

Psychophysical Properties of Music for Relaxation

Psychophysical Properties	Parameters
Tempo	Approximately 60bpm
Pitch Range	Pitches around C5 (high C)
Dynamic Variation	Small changes, e.g., between *pp–p* or *mf–f*
Melodic Complexity	Moderately simple melodies
Harmonic Complexity	Diatonic, within tonal center
Rhythmic Complexity	Very simple rhythms
Instrumental Complexity	Small ensemble/chamber-size ensemble
Lyrics/Words	Majority with no lyrics/words
Vocalization	No vocalizations
Mode	Majority in major mode
Contour	Majority with ascending and descending contours
Timbre	Mostly performed on synthesizers, followed by strings

The Music Alternate Engagement (MAE) protocol carried out at MHMC is designed in accordance with the Gate Control Theory of Pain and the use of music therapy as an attention-diversion technique. MAE consists of a menu of medical music therapy interventions aimed at actively engaging ICU patients in music and diverting them from painful procedures and sensations. The menu of interventions includes (a) active music listening, (b) therapeutic singing, (c) song phrase cued response, (d) deep breathing exercise, and (d) therapeutic instrumental playing. These interventions require either passive or active participation from the patients and are adapted to accommodate the varied functioning levels of patients. The selection of music or songs used in the MAE is predetermined by the assessment interview. Songs are picked according to the patient's music preferences and include those by their favorite artists or from their most preferred genre. Medical music therapy MAE interventions are provided in treatment rooms or in ICU patient rooms, alone or in conjunction with medical procedures.

In active music listening, patients listen to familiar songs of their choosing. Preferred song selections are either played and sung live by the music therapist or played on the compact disc player. Patients engage in active discussions with the music therapist about the songs during this process. The conversations may center on basic facts about the songs, or they can focus on the patients' associated personal memories, thoughts, and feelings in relation to the song.

Therapeutic singing in the ICU can refer to the patient's or family's participation through singing familiar songs with the music therapist. Live music played by the music therapist on the guitar is most commonly used for this intervention.

During song phrase cued response, patients listen to songs in order to generate a specific response at a designated time in the song. Live music played by the music therapist is always used for this intervention. At the end of a musical phrase of a song, the music therapist omits certain lyrics and has the patient "fill in the blanks." Patients sing the words of the original song or fill in their own words to express their thoughts and emotions at that moment. For example, a patient once substituted the words "Let it heal" to the famous Beatles' song "Let It Be."

Music with deep breathing exercise is beneficial immediately after painful or stress-inducing treatments such as the debridement of a patient's wounds. Patients are reminded of the deep breathing exercises they did during the MBI intervention and are encouraged to listen to the music and entrain their breathing with the speed of the music.

Rhythm instruments such as maracas, tambourines, small drums, and rhythm sticks are available for use during therapeutic instrumental playing. The physical limitations of ICU patients often prevent them from physical engagement in this intervention. Patients with burns to their hands are not able to manipulate instruments. At times, it may be hazardous for the patient to play instruments due to the presence of IV lines and monitor cables.

Medical music therapy interventions with ICU patients should also support the family members. Music therapy interventions are non-invasive and can support the needs of family with patients in the ICU at their various emotional, social, and cognitive development levels. For example, the Sound of Family Together (S.O.F.T.) Music Program was developed by the music therapist at MHMC (Tan et al., 2008) to address the needs of children visiting a loved one in the burn ICU. The S.O.F.T. Music Program was designed to allow the patient's child or grandchild to record his or her voice(s) on an audio media software program called *GarageBand.* Music tracks (e.g., drums, guitar, and piano) can then be laid over the vocal tracks to create a musical song/prose. The child determines the content of the audio CD with assistance from the music therapist. Content may include original songs that the child writes for the hospitalized family member; piggy-back songs (changing the lyrics of existing songs); the patient's favorite songs; the child's favorite songs, stories, poems, and special messages; and compilation of songs from CDs. The recorded tracks can then be imported into *iTunes* and burned onto a writable-compact disc. *iPhoto* can be used to take pictures of the children or grandchildren for the album cover of the audio CD. *PrintShop* is then used to design the CD cover. All software programs used for this study (i.e., *GarageBand, iTunes, iPhoto*, and *PrintShop*) are available on the MacBook laptop computer. The finished product is presented to the patient by the music therapist. The State-Trait Anxiety Inventory (STAI) is used to test the efficacy of the S.O.F.T. program. It is first administered to the child (STAI-C) and one non-hospitalized adult family member (STAI-Y) within 4 days of the patient's admission to document his or her baseline level of anxiety. The inventories are conducted again after the completion of the S.O.F.T. Music Program to evaluate its impact on the family members.

Medical Music Therapy Interventions with an ICU Patient and the Family: A Case Study

Brad and his family graciously agreed to share their experiences of the ICU and music therapy for the purposes of this chapter. The information presented below is based on recollections and reflections of Brad, his wife and children, and the music therapist. Brad and his family participated in a phone interview conducted April 27, 2008. This written case study was reviewed and approved by Brad and his family prior to publication. Consent for release and publication of this information was obtained by AMTA.

The following case example is of a young man and his family whose experience with a life-threatening illness and journey to recovery affected multiple interdisciplinary team members. Highlights from music therapy sessions are presented to exemplify the role of music therapy in addressing the psychosocial and spiritual needs of this ICU patient and his family during their ICU experience.

Brad, a 37-year-old Caucasian male acquired an infection that rapidly spread, causing sepsis and multisystem organ failure. As a result, he was admitted to the ICU and a medication-induced coma was deemed appropriate. A mechanical ventilator and dialysis machine supported Brad's essential bodily functions for several weeks.

Several members of the ICU team, including a nurse, social worker, and child life specialist, made referrals for music therapy. Reasons for referral included shock, reduction of sedative medications, and patient and family emotional distress. Multiple referrals for the same patient/family can indicate that the patient and family are in a very critical and difficult situation. Triaged accordingly, Brad's referral was categorized a high priority for music therapy services. The music therapist reviewed Brad's electronic medical record, spoke with several members of his ICU treatment team, met with his family, and provided a music therapy assessment session within 24 hours of receiving the referrals.

The shock of Brad's life-threatening illness and the ensuing upheaval of daily patterns and family role responsibilities may have resulted in an altered state of consciousness for his wife Katy during this time. Aware that significant stress is believed to negatively impact the brain's ability to make new memories and retrieve known information, the music therapist presented information in a manner that was accessible to Katy. While conscientiously softening her body posture and gestures to communicate safety and reassurance, the music therapist purposefully modified the tone and pacing of her speaking voice, use of breath, and eye contact.

In response to the music therapist's assessment questions, Katy defined her husband as a "lover of music" and described the important role of music in Brad's life, his musical preferences, and past experiences. The music therapist integrated Brad's musical preferences into the assessment session, providing interventions to address his immediate physical, emotional, and spiritual needs. Live guitar and singing were tailored to facilitate changes in physiologic variables specific to Brad's medically determined needs and in accordance with the iso principle and rhythmic entrainment. Familiar, preferred music was presented in a simplified, yet recognizable, form to promote a sense of holding, comfort, and connection for both Brad and his wife. For example, one of Brad's favorite songs, *California Stars* by Wilco, was musically adapted to therapeutically address his varied needs. The music therapist manipulated the various elements of music throughout the assessment session based on Brad's nonverbal responses to the intervention.

California Stars became a recurring theme that was integrated into many sessions during Brad's ICU stay. The music therapist, to meet Brad's multiple, changing needs over the course of his 3-week coma and 6-week ICU stay, adapted the song's musical elements and therapeutic role.

Rhythm: A simple rhythmic pattern was first performed on guitar in a manner that mirrored the erratic pattern of Brad's blood pressure and heart rates reflected on vital sign monitors. The music therapist gradually increased regularity and predictability of the rhythmic pattern until establishing a firm, steady, and predictable pattern and holding it. This adaptation was made to facilitate changes in physiologic variables in desired directions to promote recovery from shock. Simplified, organized, and predictable rhythmic patterns may also provide an appropriate and necessary form of sensory stimulation accessible to brain-injured ICU patients in a coma, thus promoting cortical recovery (Baker & Tamplin, 2006).

Tempo: In each session, the tempo of the live music provided by the music therapist reflected the combined rhythms of Brad's heart and respiration rates, blood pressure, and oxygen saturation levels. Decisions to gradually increase or decrease the speed of the live music in each session were made after consultation with Brad's nurse, who made recommendations based on his medical needs at that time.

Timbre: The music therapist played a classical guitar with nylon strings. Clear and pure vocal tones of a pleasing quality were sung to facilitate a sense of comfort, grounding, and safety. Purposeful use of the voice is believed to have particular benefit for coma patients because of its strong human connection and ability to be a shared, resonating experience between the provider and receiver of the medium (Baker & Tamplin, 2006). The music therapist hypothesized that purposeful and controlled use of the human voice could increase Brad's sense of internal and external familiarity and safety, cueing his instinctive regulatory processes to enter a state of healing and recovery, instead of fight or flight.

Pitch: A narrow pitch range, reflective of the natural speaking voice, was used. Large jumps between pitches in the song(s) were reduced through step-wise movements of smaller pitch intervals. When deemed therapeutically appropriate, pitches of a higher vocal range and jumps between pitches were purposefully used to assess Brad's ability to consistently respond to environmental stimuli.

Volume: Steps were taken to reduce all extraneous auditory stimuli in Brad's room. Live instrumental and vocal music provided was of a soft volume level.

Form: The form of Brad's preferred songs, including *California Stars*, was adhered to for the purpose of song recognition. This song was provided at different times in the sessions dependent upon therapeutic need and with consideration for the overall form of each session's progression from beginning to end. To establish familiarity, increase awareness of the environment, and create a sense of holding, the song was used at the beginning of sessions. At other times, *California Stars* was provided as the closing song in the session; the lyrics are a reflection and reminder of Brad's need to rest, the comfort of his wife's touch, and a sense of hope.

Lyrics: The lyrics of the song *California Stars* acknowledge a sense of weariness and a yearning to be somewhere else while simultaneously reminding us that strength, comfort, and hope are derived from the touch of a lover's hand, his or her encouraging words, and the vision of a new day.

California Stars – by Wilco*

I'd like to rest my heavy head tonight
On a bed of California stars
I'd like to lay my weary bones tonight
On a bed of California stars

I'd love to feel
Your hand touching mine
And tell me why
I must keep working on

Yes I'd give my life
To lay my head tonight on a bed
Of California stars

I'd like to dream
My troubles all away
On a bed of California stars

Jump up from my star bed
Make another day
Underneath my California stars
They hang like grapes
On vines that shine
And warm the lovers' glass
Like friendly wine

So I'd give this world
Just to dream a dream with you
On our bed of California stars

*Wilco, words by Woody Guthrie, music by Jay Bennett/Jeff Tweedy (1998). Los Angeles, CA: Woody Guthrie Publications, Inc.

There were times when the music therapist would alter the lyrics of the song to make direct statements of encouragement and reinforce Brad's spiritual will and desire to maintain a healing trajectory. The strong connection between Brad and his wife was also reflected in the lyric changes. Wilco's original lyrics of *California Stars* were changed by the music therapist to "Brad, we're here with you telling you why, you must keep working on holding to life. So rest your head tonight on this bed, you beautiful star" and sung as Katy sat at Brad's bedside holding his hand.

Katy reflects that the use of *California Stars* was "so special" and "exactly what Brad needed to come out of that coma." Music was integral to many aspects of Brad's life and one of his passions prior to the onset of his life-threatening illness. From Katy's perspective, the provision of music therapy sessions during her husband's ICU stay was so "helpful and comforting" at a "time when we were so emotional." She believes that Brad was able to hear the music and was listening and that it calmed him down. She further commented that provision of music therapy sessions felt very "special" and "good for her in the environment of the ICU."

The child life specialist consulted with the music therapist when it was time for Brad and Katy's children, Ben, then 7, and Sofie, then 5, to visit their dad in the ICU. Measures were taken to reduce possible traumatic sensory experiences for the children, including covering Brad's body with his sheets up to his chest, as his hands and feet had turned black with **necrosis**. Ben and Sofie spent time in the ICU as they were comfortable. Their grandparents' presence during these visits provided the children with opportunities for individualized attention, flexibility of visitation, and physical comfort as Katy tended to Brad's needs and spoke with medical personnel. Family music therapy sessions were often provided during the children's visits.

Brad, Katy, Ben, and Sofie have several favorite memories of their time in music therapy together. One particularly fond memory is of a time together, with their grandparents, after

Brad had regained consciousness and was beginning to vocalize. The family played the tone chimes and sang *Here Comes the Sun* by the Beatles. The music therapist grouped family members in dyads or triads, provided them with chimes according to the I–IV–V chords of the song, and nonverbally cued the family to play together. Brad was encouraged to vocalize "do-do-do-do" at the appropriate time in the song as the music therapist and his family sang. To maximize success, the music therapist cued breaths and sustained the last note/word of phrases before his part. Brad's family smiled and laughed together as their individual musical voices joined together in the creation of music.

Another fond memory is from a session when the music therapist used the song "Lean on Me" to facilitate exploration and discussion of the ways family members take turns helping each other. Brad, Katy, and the children rewrote portions of the song's lyrics to reflect their current feelings, needs, and means of supporting each other. These lyrics were discussed and expanded upon in the session to discuss changes in each family member's role. The music therapist sang the family's new lyrics, accompanying herself on the guitar, as Brad's children played small percussion instruments.

Ben reflects that his participation in music therapy sessions helped him "feel closer" to his dad when he visited. He remembers feeling sad during that time and states that the music therapy experiences helped him "feel better" and deal with "how hard everything was." Ben's favorite part of music therapy sessions was playing instruments, including the chimes.

Brad remembers his children laughing and having fun during these times in the ICU environment. Recalling the memory of lying in a hospital bed, watching his family play chimes and sing a Beatles song, Brad states, "It was the craziness of this experience in the context of my situation that allowed us to laugh and have fun together."

Music therapy individual and family sessions were provided until Brad was discharged from the hospital. An inpatient on four different hospital units, Brad endured 20 surgeries, multiple amputations, and 6 months in bed before he was ready for outpatient rehabilitation. For Brad, his personal experiences in music therapy brought up many feelings. Brad says it was "the incongruity of the presence of something so beautiful in such a horrible environment" that brought tears to his face many times.

Documentation of Outcomes

Many outcome measures are applied in the ICU setting. The *Acute Physiology and Chronic Health Evaluation* (APACHE II) evaluates baseline variables. Assessment tools commonly used with coma patients include the Glasgow Coma Scale (GCS) and the Rancho Los Amigos Scale. The Profile of Mood States (POMS), State-Trait Anxiety Inventory (STAI) in its various forms, and the Richmond Agitation Sedation Scale (RASS) are cited throughout the ICU literature to evaluate patient mood state, anxiety, and agitation, respectively. The *FACES Anxiety Scale* is one validated self-report measurement of anxiety that exists for adult patients on mechanical ventilation (McKinley et al., 2003; McKinley et al., 2004). Visual Analog Scales (VAS) are also used to rate pain and anxiety.

Music therapy evaluation measures used in the CCFAP project include the *Patient Progress Notes: Music Therapy – Anxiety Management* pre-post session form, the *Patient Progress Notes: Music Therap – Pain Management* pre-post session form, and the *Music*

Therapy ICU Staff Survey. Former Evanston Northwestern Healthcare music therapist Jessica Shaller Gerweck, MM, MT-BC, with assistance from Brenda Paperniak, MT-BC, and Ming-Chen Lu, MA, created these forms. In addition, statistics related to music therapy services (number of patients, family members, and sessions; total hours of music therapy; reason for referral and referral source) are recorded and tabulated for department and administrative reports.

Music therapy outcomes for ICU burn patients at MHMC are recorded and measured through the *Metrohealth Medical Center Comprehensive Burn Care Center: The Effect of Patient-Preferred Music, Relaxation Music, and Standard Care Environment on Patients in Intensive Care Units – Data Collection Form*. This music therapy form was designed by Xueli Tan, MM, MT-BC, from the Cleveland Music School Settlement, and is employed in research projects at the burn care center of MHMC. Research projects are supported jointly by the Kulas Foundation (Cleveland, OH), the Clinical Research Unit at MetroHealth Medical Center (Case Western Reserve University School of Medicines) and the Arthur Flagler Fultz Research Grant (American Music Therapy Association, 2005).

A majority of patients in ICU settings are often under heavy sedation due to pain and comfort issues, anxiety, or intubation. Their responses and, therefore, any behavioral measurable outcomes are not easily visible to the observer. Thus, measurable outcomes for research and clinical documentation purposes in the ICU setting need to be a comprehensive investigation of multi-faceted parameters such as behavioral observations, vital signs, **biomarkers**, and patient self-reports. Music therapists collaborate with health professionals such as doctors, nurses, laboratory technicians, respiratory therapists, and hospital research associates to obtain these multi-faceted parameters.

The music therapy evaluation phase of individual patient responses occurs during and after each session. Outcome measures of patient pain and anxiety pre- and post-music therapy session, changes in physiological markers (heart rate, respiration rate, blood pressure, and oxygen saturation), behavioral observations, and verbal responses are recorded in each patient's medical record following the music therapy session. On average, music therapy sessions are approximately 30 minutes in length in the ICU setting, with a range of 20–90 minutes.

Outcomes recorded on 40 ICU patients through the *Patient Progress Notes: Music Therapy – Anxiety Management* pre-post session form demonstrate a reduction of the patient's anxiety by 59.6% as rated by the patient, their family member, or nurse; an average 79.2% reduction of related patient behaviors observed by the music therapist; and an average 68% reduction of related psychosocial manifestations of anxiety as observed by the music therapist. ICU patient outcomes related to pain were recorded on the *Patient Progress Notes: Music Therapy – Pain Management* pre-post session form and demonstrate an average decrease in pain rating (patient, family, or nurse) of 71%; an average decrease in behavioral observations of pain of 94%, and an average decrease in psychosocial expressions of pain of 89%.

Integration of music therapy in the CCFAP produced positive outcomes for all involved.

Over 390 music therapy sessions were provided to patients in the ICUs of Evanston and Highland Park hospitals from July 2003 through September 2004 as part of the CCFAP project. Approximately 300 family members participated in music therapy sessions during this time. The music therapists addressed family goals of the CCFAP, including reduced stress, increased communication, increased satisfaction with the care of their loved one, and increased knowledge/provision of informational materials. Outcomes specific to the discipline of music therapy were not evaluated in the CCFAP study, though empirical evidence demonstrates that family members who participate in music therapy sessions achieve these stated goals.

ICU interdisciplinary team members report positive outcomes from music therapy for their patients and their family members as well as themselves. Twenty-five ICU interdisciplinary team members (16 nurses, 3 chaplains, 2 social workers, 2 physicians, 1 occupational therapist, and 1 medical secretary) completed the *Music Therapy ICU Staff Survey* during the CCFAP project at Evanston Northwestern Healthcare. Participants reported their perception of music therapy's impact according to a 5-point Likert scale: No Impact (1), Mild Impact (2), Fair Impact (3), Moderate Impact (4), and Great Impact (5). In terms of the impact of music therapy for ICU patients, participants reported the greatest impact on depressed mood state (average rating 4.54/5), anxiety and agitation (average rating 4.52/5), sensory integration and appropriate stimulation (average rating 4.5/5), emotional support (average rating 4.4/5), and spiritual support (average rating 4.25/5). Participants reported their perception of music therapy's impact for family members and ranked "satisfaction with quality of care of their loved one in the ICU" as the greatest outcome, with a 4.3/5 average rating. Additional positive outcomes include reduced family anxiety and agitation (average rating 4.25/5), increased emotional support (average rating 4.2/5), and eased "end of life" transitions for family members (average rating 4.2/5). Survey participants also ranked the impact of music therapy on their ICU experience as medical personnel. The greatest impact of music therapy, with an average rating of 4.5/5, was the reduction of their stress/anxiety levels during medical procedures (placement of **NG tube**, **extubation**, dressing change, minor medical procedures). An increased sense of calm within the ICU working environment was ranked as the second greatest benefit for medical personnel, with an average rating of 4.1/5. Collaboration with members of the CCFAP team greatly augmented the professional experience of the ENH music therapists through:

- facilitating open communication between the ICU staff and support service providers;
- providing greater opportunities for co-treatment in the ICU;
- developing strategies to implement music therapy aligned with a philosophy of care;
- increasing awareness of the needs of family members in the ICU;
- providing opportunities for collaboration on research and publication projects; and
- learning the phases of a large-scale, innovative, family-focused ICU project.

Follow-up Services

Patients who no longer require intensive care are transferred from the ICU to a step-down medical unit. Once patients recover further, they are transferred to a hospital inpatient rehabilitation unit, specialized rehabilitation center, or outpatient rehabilitation program. Patients expected to require continued specialized care due to their illness/injury are transferred to nursing homes with varied levels of skilled care.

Music therapists are often able to cross hospital units and continue to provide care with a focus on rehabilitative goals and maintained psychosocial support of patients and their families. In many hospital settings, this continuity of care provided by music therapists is unique and highly desired, since most other medical disciplines are unit-specific.

ICU patients and their family members may experience residual mental health issues as a result of their life-threatening illness/injury and prolonged elevated stress experiences. In the burn care and rehabilitation literature, emphasis on studying the psychological stress, coping, and treatment for relatives of burn patients surfaced from the late 1980s to early 1990s (Angermeier, 1991; Cella, Perry, Kulchycky, & Goodwin, 1988; Shelby, Sullivan, Groussman, Gray, & Saffle, 1992). Participation of close relatives in the care of burn patients is a stress-provoking adverse life event that can result in psychological maladjustment of these close relatives (Shelby et al., 1992). The researchers tested 14 adult relatives of patients with thermal burns and found that immune responses of the adult relatives decreased as depression and anxiety levels increased. Based on these findings, the researchers recommended that further work was needed to develop intervention programs that emphasize psychosocial adjustment and coping for the family (Shelby et al., 1992). Music therapy can address the numerous needs of the ICU patient's family through both providing music therapy interventions and teaching family members supportive activities that promote caretaking, comfort, and support/coping goals.

The Future of Music Therapy in Adult ICU

Promoting comfort for patients on MV and identifying strategies that reduce total time on MV are clinical priorities for the ICU medical team (Abott et al., 2001; Stone & Rusk, 1989). Physicians and nurses seek to alleviate anxiety, agitation, and fear for these patients, to reduce the risk for mortality and increased morbidity while reducing suffering. Preliminary empirical evidence supports the hypothesis that medical music therapy interventions designed to facilitate ventilator weaning and reduce total time spent on MV will also reduce patient morbidity and mortality rates and, therefore, reduce hospital costs.

Music's influence on the Reticular Activating System and other brain processes, despite damage associated with a coma, holds promising implications for the positive impact of medical music therapy. This may be particularly true for interventions designed to promote sensory regulation and appropriate stimulation, and increased arousal, orientation, and neurologic reorganization. The capacity of auditory rhythms to entrain rhythmic motor responses, regardless of cerebellar pathology, suggests that sensory rhythms can compensate for timing mechanisms in the brain that may be dysfunctional because of disease or injury (Molinari, Thaut, Gioia, et al., as cited in Thaut, 2008). Continued research must be done to understand music's influence on functions of the brain and its potential in early neurological healing and rehabilitation for ICU patients who experience critical events such as stroke, intracranial bleed, traumatic brain injuries, trauma, or medication-induced comas and neurologic surgeries.

A family-centered approach to care is a responsibility no hospital can ignore, given the risk for morbidity and mortality in the ICU and the reciprocal relationship between family satisfaction and positive patient outcomes. Music therapy interventions provided by board-certified music therapists address the varied and diverse needs of both ICU patients and their family members. Positive ICU patient, family, and staff outcomes demonstrated through the CCFAP led hospital administrators to conclude that additional research was necessary to determine the long-term benefits for families and for the hospital. Such benefits may include reduced lengths of hospital stay, increased staff retention, decreased legal action, an improved coordinated system of care, and an increased professional knowledge base about serving the families of critically ill patients (Gentling et al., 2005).

Very few research studies focus on investigating the psychosocial ramifications on children of adult burn patients. Previous studies focused on the impact of a burn on patients' adult relatives, primarily spouses and adult children. There are few studies investigating interventions that assist children in coping with their emotional reactions to their parents' burns. The only documented literature was from Angermeier (1991), a social worker who developed a desensitization process to facilitate first visits between young children and their parents with scarred burns. Thus, more research studies are needed to explore new interventions to help young children cope with family crisis and deal with their own issues of separation from the adult burn patient. Child, individual, and family medical music therapy sessions can reduce trauma associated with the ICU environment and can facilitate emotional adjustment and coping through a creative and non-threatening medium that is adapted according to the developmental abilities and understanding of each child. Most recently, the impact of the S.O.F.T. Music Program found positive results on the coping and adjustment of children of adults with severe burns (Tan et al., 2008).

There is a great need for research in the Intensive Care Unit (ICU) setting by board-certified music therapists. As stated in the introduction of this chapter, both nurses and music therapists have, for decades, championed the use of music in ICU settings to address patient and family needs. However, according to the summary of peer-reviewed articles outlined in this chapter, the number of "music therapy" research articles published by nurses far outweighs those by board-certified music therapists. There is also a need for music therapists to publish in critical care medical journals so that ICU nurses, physicians, respiratory therapists, and others are provided with accurate information about medical music therapy interventions.

It is important that medical music therapists agree upon and use consistent terminology when referring to music therapy in order to clarify the roles of music and the medical personnel and professional music therapists that employ this medium in medical settings. Our literature review reveals that critical care nurses who implemented Bonny's *Music Rx* recorded music listening programs achieved positive desired outcomes, while those who implemented music of their choosing achieved mixed results. Patient preference, self-directed use of recorded music listening, and the characteristics of the music are important factors that influence research outcomes. Music described as "sedative" is most often recommended in the literature for ICU patients.

The authors of this chapter encourage ICU music therapists to join together to conduct multi-site patient and family studies. Intensive care units are often the smallest units in the hospital with the least number of beds on the unit. It is necessary to keep a small patient census on these units to maintain the low nurse-to-patient ratio required for each patient due to their systemic and life-threatening needs. This fact, when translated to research efforts on ICU settings, means either that research studies take a long time to complete, or that completed studies are often too small in sample size to have statistical power or demonstrate significant differences. Therefore, multi-site clinical trials can be completed in a shorter period of time with a larger sample size.

In conclusion, the current state of our health care system is certain to change in the near future. Administrators that anticipate nursing shortages and continued budget crises are becoming increasingly open to non-pharmacologic methodologies, such as medical music therapy, that creatively reduce costs while improving patient and family care (Guilianelli et al., 2005). Positive physiologic, neurologic, psychosocial, and spiritual outcomes achieved through medical music therapy interventions suggest that this allied health care profession offers a non-pharmacologic, non-invasive and cost-efficient approach to patient and family care in the ICU setting that improves both patient and family outcomes, as well as overall satisfaction.

References

Abott, K., Sago, J., & Breen, C. (2001). Families looking back: One year after discussion of withdrawal or withholding of life-sustaining support. *Critical Care Medicine, 29*(1), 197–201.

Ahmad, H., Brophy, K., Grant, G. R., & Brandstetter, R. D. (1999). Benefit of music therapy for our intensive care unit (ICU) patients. *Heart & Lung, 28*(1), 79–80.

Aldridge, D. (1998). Life as jazz: Hope, meaning and music therapy in the treatment of life threatening illness. *Advances in Mind-Body Medicine, 14,* 271–282.

Almerud, S., & Petersson, K. (2003). Music therapy—A complementary treatment for mechanically ventilated intensive care patients. *Intensive and Critical Care Nursing, 19*(1), 21–30.

American Music Therapy Association (AMTA). (n.d.). Definition of music therapy. In *What is the profession of music therapy?* Retrieved April 2008, from www.musictherapy.org

Angermeier, J. (1991). A desensitization process to facilitate first visits between burn-scarred parents and young children. *Journal of Burn Care & Rehabilitation, 12*(4), 344–345.

Appleyard, M. E., Gavaghan, S. R., Gonzolez, C., Ananian, L., Tyrell, R., & Carroll, D. L. (2000). Nurse-coached intervention for the families of patients in critical care units. *Critical Care Nursing, 20*(3), 40–48.

Armistead, L., Klein, K., & Forehand, R. (1995). Parental physical illness and child functioning. *Clinical Psychology Review, 15*(5), 409–422.

Baker, F., & Tamplin, J. (2006). Interventions for patients in altered stages of consciousness. In *Music therapy methods in neurorehabilitation: A clinician's manual* (pp. 39–61) Philadelphia: Jessica Kingsley.

Barnason, S., Zimmerman, L., & Nieveen, J. (1995). The effects of music interventions on anxiety in the patient after coronary artery bypass grafting. *Heart & Lung, 24*(2), 124–132.

Bitter, J. R., & Corey, G. (1996). Family systems therapy. In G. Corey (Ed.), *The theory and practice of counseling and psychotherapy* (5th ed.) (pp. 365–443). Pacific Grove, CA: Brooks/Cole.

Blackwood, B. (2000). The art and science of predicting patient readiness for weaning from mechanical ventilation. *International Journal of Nursing Studies, 37*(2), 145–151.

Bonny, H. (1983a). Music listening for intensive coronary care units: A pilot program. *Music Therapy, 3,* 4–16.

Bonny, H. (1983b). *Music Rx: An innovative program designed for the hospital setting.* Port Townsend, WA: Institute for Consciousness and Music.

Bonny, H. L. (2002a). Autobiographical essay. In L. Summer (Ed.), *Music consciousness: The evolution of Guided Imagery and Music* (pp. 11–17). Gilsum, NH: Barcelona.

Bonny, H. L. (2002b). Cycles of experience. In L. Summer (Ed.), *Music consciousness: The evolution of Guided Imagery and Music* (pp. 238–241). Gilsum, NH: Barcelona.

Bonny, H. L. (2002c). Music listening for intensive coronary care units: A pilot project. In L. Summer (Ed.), *Music consciousness: The evolution of Guided Imagery and Music* (pp. 249–261). Gilsum, NH: Barcelona.

Bonny, H. L., & McCarron, N. (1984). Music as an adjunct to anesthesia in operative procedures. *Journal of the American Association of Nurse Anesthesia, 52*, 55–57.

Bonny, H. L., & Savary, L. M. (1973). *Music and your mind*. San Francisco: Harper & Row.

Broderick, C., & Smith, J. (1979). The general systems approach to the family. In W. B. Burr et al. (Eds.) *Contemporary theories about the family* (Vol. 2, pp. 112–129). New York: Free Press.

Bruscia, K. E. (1989). *Defining music therapy*. Gilsum, NH: Barcelona.

Byock, I. (1997). *Dying well: Peace and possibilities at the end of life*. New York: Berkley.

Cardozo, M. (2004). Harmonic sounds: Complementary medicine for the critically ill. *British Journal of Nursing, 13*(22), 1321–1324.

Cattapan, S. E., & Fahey, P. J. (2003). Weaning from mechanical ventilation: Update on the latest strategies. *Journal of Respiratory Diseases, 24*(5), 206–212.

Cella, D. F., Perry, S. W., Kulchycky, S., & Goodwin, C. (1988). Stress and coping in relatives of burn patients: A longitudinal study. *Journal of Hospital and Community Psychiatry, 39*(2), 159–166.

Ceranoglu, T. A., & Stern, T. A. (2006). Posttraumatic stress disorder in the child of an adult burn victim: A case report and review of the literature. *Journal of Intensive Care Medicine, 21*(5), 316–319.

Chlan, L. (1995). Psychophysiologic responses of mechanical ventilator patients to music: A pilot study. *American Journal of Critical Care, 4*(3), 233–238.

Chlan, L. (1998). Effectiveness of a music therapy intervention on relaxation and anxiety for patients receiving ventilatory assistance. *Heart & Lung, 27*(3), 169–176.

Chlan, L. (2006). Music intervention. In M. Snyder & R. Lindquist (Eds.), *Complementary/alternative therapies in nursing* (5th ed.) (pp. 79–92). New York: Springer.

Chlan, L., Engeland, W. C., Anthony, A., & Guttormson, J. (2007). Influence of music on the stress response in patients receiving mechanical ventilatory support: A pilot study. *American Journal of Critical Care, 16*(2), 141–145.

Chlan, L., & Heiderscheit, A. (2009). A tool for music preference assessment in critically ill patients receiving mechanical ventilatory support. *Music Therapy Perspectives, 27*(1), 42–47.

Chlan, L., & Tracy, M. F. (1999). Music therapy in critical care: Indications and guidelines for intervention. *Critical Care Nurse, 19*(3), 35–41.

Chlan, L., Tracy, M. F., Nelson, B., & Walker, J. (2001). Feasibility of a music intervention protocol for patients receiving mechanical ventilatory support. *Alternative Therapies in Health and Medicine, 7*(6), 80–83.

Clark, D. M. (1983). On the induction of depressed mood in the laboratory evaluation and comparison of the velten and musical procedures. *Advances in Behaviour Research and Therapy, 5*, 27–49.

Clarke, C., & Harrison, D. (2001). The needs of children visiting on adult intensive care units: A review of the literature and recommendations for practice. *Journal of Advanced Nursing, 34*(1), 61–68.

Conrad, C. (2008). Esoteric or exoteric? Music in medicine. *The Medscape Journal of Medicine 10*(1), 20. Retrieved February 8, 2008, from http://www.medscape.com/viewarticle/569013

Coughlan, A. (1994). Music therapy in ICU. *Nursing Times, 90*(17), 35.

Covington, H. (1998). Use of propofol for sedation in the ICU. *Critical Care Nurse, 18*(4), 34–39.

Crowe, B. J. (2004). *Music and soul making: Towards a new theory of music therapy*. Lanham, MD: Scarecrow Press.

Davis, W., Gfeller, K. E., & Thaut, M. H. (Eds.). (2008). *An introduction to music therapy: Theory and practice* (3rd ed.) Silver Spring, MD: AMTA.

de Jong, A. E. E., Middelkoop, E., Faber, A. W., & Van Loey, N. E. E. (2007). Non-pharmacological nursing interventions for procedural pain relief in adults with burns: A systemic literature review. *Burns, 33*, 811–827.

Dileo, C., & Dneaster, D. (2005). Music therapy at the end of life: State of the art. In C. Dileo & J. V. Loewy (Eds.), *Music therapy at the end of life* (pp. xix–xxvii). Cherry Hill, NJ: Jeffrey Books.

Dowling, J., & Lederer, M. A. (2005). Emergent models of implementation and communication: The Critical Care Family Assistance Program. *Chest, 128*(3), 93S–98S.

Dowling, J., Vender, J., Guilianelli, S., & Wang, B. (2005). A model of family-centered care and satisfaction predictors: The Critical Care Family Assistance Program. *Chest, 128*(3), 81S–92S.

Dowling, J., & Wang, B. (2005). Impact on family satisfaction: The Critical Care Family Assistance Program. *Chest, 128*(3), 76S–80S.

Dykeman, C., & Appleton, V. (1999). Family theory. In D. Capuzzi & D. R. Gross (Eds.), *Counseling and psychotherapy* (2nd ed.). Upper Saddle River, NJ: Prentice Hall.

Ely, E. W., Shintani, A., Truman, B., Speroff, T., Gordon, S. M., Harrell, F. E., et al. (2004). Delirium as a predictor of mortality in mechanically ventilated patients in the intensive care unit. *Journal of the American Medical Association, 291*(14), 1753–1762.

Field, T., Pickens, J., Prodromidis, M., Malphurs, J., Fox, N., Bendell, D., Yando, R., Schanberg, S., & Kuhn, S. (2000). Targeting adolescent mothers with depressive symptoms for early intervention. *Adolescence, 35*, 381–414.

Floyd, J. P., & Fernandes, J. H. (2003). Making a place for CAM in the ICU. *Registered Nurse, 66*(7), 44–47.

Fontaine, D. K. (1994). Non-pharmacologic management of patient distress during mechanical ventilation. *Critical Care Clinics, 10*(4), 695–708.

Fratianne, R. B., Prensner, J. D., Huston, M. J., Super, D. M., Yowler, C. J., & Standley, J. M. (2001). The effect of music-based imagery and musical alternate engagement on the burn debridement process. *Journal of Burn Care and Rehabilitation, 22*(1), 47–53.

Frazier, S. K., Moser, D. K., Riegel, B., McKinley, S., Blakely, W., Kim, K. A., et al. (2002). Critical care nurses' assessment of patients' anxiety: Reliance on physiological and behavioral parameters. *American Journal of Critical Care, 11*(1), 57–64.

Gagner-Tjellesen, D., Yurkovich, E. E., & Gragert, M. (2001). Use of music therapy and other ITNIs in acute care. *Journal of Psychosocial Nursing and Mental Health Services, 39*(10), 26–37.

Gaisser, D. J., & Oliva, R. (in progress). *Music therapy as an adjunctive treatment in the management of stress for patients being weaned from mechanical ventilation.* Arthur Flagler Fultz Research Fund.

Gentling, S., Grady, R., & Mattox, K. (2005). Hospital administrator's perspective: The Critical Care Family Assistance Program. *Chest, 128*(3), 103S–105S.

Goldman, J. (1992). Sonic entrainment. In R. Spintge & R. Droh (Eds.), *Music medicine* (pp. 194–208). St. Louis, MO: MMB Music.

Guilianelli, S., Kelly, R., & Skelskey, J. (2005). Critical care nurse manager's perspective: The Critical Care Family Assistance Program. *Chest, 128*(3), 118S–123S.

Guntupalli, K., McCaffree, D. R., Vender, J., Clary, G., & LoCicero, J. (2005). Project director's perspective: The Critical Care Family Assistance Program. *Chest, 128*(3), 106S–110S.

Guzzetta, C. E. (1989). Effects of relaxation and music therapy on patients in a coronary care unit with presumptive acute myocardial infarction. *Heart & Lung, 18*(6), 609–616.

Hampe, S. O. (1975). Needs of the grieving spouse in a hospital setting. *Nursing Research, 24*(2), 113–120.

Henry, L. L. (1995). Music therapy: A nursing intervention for the control of pain and anxiety in the ICU: A review of the research literature. *Dimensions of Critical Care Nursing, 14*(6), 295–304.

Heyland, D., Rocker, G., Dodek, P., Kutsogiannis, D. J., Konopad, E., Cook, D. J., et al. (2002). Family satisfaction with care in the intensive care unit: Results of a multiple center study. *Critical Care Medicine, 30*(7), 1413–1418.

Jaber, S., Bahloul, H., Guetin, S., Chanques, G., Sebbane, M., & Eledjam, J. J. (2007). Effects of music therapy in intensive care unit without sedation in weaning patients versus non-ventilated patients. *Annales Francaises d'Anesthesie et de Reanimation, 26*(1), 30–38.

Johnson, M. M., & Sexton, D. L. (1990). Distress during mechanical ventilation: Patients' perceptions. *Critical Care Nurse, 10*(7), 48–57.

Johnston, K., & Rohaly-Davis, J. (1996). An introduction to music therapy: Helping the oncology patient in the ICU. *Critical Care Nursing Quarterly, 18*(4), 54–60.

Johnstone, M. (1994). Children visiting members of their family receiving treatment in ICUs: A literature review. *Intensive and Critical Care Nursing, 10*, 289–292.

Kahn, D. M., Cook, T. E., Carlisle, C. C., Nelson, D. L., Kramer, N. R., & Millman, R. P. (1998). Identification and modification of environmental noise in an ICU setting. *Chest, 114*(2), 535–540.

Lam, P., & Beaulieu, M. (2004). Experiences of families in the neurologic ICU: "A bedside phenomenon." *Journal of Neuroscience Nursing, 36*(3), 142–155.

Lederer, M. A., Goode, T., & Dowling, J. (2005). Origins and development: The Critical Care Family Assistance Program. *Chest, 128*(3), 65S–75S.

Lee, O. K. A., Chung, Y. F. L., Chan, M. F., & Chan, W. M. (2005). Music and its effect on the physiological responses and anxiety levels of patients receiving mechanical ventilation: A pilot study. *Journal of Critical Care Nursing, 14*(5), 609–620.

Lewandowski, L. A. (1992). Needs of children during the critical illness of a parent or sibling. *Critical Care Nursing Clinics of North America, 4*(4), 573–585.

Lopez-Fagin, L. (1995). Critical care family needs: A cognitive research utilization approach. *Critical Care Nurse, 15*(4), 21–26.

Maranto, C. D. (1991). A classification model for music in medicine. In C. D. Maranto (Ed.), *Applications of music in medicine* (pp. 1–6). Washington, DC: National Association for Music Therapy.

McCartney, J. R., & Boland, R. J. (1994). Anxiety and delirium in the intensive care unit. *Critical Care Clinics, 10*(4), 673–680.

McKinley, S., Coote, K., & Stein-Parbury, J. (2003). Development and testing of a Faces Scale for the assessment of anxiety in critically ill patients. *Journal of Advanced Nursing, 41*(1), 73–79.

McKinley, S., Stein-Parbury, J., Chehelnabi, A., & Lovas, J. (2004). Assessment of anxiety in intensive care patients by using the Faces Anxiety Scale. *American Journal of Critical Care, 13*(2), 146–152.

Meade, M. O., Guyatt, G. H., & Cook, D. J. (2001). Weaning from mechanical ventilation: The evidence from clinical research. *Respiratory Care, 46*(12), 1408–1417.

Medina, J. (2005). A natural synergy in creating a patient-focused care environment: The Critical Care Family Assistance Program. *Chest, 128*(3), 99S–102S.

Melzack, R., & Wall, P. (1965). Pain mechanisms: A new theory. *Science, 150*, 971–979.

Merriam-Webster Online Dictionary. (2010). *Spirit.* Retrieved September 24, 2010, from http://www.merriam-webster.com/dictionary/spirit

Miller, A. C., Hickman, L. C., & Lemasters, G. K. (1992). A distraction technique for control of burn pain. *Journal of Burn Care & Rehabilitation, 13*, 576–580.

Morrison, W. E., Haas, E. C., Shaffner, D. H., Garrett, E. S., & Fackler, J. C. (2003). Noise, stress, and annoyance in a pediatric intensive care unit. *Critical Care Medicine, 31*(1), 113–119.

Moser, D. K., Chung, M. L., McKinley, S., Riegel, B., An, K., Cherrington, C. C., et al. (2003). Critical care nursing practice regarding patient anxiety assessment and management. *Intensive and Critical Care Nursing, 19*(5), 276–288.

Motler, N. (1979). Needs of relatives of critically ill patients: A descriptive study. *Heart & Lung, 8*(2), 332–339.

Motler, N. C., & Leske, J. S. (1983). *Critical Care Family Needs Inventory.* Unpublished manuscript.

Mynchenberg, T. L., & Dungan, J. M. (1995). A relaxation protocol to reduce patient anxiety. *Dimensions of Critical Care Nursing, 14*(2), 78–85.

National Institute on Drug Abuse. (n.d.). *Pain and opiophobia*. Retrieved December 19, 2007, from http://www.nida.nih.gov/ResearchReports/Prescription/Prescription6a.html

O'Sullivan, R. J. (1991, September). A musical road to recovery: Music in intensive care. *Intensive Nursing Care, 7*(3), 160–163.

Pochard, F., Lanore, J. J., & Bellivier, F. (1995). Subjective psychological status of severely ill patients discharged from mechanical ventilation. *Clinical Intensive Care, 6*(2), 57–61.

Prensner, J. D., Yowler, C. J., Smith, L. F., Steele, A. L., & Fratianne, R. B. (2001). Music therapy for assistance with pain and anxiety management in burn treatment. *Journal of Burn Care & Rehabilitation, 22*(1), 83–88.

Radocy, R. E., & Boyle, D. J. (1997). *Measurement and evaluation of musical experiences*. New York: Schirmer Books.

Richards, K., Nagel, C., Markie, M., Elwell, J., & Barone, C. (2003). Use of complementary and alternative therapies to promote sleep in critically ill patients. *Critical Care Nursing Clinics of North America, 15*(3), 329–340.

Robillard, D., Shim, S., Irwin, R., Katonah, J., Wren, R., Grieg, J., et al. (2005). Support services perspective: The Critical Care Family Assistance Program. *Chest, 128*(3), 124S–127S.

Rychener, M. (2005). *CCFAP final music therapy report*. Unpublished document to department heads at ENH and CCFAP funders.

Schor, E. L. (2003). Family pediatrics: Report of the task force on the family. American Academy of Pediatrics Task Force on the Family. *Pediatrics, 111*(6, Pt. 2), 1541–1571.

Shaller, J., & Rivera Smith, C. (2002). Music therapy with adolescents experiencing loss. *The Forum, Association for Death Education and Counseling, 28*(5), 1, 3–4.

Shantin, L. (1970). Alteration of mood via music: A study of the vectoring effect. *Journal of Psychology, 75,* 81–86.

Shelby, J., Sullivan, J., Groussman, M., Gray, R., & Saffle, J. (1992). Severe burn injury: Effects on psychologic and immunologic function in non-injured close relatives. *Journal of Burn Care & Rehabilitation, 13*(1), 58–63.

Siegel, K., Mesagno, F. P., Karus, D., Christ, G., Banks, K., & Moynihan, R. (1992). Psychosocial adjustment of children with a terminally ill parent. *Journal of the American Academy of Child and Adolescent Psychiatry, 31*(2), 327–333.

Skelskey, J., Robillard, D., & Irwin, R. (2005). Project coordinator's perspective: The Critical Care Family Assistance Program. *Chest, 128*(3), 111S–117S.

Sloboda, J. (1999). Music—Where cognition and emotion meet. *The Psychologist, 12,* 450–455.

Sprague, S., & Hopkins, P. D. (2003). Use of inspiratory strength training to wean six patients who were ventilator-dependent. *Physical Therapy, 83*(2), 171–181.

Stone, S. K., & Rusk, F. (1989). The effects of music therapy on critically ill patients in the intensive care. *Heart & Lung, 18*, 291.

Stubbs, T. (2005). Experiences and perceptions of music therapy in critical illness. *Nursing Times, 101*(45), 34–36.

Szokol, J. W., & Vender, J. S. (2001). Anxiety, delirium, and pain in the intensive care unit. *Critical Care Clinics, 17*(4), 821–842.

Tan, X., Yowler, C. J., & Fratianne, R. B. (2008). *Sound of Family Together (S.O.F.T.) Music Program: A randomized-controlled study to investigate the effect of music therapy on the coping and adjustment of children of adults with major burns.* Unpublished manuscript.

Tan, X., Yowler, C. J., Super, D. M., & Fratianne, R. B. (2010). The efficacy of music therapy protocols for decreasing pain, anxiety and muscle tension levels during burn dressing changes: A prospective randomized crossover trial. *Journal of Burn Care & Research, 31,* 590–597.

Taylor, D. B. (1997). *Biomedical foundations of music as therapy*. St. Louis, MO: MMB Music.

Thaut, M. H. (1989). Music therapy, affect modification, and therapeutic change: Towards an integrative model. *Music Therapy Perspectives, 7,* 55–62.

Thaut, M. H. (2008). *Rhythm, music, and the brain: Scientific foundations and clinical applications* (pp. 55–59). Florence, KY: Routledge.

Tijunelis, M. A., Fitzsullivan, E., & Henderson, S. O. (2005). Noise in the ED. *American Journal of Emergency Medicine, 23*, 332–335.

Tracy, M. F., Lindquist, R., Watanuki, S., Sendelbach, S., Kreitzer, M. J., Berman, B., & Savik, K. (2003). Nurse attitudes towards the use of complementary and alternative therapies in critical care. *Heart & Lung, 32*(3), 197–209.

Turnbull, A., & Turnbull, H. R. (1990). *Families, professionals, and exceptionality: A special partnership* (2nd ed.). New York: Macmillan.

Twiss, E., Seaver, J., & McCaffrey, R. (2006). The effect of music listening on older adults undergoing cardiovascular surgery. *British Association of Critical Care Nurses, 11*(5), 224–231.

Updike, P. (1990). Music therapy results for ICU patients. *Dimensions of Critical Care Nursing, 9*(1), 39–45.

Wasser, T., Pasquale, M. A., Matchett, S. C., Bryan, Y., & Pasquale, M. (2001). Establishing reliability and validity of the Critical Care Family Satisfaction Survey. *Critical Care Medicine, 29*(1), 192–196.

White, J. M. (1999). Effects of relaxing music on cardiac autonomic balance and anxiety after acute myocardial infarction. *American Journal of Critical Care, 8*(4), 220–230.

White, J. M. (2000). State of the science of music interventions: Critical care and perioperative practice. *Critical Care Clinics of North America, 12*(2), 219–225.

Wilkins, M. K., & Moore, M. L. (2004). Music intervention in the ICU: A complementary therapy to improve patient outcomes. *Evidence-Based Nursing, 7*(4), 103–104.

Wong, H. L., Lopez-Nahas, V., & Molassiotis, A. (2001). Effects of music therapy on anxiety in ventilator-dependent patients. *Heart & Lung, 30*(5), 376–387.

Wright, L., & Fuwiler, R. (1974). Long range emotional sequelae of burns: Effects on children and their mothers. *Pediatric Research, 8*(12), 931–934.

Yalom, I. D. (1995). *Interpersonal learning. Theory and practice of group psychotherapy* (4th ed.) (pp. 17– 46). New York: Basic Books.

Zimmerman, L., Nieveen, J., Barnason, S., & Schmaderer, M. (1996). The effects of music interventions on postoperative pain and sleep in coronary artery bypass graft (CABG) patients. *Scholarly Inquiry for Nursing Practice, 10*(2), 153–174.

Appendix

METROHEALTH MEDICAL CENTER
COMPREHENSIVE BURN CARE CENTER

Music Therapy Research Assessment

Name: ________________________ M / F Age: ______________

Admission Date: _________________ Inpatient / Outpatient

TBSA: ____________ Degree of Burn: ___________________________

Location of Burn: ____ face ____ head ____ neck ____ chest ____ back

____ buttocks ____ hands ____ feet ____ upper extremities

____ lower extremities ____ perineum

Music History

Experience in/with music instruction?

____

Musical/performing groups?

____

Music therapy?

____

Music Preferences

Preferred Styles:

Folk/Traditional Musicals Religious Rap Classical Country Popular

1940s 1950s 1960s 1970s 1980s 1990s/present

Others: ______________________________

Favorite artists: ____

Favorite songs: ____

Favorite radio stations: ____

MUSIC-BASED IMAGERY

Description of safe/relaxing place.

Visual:

____
____
____

Auditory: __________________________________
____
____

Olfactory: __________________________________
____
____

Kinesthetic: __________________________________
____
____

Taste: __________________________________
____
____

Comments:

____
____
____

If duplicated or adapted for clinical and/or research use, please reference source: Music Therapy Department, The Cleveland Music School Settlement in collaboration with MetroHealth Medical Center.

PATIENT PROGRESS NOTES
MUSIC THERAPY – ANXIETY MANAGEMENT

Patient's Name:________________ Age:______ Sex:______ Hospital/Unit:________________
Primary Diagnosis:________________ Referred By:________________

Intensity of Anxiety *Prior to* Music Therapy Intervention:

I. Patient Self-Rating

1	2	3	4	5	6	7	8	9	10
No Anxiety				Moderate Anxiety					Worst Anxiety Possible

II. Observations

Behavioral

____ Biting of lip	____ Grimacing	____ Guarding body part	~HR/BP________
____ Clenched fists	____ Clenching/grinding teeth	____ Sweating	~Respiration ________
____ Eyes wide open	____ Rocking	____ Crying, moaning	~Vocal Intensity/Speed_____
____ Eyes closed tightly	____ Repetitive movements	____ Other________	~Vocal Pitch________

Psychosocial

____ flat affect	____ withdrawn	____ unable to sleep	____ tired	____ tearful
____ sad	____ isolated	____ loss of control	____ bored	____ lonely
____ bright affect	____ guarded	____ sleep disturbance	____ frustrated	____ nauseous
____ anxious/worried	____ resistant	____ other:________________		

III. Patient's Description of Anxiety________________

____

Intensity of Anxiety *After* Music Therapy Intervention:

I. Patient Self-Rating

1	2	3	4	5	6	7	8	9	10
No Anxiety			Moderate Anxiety				Worst Anxiety Possible		

II. Observations

Behavioral

____ Biting of lip	____ Grimacing	____ Guarding body part	~HR/BP________
____ Clenched fists	____ Clenching/grinding teeth	____ Sweating	~Respiration ________
____ Eyes wide open	____ Rocking	____ Crying, moaning	~Vocal Intensity/Speed_____
____ Eyes closed tightly	____ Repetitive movements	____ Other________	~Vocal Pitch________

Psychosocial

____ flat affect	____ withdrawn	____ unable to sleep	____ tired	____ tearful
____ sad	____ isolated	____ loss of control	____ bored	____ lonely
____ bright affect	____ guarded	____ sleep disturbance	____ frustrated	____ nauseous
____ anxious/worried	____ resistant	____ other:________________		

III. Patient's Description of Anxiety________________________________

____

IV. Session Observations________________________________

____

____

____

V. Patient Statements________________________________

VI. Signature________________ Phone________ Pager________ Date________

Board Certified Music Therapist

PATIENT PROGRESS NOTES
MUSIC THERAPY – PAIN MANAGEMENT

Patient's Name:________________________________Age:______Sex:______ Hospital/Unit:________________
Primary Diagnosis:_____________________________________Referred By:_____________________________

Intensity of Pain *Prior to* Music Therapy Intervention:

I. Patient Self-Rating

1 2 3 4 5 6 7 8 9 10
No Pain — Moderate Pain — Worst Pain Possible

II. Observations

Behavioral

____ Biting of lip	____ Grimacing	____ Guarding body part	~HR/BP______________
____ Clenched fists	____ Clenching/grinding teeth	____ Sweating	~Respiration ____________
____ Eyes wide open	____ Rocking	____ Crying, moaning	~Vocal Intensity/Speed_____
____ Eyes closed tightly	____ Repetitive movements	____ Other______________	~Vocal Pitch____________

Psychosocial

____ flat affect	____ withdrawn	____ unable to sleep	____ tired	____ tearful
____ sad	____ isolated	____ loss of control	____ bored	____ lonely
____ bright affect	____ guarded	____ sleep disturbance	____ frustrated	____ nauseous
____ anxious/worried	____ resistant	____ other:________________________		

III. Patient's Description of Pain____
IV. Location of Pain____

Intensity of Pain *After* Music Therapy Intervention:

I. Patient Self-Rating

1 2 3 4 5 6 7 8 9 10
No Pain — Moderate Pain — Worst Pain Possible

II. Observations

Behavioral

____ Biting of lip	____ Grimacing	____ Guarding body part	~HR/BP______________
____ Clenched fists	____ Clenching/grinding teeth	____ Sweating	~Respiration ____________
____ Eyes wide open	____ Rocking	____ Crying, moaning	~Vocal Intensity/Speed_____
____ Eyes closed tightly	____ Repetitive movements	____ Other______________	~Vocal Pitch____________

Psychosocial

____ flat affect	____ withdrawn	____ unable to sleep	____ tired	____ tearful
____ sad	____ isolated	____ loss of control	____ bored	____ lonely
____ bright affect	____ guarded	____ sleep disturbance	____ frustrated	____ nauseous
____ anxious/worried	____ resistant	____ other:________________________		

III. Patient's Description of Pain__________________
IV. Location of Pain____
V. Session Observations____
____
____
____
VI. Patient Statements____
VII. Signature____________________________Phone______________ Pager______________ Date__________
Board Certified Music Therapist

Critical Care Family Assistance Program (CCFAP) **Discipline:____________________** **Primary Shift: Morning / PM**

<u>Music Therapy ICU Staff Survey</u>

Hospital: EH HPH GBH

Please circle one number per line to indicate how strongly you agree or disagree with the following statements regarding music therapy and its impact on patient, family, and staff care. If you have not experienced music therapy, please complete the survey as you "foresee the impact" of music therapy in the ICU setting. Thank you for your time and feedback.

	No Impact	Mild Impact	Fair Impact	Moderate Impact	Great Impact	Not Applicable
<u>Staff Evaluation of the benefit to ICU patients</u>	1	2	3	4	5	N/A
1. Music Therapy…						
A. reduces a patient's level of anxiety and agitation.	1	2	3	4	5	N/A
B. reduces a patient's level of pain.	1	2	3	4	5	N/A
C. provides pre- and post-surgical patient support.	1	2	3	4	5	N/A
D. reduces a patient's depressed mood state.	1	2	3	4	5	N/A
E. provides emotional support to the patient.	1	2	3	4	5	N/A
F. provides spiritual support to the patient.	1	2	3	4	5	N/A
G. provides appropriate sensory stimulation for patients.	1	2	3	4	5	N/A
H. eases the "end of life" transition for patients.	1	2	3	4	5	N/A

I. reduces feelings of isolation/frustration for LTS patients	**1**	**2**	**3**	**4**	**5**	**N/A**
J. positively contributes to the quality of care of patients.	**1**	**2**	**3**	**4**	**5**	**N/A**

	No Impact	**Mild Impact**	**Fair Impact**	**Moderate Impact**	**Great Impact**	**Not Applicable**
Staff Evaluation of the benefit to family members	**1**	**2**	**3**	**4**	**5**	**N/A**
2. Music Therapy…						
A. reduces the level of anxiety/agitation in family members.	**1**	**2**	**3**	**4**	**5**	**N/A**
B. provides emotional support to family members.	**1**	**2**	**3**	**4**	**5**	**N/A**
C. provides spiritual support to family members.	**1**	**2**	**3**	**4**	**5**	**N/A**
D. eases the “end of life” transition for family members.	**1**	**2**	**3**	**4**	**5**	**N/A**
E. reduces feelings of isolation/frustration for LTS families.	**1**	**2**	**3**	**4**	**5**	**N/A**
F. improves the quality of care for family members.	**1**	**2**	**3**	**4**	**5**	**N/A**
G. improves family members’ satisfaction with quality of care of their loved one in the ICU.	**1**	**2**	**3**	**4**	**5**	**N/A**

Staff Evaluation of the benefit to ICD staff members	No Impact	Mild Impact	Fair Impact	Moderate Impact	Great Impact	Not Applicable
	1	2	3	4	5	N/A
3. Music Therapy…						
A. promotes a calming/relaxingworking environment.	1	2	3	4	5	N/A
B. reduces my levels of stress/anxiety during medical procedures (placement of NG tube, extubation, dressing change, PT/OT, minor medical procedures).	1	2	3	4	5	N/A
C. when present, reduces stressful interactions between families/patients and ICU staff members.	1	2	3	4	5	N/A
D. during the withdrawal of life support/end of life, supports my own professional and personal process.	1	2	3	4	5	N/A
E. I refer my patients and their family members to music therapy.	**Never**	**Rarely**	**Sometimes**	**Often**	**Always**	
F. I access the lending listening library materials for for use with my patients and their family members.	**Never**	**Rarely**	**Sometimes**	**Often**	**Always**	

Years in ICU environment: 1–5 6–10 11–15 16–20 21 or more

Number of times your patients, their family members, and/or yourself have received music therapy services:

1–5 6–10 11–15 16–20 21 or more

Additional comments: ______________________________

____

____

METROHEALTH MEDICAL CENTER
COMPREHENSIVE BURN CARE CENTER

The Effect of Patient-Preferred Music, Relaxation Music, and Standard Care Environment on Patients in Intensive Care Units

Data Collection Form

Patient code: _______________ Age: _____________ Female / Male
Diagnoses: ____
TBSA Burn (BICU): ____________ Degree of Burn (BICU): ________________
Past Medical History: ____
Date: _________________ Research Day: 1 2 3 (circle one)
Condition (circle one):
Standard ICU (TV/no TV) / Relaxation music / Patient-preferred: _______________
Volume Level: ____________dBA

Location of Burn (BICU):

Face		Hands	
Head		Feet	
Neck		Upper Ext.	
Chest		Lower Ext.	
Stomach		Perineum	
Back		Buttock	

Medication:

Pain Medicine	Dosage	Time	Anxiety Medicine	Dosage	Time
Oxycodone (PO)			Ativan Circle one: IV / PO		
Tylenol with Codeine (PO)			Xanax (PO)		
Percocet (PO)			Versed (IV)		
Motrin (PO)			Others: ____________		
Vicodin (PO)					
Morphine Circle one: IV / IM / PO					
Demerol Circle one: IV / IM / PO					
Dilaudid Circle one: IV / IM / PO					
Fentanyl Circle one: IV / IM / PO					
Others: _______________					

Time elapsed after dressing change (BICU): __________________________
Patient code: _____________ Date: _________ Day 1 2 3 (circle one)

HEMODYNAMIC PARAMETERS

Time	HR	RR	BP	Cortisol (Serum / Saliva)	IgA (Serum / Saliva)
Baseline					
START MUSIC	-----	-----	-----	------------------	------------------
15 mins				------------------	------------------
30 mins					
STOP MUSIC	-----	-----	-----	------------------	------------------
30 mins					

Patient's Self-Report for Comfort, Pain, and Anxiety Levels

Comfort: 0 1 2 3 4 5 6 7 8 9 10
(least) (most)

Pain: 0 1 2 3 4 5 6 7 8 9 10
(least) (most)

Anxiety: 0 1 2 3 4 5 6 7 8 9 10
(least) (most)

If duplicated or adapted for clinical and/or research use, please reference source: Music Therapy Department, The Cleveland Music School Settlement in collaboration with MetroHealth Medical Center.

CHAPTER 4

General Medical/Surgical

Joey Walker
Judy Nguyen Engel
Deanna Hanson-Abromeit
Joanne V. Loewy
Soozie Cotter-Schaufele

Music therapy in adult general medical and surgical settings has unique challenges due to the variety of environments, diagnoses, and experiences of the patients. Patients may be young adults in their early 20s just finishing college and beginning a career, middle age adults with careers and young families, or older adults with a wealth of life experiences. The diagnoses seen in adult medical and surgical units are varied, and the settings are specialized. Historically, it has been recognized that patients who were very sick improved if they were close to the nurse's station, and that those with acute, serious illnesses received better treatment if the patients were grouped according to diagnosis (Society of Critical Care Medicine, 2001–2009). More recently, with changes in the increased scope of coverage influenced by insurance companies and advances in medical technologies, the hospital environment has changed from a long-term setting to one that is more short term.

In the 1970s and 1980s, the average length of a hospital stay was 7 to 8 days. In the 1990s, it declined to a little over 6 days (DeFrances, Hall, & Podgornik, 2005). Based on the most recent national hospital survey statistics (DeFrances, Lucas, Buie, & Golosinskiy, 2008), the average hospital stay is now 4.8 days, with variation in length of stay based on age, gender, and region of hospitalization. The average age of inpatients has been increasing since 1970; 38% of hospitalized inpatients are over the age of 65 with an average length of stay of 5.5 days. Those ages 45–64 have an average length of stay of 5 days, and those between ages 15–44 are hospitalized for an average of 3.4 days. The average length of stay for male patients is slightly higher (5.2 days) than females (4.5), with regional averages ranging between 4.2 in the Midwest to 5.3 days in the Northeast (DeFrances et al., 2008).

The decline in the length of hospitalization is attributed to advances in technology and pharmacology, which contribute to earlier diagnosis, safer surgical procedures and shorter recovery from operations, the availability of post-acute care alternatives, and shifts in insurance and Medicare coverage (DeFrances et al., 2005). Inpatient units are decreasing in size and number of staff. The characteristics of the patients on the inpatient units tend to be more severe in nature, thus requiring more brief, individualized services at the bedside. In addition, trends in hospitalization have moved toward more outpatient treatment and shorter hospital stays. Music therapists should be prepared to provide mostly brief, short-term services to adult patients in both the inpatient and outpatient general medical and surgical setting. With the decline in inpatient services, there has been an increase in outpatient clinics and clinic-based staff. These clinics tend to be specialized by diagnosis.

The adult general medical/surgical hospital setting spans a variety of hospital units, specialty medical care, diagnoses, lengths of stay, and age ranges. This requires the music therapist to have a wide basis of general knowledge. Some of the more common areas of clinical practice for music therapy in the adult medical/surgical setting are neurology, burn, orthopedics, dermatology, post surgical, and internal medicine. Post surgical in the general medical/surgical context is considered a step up toward discharge that may follow admittance into a medical intensive care unit (see Chapter 3). *Internal medicine* is an umbrella term for the specialized prevention, diagnosis, and non-surgical treatment of diseases in adulthood. Internal medicine includes 13 subspecialties: adolescent medicine, allergy and **immunology, cardiology, endocrinology, gastroenterology,** geriatrics, **hematology**, infectious disease, **nephrology**, **oncology**, **pulmonology**, **rheumatology**, and sports medicine (American College of Physicians, n.d.).

This chapter will provide an overview of music therapy clinical practice in the adult general medical/surgical units. The hospital music therapist will likely visit multiple general medical/surgical units that are organized according to diagnosis or specialty, thus working with patients and families with varying diagnoses. The hospital music therapist must be knowledgeable in the diagnoses and procedures of patients he or she will be treating. While it is quite challenging to be familiar with all diagnoses and procedures, there are some common needs for hospitalized patients and their families. The context of age (e.g., adolescents or elderly) is relevant and should be considered when planning interventions. Music therapy with adults diagnosed with cancer is a specialty area of practice and is discussed at length in Chapter 5. Some music therapists in the general medical/surgical units may also see patients who are participating in rehabilitation; however, diagnosis and music therapy in rehabilitation are not included within the scope of this chapter. Much of the content related to treatment can be transferred to a diagnosis not specifically discussed as long as the music therapist has relevant treatment goals and viable interventions appropriate to the acute setting.

Common Specialty Units in Adult General Medical/Surgical Served by Music Therapy

Internal medicine – diagnosis and non-surgical treatment of disease in adults
- Cardiology – disorders of the heart and blood vessels
- Endocrinology – the system that deals with disorders of hormones
- Gastroenterology – digestive diseases
- Infectious disease – caused by biological agents such as a virus, bacterium, or parasite
- Nephrology – function and disease of the kidney
- Pulmonology – diseases of the lung and respiratory tract
- Rheumatology – diagnosis and treatment involving the muscles and/or joints

Neurology – function and diseases of the brain

Post surgical – following an inpatient or outpatient surgical procedure; may be following a stay in an intensive care unit

Burn – specialized burn treatment; some hospitals may also house pediatric burn patients

Orthopedics – diagnosis and treatment of problems of the **musculoskeletal** system

Intensive care units may be located within these specialty designations. For example, if patients have been placed on a ventilator, they may be initially housed on the Intensive Pulmonary Care Unit (IPCU). Ventilation is often a long-term medical intervention that requires continued hospitalization. Many ventilated patients remain in intensive care until they can be weaned off of the ventilator. (Chapter 3 provides information related to music therapy in adult intensive care units.) Once patients are breathing on their own, they may be placed on a general adult unit until they are ready for discharge. When patients have more specialized needs, music therapists may follow them from a higher level of care (e.g., ICU), to the general specialty area, and then into the outpatient clinic for follow-up services. Music therapists can provide for longer-range goals that are adaptable to the changing medical stability of the patient during medical treatment, and they can provide for continuity of care throughout hospitalization.

Currently, nurses author the majority of the literature discussing the use of music as a treatment strategy with adult populations in the general/medical and intensive care medical settings. The term *music therapy* is loosely applied to the use of recorded music as a nursing intervention and does not imply that the treatment modality is one of specialization by a board-certified music therapist. Few research or clinical studies have been documented in the literature that utilize live, interactive, music-based strategies, or employ the expertise of the board-certified music therapist (Chen, Hayden, Sneden-Riley, & Clair, 2004; Engen, 2005; Mandel, Hanser, Secic, & Davis, 2007; Wiens, Reimer, & Guyn, 1999) for adult medical/surgical patients.

In reviewing the literature, the use of music as a therapeutic modality is clearly recognized as beneficial to the adult medical/surgical patient. The majority of the research related to specialties of adult medical/surgical has focused on cardiology (e.g., Cadigan et al., 2001; Chan et al., 2006; Mandel et al., 2007; Sendelbach, Halm, Doran, Miller, & Gaillard, 2006; Tusek, Cwynar, & Cosgrove, 1999; Voss, Good, Yates, Baun, Thompson, & Hertzog, 2004; Zimmerman, Nieveen, Barnason, & Schmaderer, 1996) and gastroenterology (e.g., Chlan, Evans, Greenleaf, & Walker, 2000; Hayes, Buffum, Lanier, Rodahl, & Sasso, 2003; Schiemann, Gross, Reuter, & Kellner, 2002; Smolen, Topp, & Singer, 2002; Uedo et al., 2004), with those studies looking at the efficacy of music as either procedural or surgical support. With few exceptions, most research has been conducted by nurses and has used recorded music selections, with music listening as the primary intervention strategy. Positive outcomes have been reported in the majority of these studies.

The management of pain during surgery and procedures is of concern for adult medical/surgical patients. Researchers have found decreased pain perception in patients who used music listening as a coping strategy (Chan et al., 2006; Good, Anderson, Ahn, Cong, & Stanton-Hicks, 2005; Good, Stanton-Hicks, et al., 2001; Kane et al., 2004; Kshettry, Carole, Henly, Sendelbach, & Kummer, 2006; Nilsson, Rawal, & Unosson, 2003; Tse, Chan, & Benzie, 2005; Voss et al., 2004; Zimmerman et al., 1996). Anxiety reduction is also of interest, and the majority of studies have found a reduced level of anxiety in the patients who listened to music (Buffum et al., 2006; Chlan et al., 2000; Cooke, Chaboyer, Schluter, & Hiratos, 2005; Hamel, 2001; Hayes et al., 2003; Lopez-Cepero Andrada et al., 2004; Padmanabhan, Hildreth, & Laws, 2005; Sendelbach et al., 2006; Twiss, Seaver, & McCaffrey, 2006; Uedo et al., 2004; Voss et al., 2004; White, 1999).

Some studies showed improved physiological responses, although the outcomes were inconsistent in the type (e.g., blood pressure, heart rate, respiration rate) and significance (Buffum et al., 2006; Chan et al., 2006; Hamel, 2001; Lazaroff & Shimshoni, 2000; Leardi et al., 2007; Mamaril, Windle, & Burkard, 2006; Smolen et al., 2002; Tse et al., 2005; Tusek et al., 1999; White, 1999). Several studies found that patients had improved perception of the procedure and better psychological outcomes when using music (Bampton & Draper, 1997; Chlan et al., 2000; Heiser, Chiles, Fudge, & Gray, 1997; Schiemann et al., 2002; Smolen et al., 2002; Thorgaard, Henriksen, Pedersbaek, & Thomsen, 2004; Tusek et al., 1999).

Music listening has also been shown to be a cost-effective strategy with regard to procedures: reducing time of intubation after surgery (Twiss et al., 2006), requirements for **analgesia** (Nilsson et al., 2003; Schiemann et al., 2002; Tse et al., 2005), and sedatives during procedures (Smolen et al., 2002). Due to these myriad benefits, music listening is highly recommended as a non-pharmacolgical intervention or **adjuvant**.

Music therapy interventions that engage the patients in active music opportunities that include live music have also demonstrated positive outcomes. Cardiac rehabilitation paired with multiple (four to six) music therapy sessions showed significant outcomes in systolic blood pressure and pre- and post-treatment scores of stress and anxiety. Music therapy participants also had lower levels of trait anxiety and higher levels of general health and social functioning than those receiving cardiac rehabilitation alone. The music therapy sessions included singing, instrument playing, and relaxation and imagery with recorded music (Mandel et al., 2007).

Music therapy with patients with chronic obstructive pulmonary disease (COPD) is an emerging area of music therapy practice in the medical setting. Warm-up posture and breath management exercises paired with choral speaking and singing for outpatients diagnosed with COPD demonstrated significant changes in breath control and support following 6 weeks of twice weekly music therapy sessions. Participants also demonstrated obvious changes in breathing patterns and had increased levels in mental and social health (Engen, 2005).

Neurologic Music Therapy techniques (Thaut, Thaut, & LaGasse, 2008) were adapted to be appropriate for three inpatients admitted for advanced stage COPD. Rhythmic Auditory Stimulation and Respiratory Cuing were intended to regulate gait and breathing, increase endurance, and manage fear and anxiety and were co-facilitated with the physical therapist. Patients walked farther with the music and perceived less shortness of breath and a decreased recovery time for oxygen saturation than without music therapy (Chen et al., 2004). While researchers have focused on some areas of specialization more frequently than others and have mostly studied the use of recorded music, clinical practice by board-certified music therapists has been integrated throughout the hospital using a variety of techniques that are beneficial for adults and their families.

Music Therapy Practice on the Adult Medical/Surgical Unit

Due to the shift to shorter hospital stays, therapy services have also shifted. What was primarily a treatment model that focused on goals and objectives for long-term hospitalization has now moved to one of **acute** inpatient and outpatient services with consideration for the patient and family. Inpatient units are declining in size but are catering more to the specific needs of the patients. Hospital environments are changing rapidly in order to appear less sterile and medical, and more comfortable and family-centered. For example, more patient rooms are being designed as private rooms with less prevalence of the semi-private double rooms common in the past. Medical equipment may be housed in attractive cabinetry, and the rooms may be decorated with artwork, televisions and DVD players, and sound systems that allow for personal playback of music or unit-based systems. The needs of the patient's family members are taken into consideration, and collaborative treatment between disciplines is occurring for more efficient and viable services. In fact, music therapy fits particularly well into those facilities committed to a family-centered care orientation, a transformation in medical care philosophy that emerged from pediatrics and is quickly becoming a standard philosophy of care among adult patients. Music therapy provides normalization and comfort in conjunction with this shift toward improved patient and family care, and reflects this shift in the provision of patient services.

Family-Centered Care in the Adult Setting

Music therapists and the services offered by a music therapy program are an integral component of family-centered care throughout the hospital. A patient is rarely hospitalized without a family member or friend providing part of his or her care. Family members are affected by the medical procedures that patients endure. Music therapy can address family needs that arise during, and due to, hospitalization.

Sometimes relationships are strained due to the severity of the diagnosis or prognosis, or due to a past family history. Families and patients may benefit from relief from tension, boredom, or lack of sensory stimulation. Engaging musically can support family interactions, provide a catalyst for family communication, and create a sense of normalcy. Singing familiar songs, playing instruments, or simply listening allows the family to connect within the context of fond memories, shared experiences, and possibly happier or more peaceful times. Music can reduce the level of tension in the environment or within the individuals. Music can also facilitate spiritual expression and support. Music, whether recorded or live, can generate an environment of peacefulness and calm amidst the chaos and activity of the hospital unit. Using the iso principle, the music therapist can facilitate a musical experience that matches the patient and family at their current physical and emotional state, gradually altering the musical elements to effect change. In addition, most cultures and faith traditions utilize music. Music, as a nonverbal form of communication, addresses the diversity of patients and their families that may exceed the language resources of the medical staff. The following is a case study detailing how music therapy can impact family relationships.

Case Study Example

A young father, after attempting suicide by a self-inflicted gunshot wound to the head, was hospitalized for palliative care. A music therapy referral was made for family support. The family, except for the patient's 4-year-old daughter, was gathered in the hospital room, along with the hospital chaplain. The music therapist approached the room, carrying her harp, and quietly knocked on the door. After she was motioned inside, the music therapist noticed that the room was darkened and the extended family was gathered around the patient's bedside praying and crying. In listening to the family members, she also quickly recognized that English was not the primary language. Due to the gravity of the situation, the music therapist realized that it was not appropriate to ask questions and that this session would require astute observation and unobtrusive actions. She made eye contact with the hospital chaplain, who had been in attendance ever since the patient was admitted, shortly before the music therapist's arrival. He approached her and quietly communicated that the family wanted her to play softly as they prayed together. The music therapist grabbed an empty chair and positioned herself near the bedside, close to the patient's head, yet without blocking the family's access. Because little was known about the patient or family musical preferences, the therapist began improvising slow, simple, and predictable melodic patterns on the harp using a soft dynamic so as not to disturb their prayers and conversation. It was her intention to provide a continuous flow of music in an effort to create structure and support to the family members through an auditory stimulus. While she played, the music therapist was attentive to the immediate responses and potential needs of the family members.

Shortly after the music therapist's arrival, a family member entered and indicated that the patient's 4-year-old daughter had asked to see him. Following a brief discussion, the family decided to support her request. As she entered the room, the child was assured that it was her daddy in the bed. The patient's wound and eyes were covered, so his face was only partially visible. Initially the child looked at her father and then ran away. She sat away from the bedside on a sofa with a young woman presumed to be her mother. The child made intermittent eye contact with the therapist. She eventually moved towards the music therapist and stood next to her for several minutes. The music therapist transitioned into playing "Twinkle, Twinkle Little Star" for the child in the same tempo and dynamics as the improvised music, humming as she played. The child continued to make brief eye contact with the music therapist, then shyly looked to her father, before returning to her mother on the sofa, away from her father. Shortly she indicated that she wanted to leave and left the room with her mother. The therapist transitioned back to improvised music.

During this time the family members had moved away from the bedside; most had stopped crying, and all were visibly calmer. The therapist had been playing for an hour. As the family began to move in and out of the room, the therapist gradually stopped playing by slowing the tempo and fading the volume. She informed one family member sitting on the sofa that she was leaving, and if they would like her to come back, they should ask the nurse to page her.

Later that day, the music therapist was paged to return. As she entered the room, the family members were gathered in various spots around the room. They requested that she play again, so she positioned herself in the same spot and began to improvise on the harp in a similar manner as in the earlier session. The music therapist noticed the patient's daughter looking at her and gave her a gentle, encouraging smile. The child approached the music therapist and asked if she could hear the star song again. As the music therapist played and hummed, the child sang the words in English. She then began to move closer to her father, so the music therapist suggested she sing to him. The child put her hand on her father's arm and sang "Twinkle, Twinkle Little Star" many times before saying, "Now he can know it's me, and he won't be ascared [sic]." (She seemed concerned that he was feeling afraid of the dark because his eyes were covered.) The family wept in response to her actions and words, thanked the music therapist, and asked her to continue playing for a while longer. The young man died shortly thereafter.

Overview: Although English was not the primary language of this family, the improvised music created an auditory environment that appeared to communicate comfort, caring, and support. The familiar children's song provided a normalized stimulus that assisted in easing the child's fears and supporting her efforts in understanding and coping with the situation. Perhaps the music even provided some sense of peace and comfort to the patient.

Music therapy not only may help the patient and family to improve their personal coping abilities with a situation, but may also allow them to be more receptive and engaged in their medical care. For example, an adult child of a patient may express anxiety for his or her parent by accusing the nursing staff of not providing the parent with enough pain medication or other comfort measures. A sensitive music therapist who can utilize the therapeutic function of music to facilitate change may help the adult child reduce tension, have an opportunity to express his or her concerns, and be better able to recognize that the parent is receiving quality care. Music therapy may assist and offer patients and families more effective methods to communicate their concerns to the nursing and medical staff. This, in turn, also supports a more relaxed atmosphere for the nursing and medical staff.

The hospitalization itself may not be the only situation that challenges the well-being of the patient and family. During hospitalization, follow-up visits, and outpatient care, patients can move from unit to unit, interacting with a variety of hospital personnel. Different people staff each unit of the hospital, with changes at each shift. The number of nursing and medical staff that a patient or family members interact with can be quite high. The music therapist, often the only music therapist on the unit or at the hospital, has the privilege of following the family as the patient is moved among units due to changing medical needs. Continuity of care offers a more humanistic and holistic care model that helps patients and families to feel more satisfied.

Continuity of care affords the music therapist with the opportunity to develop a meaningful rapport with the patient and his or her family. Sometimes the family members may see the music therapist as a neutral party and may share concerns or ask questions that they may not otherwise initiate. The music therapist may be the staff member with whom the patient has had the longest relationship during hospitalization. This relationship may also allow the therapist to see a positive aspect of the hospitalization that may not always be evident. For example, when the patient or family is questioning medical care decisions, the music therapist may be available to offer support, listen without judgment, and facilitate resolution. Often after verbalizing a problem or dilemma, a patient or family member is able to clarify pertinent questions or decisions and direct them to the appropriate staff member with assistance from the music therapist. The music therapist can also be an advocate for patients and families. For example, if several medical specialty areas are working with a patient and there is not a case manager involved, the music therapist may provide the knowledge, information, and stability to ensure that the patient receives the best quality of care.

While the types of services offered in music therapy will depend on the needs of the patient and family during their hospital course, the music therapist will frequently remain constant. The opportunity to provide such continuity of care is one of the greatest benefits the music therapist on the adult general medical/surgical unit can provide to the patient and family. For example, individual family services are most appropriate for a patient on an intensive care unit, or one who is recovering from a complicated surgery. As the patient becomes more stable, individual services may continue with the addition or substitution of group services facilitated by the same music therapist. The patient may be receiving services from multiple professionals that require careful coordination or co-treatment. Once the patient is discharged, the music therapist can be available to the patient and family for procedural or emotional support during outpatient visits.

Co-treatment

Co-treatment can be advantageous for patients as well as staff. Coordination of multiple services within the constraints of hospitalization and planning around staff schedules can be challenging and inefficient. Scheduling services continuously throughout the day can be exhausting and frustrating for the patient and can contribute to issues of noncompliance and reduced patient satisfaction. Coordination and integration of professional services can alleviate frustration and anxiety for both the patient and staff. In addition, co-treating increases awareness and understanding of the represented professions, contributes to knowledge of the patient and family from multiple perspectives, and functions as a direct focus on the best interests of the patient and family. Music therapists on the adult units co-treat with therapeutic recreation specialists; occupational, physical, and speech therapists; social workers; chaplains; and nursing and medical staff.

With the added medium of music and the collaborative skills of the therapists, many situations in the hospital may become more pleasant, effective, and beneficial for the patient and staff members. For example, the music therapist assists the physical therapist or nurse with walking a patient down the hall after surgery. In this situation, using preferred patient music as the focus, the music therapist is able to facilitate changes in the musical elements (e.g., changes to the tempo or dynamics of the live music) to provide a structure and cuing mechanism for the ambulation of the patient. The music fosters motivation and creates a positive association and focal point for the motor task. The patient may experience less pain, and for both the patient and staff, the task may be perceived as easier in time and effort.

Outpatient Services

If possible, outpatient services will be the first option for treatment or may be utilized as a follow-up to a hospital admission. Outpatient services are continually being expanded with more options available to patients. Hospitals are adding amenities such as Internet access, more attractive and comfortable décor, televisions, play areas with activities for children, and other furnishings to create a family-friendly and comfortable environment in their outpatient clinics. Freestanding specialized care clinics, often associated with larger medical centers, are emerging in communities to accommodate patients closer to their homes. Specialized care clinics do not require patients to navigate the vast hallways of large bustling medical centers, but they allow clients to park nearby and frequently offer less wait time for services.

Music therapy programs can support the shift to outpatient clinics by including services to the outpatient areas to improve comfort, reduce anxiety and pain, provide procedural support, and offer an overall more pleasant experience. While one-to-one interventions are still the most common manner of providing treatment, group music therapy services work particularly well in the outpatient clinics. Group music therapy services are cost-effective and can be of great benefit to patients. Following discharge, a patient may participate in an outpatient group that has been designed to address a specific diagnosis. In the outpatient clinics, patients with similar needs can be placed in a group together so that they gain support from each other and benefit from the treatment interventions facilitated by the music therapist. Group services provide a beneficial and cost-effective treatment alternative for the patient, as well as the hospital or clinic.

One Midwestern hospital offers hospital-wide monthly Karaoke to both inpatients and outpatients. Inpatients that are stable enough are transported to the hospital gymnasium for an afternoon of singing and socializing. Staff, patients, and families from across the hospital and outpatient clinics look forward to this shared experience that celebrates music, fun, and people. Patients have been known to schedule their outpatient visits to correspond with the monthly Karaoke. One young adult patient with cystic fibrosis schedules her outpatient clinic visits and routine inpatient admissions for "tune ups" with the monthly Karaoke schedule. Songs with sustained notes are difficult for her to sing and restrict her normal breathing, so she knows which popular songs have short phrases. When she attends Karaoke, she is able to select music that she can sing in a successful manner. Sometimes she practices new material in this safe environment and then after discharge is able to have more success in her home environment where she sings Karaoke at a local establishment.

Music Therapy Treatment Process on the Adult Medical/Surgical Unit

One-to-one sessions are an integral part of a music therapist's caseload in the general hospital. Presently, patients on the inpatient units have a higher acuity, meaning, in general, they have more complex medical concerns. Therefore, the music therapist will provide services to medically compromised inpatients on a one-to-one basis in various areas of the hospital. Music therapists need to assess, as well as provide treatment, within one to two sessions in the acute setting of the general hospital. Services will often involve patient family members in varying levels of integration. While the majority of services tend to be individualized, there are always exceptions due to medical or placement needs. Objective, measurable information also needs to be communicated and documented as to the efficacy of interventions in order to ensure that music therapy services continue to remain a viable component in the quality of care in the general hospital.

In this era of brief treatment practices, every interaction is important and must be treated as if it will be the only session that is provided. The music therapist must hold an understanding of multiple diagnoses and be able to multitask in a manner that is focused and genuinely present for each patient. Even when careful assessment has been completed before entering a patient's room, the music therapist must remain open and flexible to the changing needs of each patient and family as they occur. For example, the music therapist has received a referral to reduce pain perception for Maria. When the music therapist makes an initial visit, he finds Maria in tears because of some medical information she has just received. Clearly Maria needs support, validation, and a means of emotional expression. In this case, the music therapist is flexible and offers interventions that provide support and encourage expression of feelings rather than work to reduce pain perception. The music therapist must be flexible, able to think and assess quickly, provide aesthetically pleasing services, and provide successful and measurable outcomes for patients, family, and staff, all within a brief treatment period.

Referral

The referral process on adult general medical/surgical units varies based on the size of the hospital and the specific units that offer music therapy services. A physician referral may be a requirement for billing purposes, reimbursement, and standards of practice. However, an identified need for music therapy is often initiated by other clinical staff such as nurses, social workers, occupational and physical therapists, chaplains, psychologists, physician assistants (PA), unit clerks, certified therapeutic recreational specialists, the music therapist, as well as the patients or their families. Some units may have standing orders for music therapy treatment based on prior experiences, relationships with unit staff, and demonstrated patient outcomes. On these units, music therapy will be indicated for all patients that fall within a certain criteria without a separate referral. Other units may make referrals on a case-by-case basis. The patient load of the music therapist is based on the number of referrals.

Information from the referral should be general and basic: enough to prepare the music therapist for the assessment process, but not enough to be time prohibitive for the staff making the referral. Keeping the referral process short and simple facilitates easier access and management. Minimal information for the referral should include patient name, hospital location, age, gender, diagnosis, and reason for the referral. Contact information of the person making the referral should also be obtained. The reason for the referral will give the music therapist a sense of appropriate goals and objectives. Some hospitals may allow the music therapist to design a referral form, whereas other facilities have a general referral/consultation form that is used for all referrals across disciplines.

The referral form and the implementation of a referral process can be a critical factor in the provision of services to patients, as well as the continued education and communication among staff. There may be some misconceptions that patients must have a musical background or an interest in music in order to be referred for music therapy. The referral form can be used as a mechanism for identifying patients who are in the greatest need for music therapy services. It can also serve as a teaching mechanism for rotating residents and floating nurses who tend to be a part of the modern-day hospital environment. Education of the staff on the role and efficacy of music therapy will result in appropriate patients for referral. The example referral form from Beth Israel Hospital, New York (Figure 3) has a checklist on the front with corresponding identifiers and descriptors on the back. If a practitioner is able to identify an area of need for the patient, he or she can turn over the form and read about what services a music therapist might provide. In this way, staff can be more informed about music therapy and its appropriateness for the patient. Offering a comment section may challenge the person making the referral to give particular details about a specific patient, and an account of what the music therapist might attend to when assessing the patient and family, thus increasing awareness of music therapy services and appropriateness of referrals.

Referrals can be made electronically, on paper, or more informally by email, phone, or casual conversation. For example, a nurse might be passing the music therapist in the hall and give a room number with a referral reason such as, "Please go see him now. He used to play the piano and has no family that visits," or "She is very agitated. Can you get her to calm down?" Referrals may also be obtained during the multidisciplinary rounds conducted on each unit. Some units have rounds daily, where each patient on the unit is discussed and potential referrals are generated. The music therapist might ask questions that compel staff to think about how music can assist in the care of a patient and family. For example, "Mrs. G. is concerned about her endoscopy tomorrow. Maybe we can provide some music before and during the procedure. I can contact the lab technician and doctor today about escorting her to the procedure." The music therapist can also solicit referrals, which tends to happen during the rotation of new staff or when a new music therapy program is being developed or upgraded.

BETH ISRAEL MEDICAL CENTER
Department of Social Work and Home Care Services
Armstrong Music Therapy Program

MUSIC THERAPY REFERRAL FORM (Side A)

Name of Patient: ______________________________________
Diagnosis: ____
Floor & Room: ____
Primary Language of Patient: _________________________________ English: __yes __ no
Caretaker(s) Name: ____
Primary Language of Caretaker: _______________________________ English: __yes __ no
Relationship to Patient: __mother __father __sibling
__foster parent __relative __friend

Reason(s) for Patient's Referral to Music Therapy (definitions on reverse side)
Check areas that apply:

Anxiety/Fear: ( ) Separation anxiety ( ) Pre or post operative anxiety ( ) General anxiety
Pain/Stress: ( ) Breathing difficulties ( ) In need of tension release

Expressive Difficulties: ( ) Depression or nonverbal ( ) Acting out or hyperactive

Coping: ( ) Facing the illness ( ) Self-esteem ( ) Communication/ Socialization

In Loss of Consciousness: ( ) Increase awareness ( ) Increase stimulation or use of imagery
Other Specify: ____
____

Comments: ____
____
____

Person Referring: ____ Ext: _______ Date:_______

Please place referrals in 6 Dazian Music Therapy Room Box or in the Music Therapy Referral envelope slots located at the Nurse's station.
*Dr. Joanne Loewy, DA, MT-BC, ext #: XXXX/internal page: XXXXX
*Kristen Stewart, MA, MT-BC, ext #: XXXX /internal page: XXXXX

REFERRAL FORM (Side B)

I. Anxiety/Fear	Music therapy soothes, familiarizes, and/or activates:
A. Separation anxiety	Chanting, musical holding, and collaborative musical experiences create a feeling of safety in the hospital.
B. Pre/Post operative anxiety	Making music relaxes and eases the mind and body of tension and fear stimulated by hospital procedures.
C. General anxiety	Musical experiences help patients make sense of their fears through a non-threatening medium.
II. Pain/Stress	Clinical improvisation provides an alternative, nonverbal means of release for a patient in discomfort:
A. Breathing and vocalizing	Life rhythms and tonal intervallic synthesis help a patient synchronize and deepen the breathing process. Toning stimulates the connection between the body breath and feeling states.
B. Tension release	Opening channels of musical creativity stimulates the body's need to release tension.
III. Expressivity	
A. Depression, nonverbal/inactivity	Structured and unstructured therapies help elicit feelings that may be "muted" or "blocked."
B. Acting out or hyperactivity	The implicit structure of music therapy techniques such as African drumming song sensitation and instrumental composition offers patients a safe means of channeling their excessive amounts of energy.
IV. Ego Strength/Coping	
A. Facing the illness	The metaphoric use of music in song selection and composition offers patients a safe way into understanding and adjusting to their illness.
B. Self-esteem	Performing and tape creating strengthen a patient's feeling of worth during this fragile time.
C. Communication/Socialization	Community singing, drumming circles, and collaborative free improvisations foster communications between patients and within families.
V. Loss of Consciousness/Coma/ICU	
A. Awareness	The use of familiar melodies helps patients become oriented or tuned into a state of safe grounded, familiarized awareness.
B. Stimulation	The use of music and guided imagery stimulates the healing process.

Figure 3. Music Therapy Referral Form for General Medical/Surgical

Clearly, most patients in the hospital could benefit from music therapy services; however, there are some patients who may benefit more than others from the direct services of the music therapist. Frequently, the music therapist will have to prioritize referrals so that the patient load can be managed effectively. Those who have an identified need (e.g., pain management, anxiety, sensory stimulation) in addition to one or more of the following criteria may be placed on a priority listing for individualized music therapy services: anticipated or experienced prolonged hospitalization, isolation, minimal or no family or other support from outside the hospital, symptoms of withdrawal and/or depression, and not receiving ancillary services (i.e., they are not being seen regularly by clinical staff other than nursing and medical staff). Patients who do not meet the prioritization criteria may be better suited for group music therapy services, music-based activity sessions (e.g., volunteers who play an accompaniment instrument and sing with patients, or an entertainer), or therapeutic music activities that can be implemented by nursing staff (e.g., standard relaxation recordings).

Sample Referral Criteria for Prioritization

- Prolonged hospitalization
- Isolation
- Lack of family/other support systems or concerns with family interactions, coping
- Withdrawn and/or depressed
- Few, if any, ancillary services (such as PT/OT)

Sometimes it may be necessary for the music therapist to upgrade criteria for referrals. This would be relevant on a unit where staff has seemingly referred only one particular type of patient or treatment need. In such a case, the objective would be to increase the staff's understanding of what music therapists do, and how this service may expand and facilitate the depth and level of care provided by the team. For example, at Beth Israel Hospital, in 1 month there were 15 referrals on the Family Medicine unit. Each referral was for a patient over the age 85, diagnosed with dementia and disorientation, and in need of stimulation. In addition, several patients with sickle cell disease had also been admitted during the month and were inadvertently overlooked by the team. The music therapists were familiar with these particular patients from the outpatient clinic. A prioritization of these referrals was necessary in order to meet the needs of the patient and the unit. In addition, re-familiarizing and re-educating the unit staff on how music therapy could address patient needs helped to increase the level of knowledge on the variety of issues and types of referrals that would be appropriate for music therapy.

Working and communicating with staff directly after a referral has been generated is invaluable to the integration of music therapy services within the hospital. It is also important to follow up with written documentation and to make an effort to personally educate and reinforce other disciplines that have made appropriate referrals. Checking back with the medical or clinical staff that made the referral, and confirming how the referral led to a goal-directed intervention as well as the outcome of that experience, may be the single most effective method of referral, team, and program building. For example, "Thanks, Dr. M. Your referral of Sarah for music therapy was invaluable. I noticed that the chart reflected that she hasn't eaten in two days. I invited her to the music therapy session when I received your referral form, where you checked "fear/anxiety" in the problem list. After attending the session, she went back to her room and ate a cup of yogurt and two pieces of toast. Thanks—keep those referrals coming."

Prior to visiting directly with the referred patient, the music therapist should review the chart and, when possible, visit with the referring staff member and the nurse currently assigned to the patient. Pre-assessment information gathered from the patient chart and/or staff may be enough to ascertain the priority for individual music therapy sessions. Sometimes the gathering of pre-assessment information is not possible due to the emergent need for services. At other times, the music therapist may not have immediate access to the patient, but can gather pre-assessment information. Minimally, the music therapist should check in with the patient's nurse before each visit in order to be informed of any relevant changes that may have occurred since the time of the referral, last visit, or within the last several hours. It is also helpful to determine the patient's availability and preferences, both musically and other, if known by the staff. Due to the acute nature of the setting and, at times, the lack of understanding for referral, it is essential that the music therapist have the ability to quickly assess the individual needs of the patient.

Pre-assessment Information

Reason for referral

Review the chart

- Medical course history
- Age
- Gender

Discuss patient with referral sources and/or patient nurse-on-duty

- Availability
- Current medical status (level of pain, responsiveness, etc.)
- Family support, issues, or concerns
- Mood/well-being in last several hours
- Preferences, musical and other (if known)

Determine infection control and other restrictions (e.g., NPO – Latin for *nil per os* or nothing by mouth)

Infection control and universal precautions

Prior to entering a hospital unit or patient's room, the music therapist must be familiar with infection control and universal precautions. The Centers for Disease Control and Prevention (1996) provides guidelines for infection control and universal precaution policies. Infection control relates to policies and procedures that minimize the risk to hospital staff and patients from infectious diseases. The level of risk will vary depending on the hospital unit and patient diagnosis.

Universal precautions relate to specific infection control practices for all patients to prevent the transmission of human immunodeficiency virus (HIV), hepatitis B virus (HBV), and other blood-borne pathogens. Universal precaution practices involve appropriate techniques when handling blood and/or needles (Centers for Disease Control and Prevention, 1996). While the music therapist is not likely to come into contact with blood or bodily fluids that require universal precautions, it is very important that he or she is knowledgeable of the practices and abides by them. Once a year, employees may be required to renew their competence on infection control and universal precautions by reading prepared materials or attending a staff inservice, followed by passing a competency test.

Infections are present in all hospital settings, but some units and patient populations require special attention. The music therapist will come in contact with more infection control restrictions on intensive care and burn units and with patients who are at higher risk for acquiring or transmitting infections, such as patients who are **immunocompromised**, have experienced a major trauma or multi-organ failure, or have been diagnosed with cystic fibrosis (Siegel, Rhinehart, Jackson, Chiarello, & Healthcare Infection Control Practices Advisory Committee, 2007). Medical staff will generate the recommendations for the type and duration of infection control precautions for a particular unit or patient; however, it is important that music therapists understand and abide by these regulations for the safety of staff and patients, in addition to themselves.

Infection control restrictions change how the music therapist approaches a patient, what instruments and materials can be brought into the room, and how and when the therapist will clean the instruments and materials. Infection control also guides a range of practices, from correct hand-washing policies to isolation safety measures. For instance, there are several types of isolation: **contact isolation**, **strict contact isolation**, and **respiratory isolation**. The infection control protocol will vary for each specific type. For example, for a patient who is on contact isolation, the protocol for all staff stipulates that hands must be washed before and after entering the patient room, the staff must be gloved and gowned throughout the visit, and gowns and gloves must be properly disposed of after the session.

When the music therapist is working within infection control guidelines, any equipment or instruments brought into a patient room must be wiped down before and after a session with medical-grade sanitation wipes. Even sheet music must be wiped down; using lyric sheets inserted into top-loading sheet protectors is a convenient way to keep the music clean without destroying it. The music therapist must follow each of these precautions, which includes playing the guitar or other instruments while wearing gloves. Wearing extra tight gloves increases the success in playing guitar, whether finger picking or strumming. The following example illustrates how infection control precautions can be followed in the context of a music therapy session.

Case Study Example

The music therapist received a referral from the Neuro Intensive Care Unit to see a 22-year-old female patient. Betsy was in a comatose state, supported by a ventilator, and was on a scheduled tube feeding. She was on contact isolation precautions due to **MRSA (Methicillin-resistant Staphylococcus aureus)**, requiring any person interacting with her to be gowned and gloved. The referral requested tactile, auditory, and olfactory stimulation, as well as opportunities to improve quality of life.

Following the Neuro Intensive Care protocol, the music therapist found Betsy's nurse to discuss the patient's current condition. The nurse agreed that music therapy would be appropriate at that time and stated that members of Betsy's family were in the room and were expecting the music therapist's arrival. From the doorway, the music therapist identified herself to the gowned and gloved woman sitting in a chair next to the hospital bed, holding the patient's hand. The woman introduced herself as Betsy's mother, Carol. The music therapist noticed that Carol appeared to have been crying and so asked, "Is this a good time for music?" Carol nodded and said, "We've been waiting for you; the nurses mentioned you and we've been patiently waiting." The music therapist then asked, "What type of music does Betsy enjoy?" Her mother answered that she liked country music and current pop music.

The music therapist then proceeded with the infection control protocol by washing her hands with soap and water at the sink, covering her clothes with a gown and putting on gloves. She unpacked the guitar, wiped it down with medical grade sanitation wipes, and organized her music, already in top-loading clear sheet protectors.

The music therapist entered the room and approached the bedside. The music therapist greeted Betsy and her mother. "Hi, Betsy. I'm the music therapist. The nurse called me and said you might enjoy listening to your favorite music. Your mom is here. She said you like country and current pop music; I think I can play those." The music therapist spoke directly to Betsy as if she could reciprocate in the conversation, and included her mother as well. The music therapist continued, "Your mom's doing great holding your hand, showing you her support," to which Carol smiled.

The music therapist, still assessing the situation, observed that Betsy made no purposeful movements to an unfamiliar voice and showed no signs of pain. She did note that Betsy's mother was actively listening, she answered for Betsy, and she appeared tearful. Based on these observations, the music therapist determined that music therapy session goals would include increasing the quality of life and coping skills for Betsy's mother.

The music therapist began to hum the melody to "Up!" (Twain & Lange, 2002), recorded by Shania Twain, and cued Carol to stand closer to the bedside. The music therapist continued to hum the first verse while simultaneously developing a task analysis of the music therapy session. Before continuing on to the next verse, the music therapist stopped and waited for almost a minute, to allow for any delayed response and to observe any positive or negative behavioral cues that Betsy might be displaying in response to the presented sensory stimulus. Certain that Betsy showed no negative signs, the music therapist continued to hum the next verse and chorus, modifying the strum to a finger-picking strum pattern. This allowed for a continuation of the auditory stimulus with a slight modification to promote sensory stimulation. Again, the music therapist paused between verse and chorus to observe for any response from Betsy. When observing the patient, the music therapist must take into consideration responses of the entire body. Consistent observation of the patient and any other participants throughout the music therapy session is an important and necessary skill the therapist must have in order to inform the direction of the session.

Not noticing any response to the change in auditory stimulation, the music therapist continued by singing the next verse. Immediately after the music therapist began to sing, Betsy's eyebrow rose. The music therapist then continued to play the guitar, but shifted from singing to humming in order to evaluate Betsy's response. The music therapist considered whether Betsy's physiological cue was positive (e.g., recognition of a familiar song, indication of preference, reinforcement to music therapist to continue), negative (e.g., increased pain, overstimulation, disapproval of music choice), or insignificant (involuntary body movement). Still unsure, the music therapist thought it best to keep the stimulus unchanged, so she continued to finger pick on the guitar and hum another verse. Without any further responses, the music therapist modified the stimulus by transitioning to another song.

Continuing with the patient's preferred songs, the music therapist began to hum "Travelin' Soldier" recorded by the Dixie Chicks (Robison, 1996). She hummed the entire song, noting that Betsy showed no signs of distress. The music therapist decided to begin singing the lyrics and was able to continue with no negative signs. Offering increasing layers of stimulation is a technique used by music therapists to increase sensory stimulation in a manner that is tolerable to a patient who may be sensitive, unresponsive, or demonstrating limited responsiveness to the presented stimuli. Because Betsy was not demonstrating any negative responses to the singing and accompaniment, the music therapist decided to add additional sensory stimuli. As she began to sing the Dixie Chick's version of "Landslide" (Nicks, 1974), the music therapist asked Carol to stroke her daughter's hand; this resulted in layered sensory stimuli of auditory and tactile stimulation.

The music therapist transitioned to another song recorded by Shania Twain, "Forever and for Always" (Lange & Twain, 2002) and instructed Carol to stroke Betsy's arm moving up to her shoulder. Carol requested the Martina McBride song "In My Daughter's Eyes" (Lovelace & Paisley, 2003). The music therapist began singing the requested song and instructed Carol to stroke Betsy's face and head. Betsy displayed a furrowed brow and the music therapist responded by asking Carol to cease the tactile stimulation. The music therapist continued the song with the finger-picking strum accompaniment, but further reduced the stimulation to Betsy by humming the melody rather than singing the lyrics. After humming several verses with no further signs of overstimulation, the music therapist returned to singing the lyrics. As the music therapist began to sing, Carol appeared tearful and began singing along with the music therapist. As they continued to sing, the music therapist encouraged Carol to resume stroking Betsy's face and head.

Layering the sensory stimulation in a progressive manner takes into consideration the patient's ability to organize and regulate the stimulation. To bring closure to the session, the music therapist must reverse the level of sensory stimulation in a sequential manner so as not to abruptly change the sensory regulation of the patient. With this patient, the music therapist asked Carol to discontinue massaging Betsy's head while the music therapist continued to sing and play the guitar. Once the tactile stimulation was completed, the music therapist waited and observed Betsy. She showed no signs of distress at the change in sensory stimulation, so the music therapist changed from singing to humming while continuing to accompany with the guitar. Again, with no observed changes in Betsy's responses, the music therapist subtracted the guitar accompaniment and continued to hum. The music therapist gradually stopped humming, concluding the music therapy session. Since this was the first session with Betsy and her contact isolation status, the music therapist did not consider using other type of tactile (instruments or fabric) or olfactory stimulation.

Reinforcing Carol, the music therapist thanked her for her participation and reinforced the value of her support to Betsy. The music therapist also thanked Betsy for participating in the music therapy session and stated, "I'd like to come back to visit you again, but if I'm unable, someone else from the music therapy department would be glad to visit you another day." Again, the music therapist thanked Carol for being such an integral part of the music therapy session. Carol smiled and followed the music therapist out of Betsy's room. Carol shared, "The music and touching her was so much more than I expected from the music therapy session. When the nurses told me about it, I thought we'd just listen to some of Betsy's favorite songs, but you gave me an opportunity to do something for my daughter." Carol began to cry and said, "This is the first time in three days that I've felt useful."

The music therapist reinforced Carol's statements and encouraged her to maintain her strength for the long medical process. Carol stated, "I'm taking it one day at a time and today has been a good day." The music therapist discussed with Carol other ways to provide support for her daughter that also created a sense of empowerment for herself. The music therapist suggested several ideas to assist Betsy, such as bringing favorite CDs to play for her or reading preferred books aloud, as well as providing Betsy with a familiar object or scent. She also suggested that Carol invite some of Betsy's friends to visit and talk about current events that would be of interest to Betsy. The music therapist also suggested that Carol take time out to care for herself each day by taking a walk, returning home in order to rest, or running errands. The music therapist also offered options for emotional support through a support group or journaling. Carol also considered writing a daily letter to Betsy and reading it out loud. After further conversation, Carol committed to bringing in some of Betsy's favorite CDs and to read aloud to her in order to create a familiar sound environment, particularly when the music therapist was not available.

Assessment

Gathering as much information as possible before interacting with the patient can better prepare the music therapist for more confident and appropriate interactions and therapeutic interventions. This is particularly true for the entry-level music therapist in the hospital setting. During the assessment process, the therapist must be completely focused on the patient and occurrences in the environment. Attention of the therapist may need to be redirected (e.g., interruptions by medical personnel), but the primary focus is to remain on providing a meaningful and musical interaction with the patient. Considering the acute nature of the hospital setting, therapeutic interventions must be beneficial within the context of one session. Remaining in the moment is particularly critical, as this may be the only opportunity for a therapeutic intervention with that particular patient.

Assessment in the hospital setting differs from music therapy assessments with other populations and settings. Hospital-based music therapy assessments may range in time from only a few minutes to the entire session. Individuals who are medically fragile may enter the hospital in their most vulnerable of states. To be admitted to the hospital, one has to undergo a myriad of tests and several series of seemingly invasive questions. The music provided and explored during an assessment may unlock many layers of emotional need. The music therapist's initial assessment session, therefore, should have enough structure to contain and provide a feeling of safety for the patient. At the same time, the assessment can provide space and a feeling of openness and exploration that gives a patient the means to feel playful and empowered. Patient might not have had such an experience during their hospital stay prior to a visit from the music therapist. Many patients speak about how music therapy provides nurturance, joy, and clarity amidst a particularly frightening time.

Each patient interaction in a medical facility has some level of surprise and unpredictability. Prior to approaching the patient's room, the music therapist should be prepared for a session that will address the full treatment process. Approach to the adult hospitalized patient must be done in a nonjudgmental, nonthreatening, and open manner. Critical to the assessment process are the entry into a patient's room and the climate of the atmosphere within the room (Loewy, 1994, 2000).

If the patient's door is closed and the nurse has indicated that he or she is awake, then the music therapist should knock and wait for a reply. If no reply is forthcoming, the music therapist should knock again and slowly open the door while expressing an audible greeting (e.g., "Mr. Peterson? I'm Jennifer from music therapy. May I come in?"). Respect of the patient's immediate needs, interests, and desires are of utmost importance, and the music therapist should not be personally insulted if the patient denies services. In the hospital environment, patients often have little opportunity for autonomous choices. Music therapists can empower patient choice by offering the patient the opportunity to have the therapist stay or come back.

Resistance is a meaningful aspect of music therapy assessment and treatment. The quality of a patient's or family's resistance is worth exploration. Some of the most trusted working music therapy relationships have been initiated through months of allowing and accepting resistance and/or refusal of music therapy services. Consideration of the patient's resistance may be a valuable part of the treatment process. It may provide the therapist with information on how the patient is coping with the hospitalization and/or illness (Ferraz, 2003; Scheiby, 2002). The therapist should have, and maintain, unconditional acceptance of the patient's refusal of music therapy services and understand that such rejection of services is not to be taken personally. In some cases, the patient may just not be interested in receiving music therapy services. Regardless of the patient's initial response to the music therapist, if the music therapist commits to coming back, it is important that he or she follows through on the commitment.

Utilizing basic manners, etiquette, and conversational skills in approaching the patient's room is highly relevant to building rapport with the patient. The entry into the room will be based on the dynamics surrounding the doorway. Coming into a patient's room too eagerly, too briskly, or too definitively does not show respect for the patient's and family's sense of self and their need for respect and privacy. Being too forceful about what music therapy provides does not always give patients and families the option to refuse the service. Once in the room, the therapist can offer a firm handshake or appropriate and natural greeting, as well as reference, or linkage, to fellow medical staff. In addition, a direct statement about music therapy that mentions the referral and process of assessment may orient the patient and family to the service and inform them of its cohesiveness to other services offered in the hospital environment. These simple and direct factors are often overlooked or misguided and lead to rejection of services and misconceptions about what music therapy may, or may not, provide for patients during their stay. The music therapist's introduction to the patient is critical to the acceptance of services.

It is especially useful that music therapists announce themselves directly to patients and staff in a clear, concise way. Even if feeling anxious or nervous, it is important that the music therapist appear confident and competent. Sometimes an intern, a newly trained music therapist, or an experienced therapist who is introducing music therapy into a new area or institution may unintentionally enter a patient's room showing anxiety. For example, the therapist might not make direct eye contact with the patient or may present services without ready explanation of potential treatment goals or areas of need. It is reasonable and likely that patients will be skeptical and have no contextual conception of music therapy and, furthermore, why it is being offered specifically to them. Because music therapy may be an unfamiliar service to many patients in the hospital setting, the music therapist needs to maintain a stance of confidence, yet not appear defensive. The music therapist can anticipate questions of all kinds and be ready to answer in a way that provides clarity and comfort.

Some music therapists think that introducing the provision of "music" might have influence in convincing patients and families to accept the modality. In actuality, an avoidance of the word *therapy* can misguide the patient and/or family. In fact, upon assessment, it may be that the patient does not want music, or that therapy is not something that would be beneficial to the patient at the time of entry or upon the first initial contact. It is an ethical responsibility to include the word *therapist* in introducing oneself, and to include the word *therapy* upon introduction of the modality, if, in fact, one is providing music therapy services or if one's job title is, indeed, "music therapist."

In working as a music therapist within an auxiliary department, the music therapist clearly represents the music therapy modality and, furthermore, makes clear distinctions, when necessary, between the department that he or she is a part of, and the function he or she will serve in performing music therapy or music therapy assessment. For example, "I am part of the Rehabilitation Therapy team. I am a music therapist . . ." or "I am part of the Department of Social Work. Whereas the social worker will be assisting with your discharge planning, I am here to provide pre-surgery support. One way I can do that is with music-based relaxation."

Assessment in the acute setting involves the therapist making detailed observations and interpretations of the ambience in the room, while also trusting his or her therapist intuition. Much of the assessment can be a multisensory experience, and the therapist must be able to multi-task. In other words, the therapist must be able to observe details of the environment while engaging the patient and processing mental notes to determine the next course of treatment. A useful tool to assess a patient's needs is the Assessment Overview. The Assessment Overview, found in the Appendix to this chapter, was created to assist beginning hospital-based practicum students or interns, but it also provides a quick reference or reminder for experienced therapists working in or transitioning to a medical practice. It was designed to help the music therapist organize his or her thoughts before entering a patient room and, once in the room, to assess possible goals for the session, identify crisis, and survey the patient's or family's situation.

Once inside the room, the music therapist observes the immediate physical environment (e.g., what is on the walls, such as pictures of family members, pets, or drawings from children or grandchildren); type and amount of medical equipment; the level of lighting; and sensory stimulation. The music therapist also notes the evidence of personal interests (e.g., what the patient is reading or doing); the level of eye contact (e.g., where is the patient focus—on the TV, out the window, or directly at the therapist); the type and style of communication; the presence or lack of family members and their relational interactions; and the energy, tension, and anxiety levels of the patient and others in the room. The music therapist makes these observations while he or she is simultaneously building rapport and forming ideas for the immediate needs and treatment goals of the patient and family.

Often the guitar or other musical instrument in the therapist's hand offers a stimulus that takes the focus off of the illness or hospitalization and creates common ground for a positive interaction. Some patients (adults, children, and especially teenagers) will be particularly turned off to the modality upon seeing a cart full of instruments. It may remind them of things that are "babyish" or events they are missing in school. It could remind an adult patient of children or grandchildren who have not visited, or who have not been informed about the patient's illness or hospitalization. At other times, the musical instruments may evoke a feeling of playfulness, taking the patient out of the role and/or focus of being ill. For patients with family or friends present in the room, having a united focus of instrument play can reduce tension, change mood, encourage expression of feeling, and help people relate to one another on the same level of common experience. Selected instruments must be age-appropriate; aesthetically pleasing in an aural, visual, and tactile sense; easily cleanable; and meet the individual needs of each patient.

Using a repertoire of song selections, the music therapist establishes rapport more quickly than if one were just standing in the room talking. Songs are also a positive way to engage family members and visitors in the patient room. Memories and emotions associated with a particular piece are triggered through the song. These can elicit conversation and expression of feelings. Often people are drawn closer together as they are able to reminisce about positive aspects of their lives. Any requests of music that the therapist does not know are important to fulfill. When possible, the therapist finds and learns the requested song prior to a return for a follow-up visit. This demonstrates respect for patients and validates their lives. If the patient will not be receiving follow-up services due to imminent discharge, the therapist locates a similar substitute in the standard repertoire of songs.

The music therapist in the adult hospital environment must possess a high level of musicianship and a wide variety of repertoire due to the range of ages, cultural backgrounds, and music preferences encountered in patients and their families. While recorded music can be beneficial and appropriate, most of the time music therapists actively create music in the moment through improvisation or composition, or by using pre-composed songs of patient preference. General knowledge, comfort, and familiarity with songs in a variety of styles and genres, and across eras that encompass the age ranges of potential patients, will ensure that the therapist is prepared for the rapidly changing diversity encountered in medical music therapy.

To prepare for such a diverse musical repertoire, medical music therapists will often have readily available a collection of assorted song books, credible Internet-based websites that provide song lyrics, and access to a good music library. Many hospital music therapy programs create their own music songbooks. These songbooks can be a collection of the most requested or popular songs from a given era or genre to provide quick access to major repertoire and availability for patients and families.

For example, one music therapy program created a songbook for the hospital that was over 300 pages. Songs were organized by genre (e.g., folk, country, spiritual) and decade (e.g., songs of the 20s through the 90s). They had been transposed into singable keys and contained lyric sheets in a readable print for the average adult patient. A corresponding copy contained chords for the therapist or others interested in accompanying. Compilation songbooks can be an invaluable resource for the music therapist in the hospital setting. Of course, it is the music therapist's responsibility to abide by copyright and fair use laws when creating a songbook for use in the hospital. Consulting with the hospital attorney or a knowledgeable expert in music and copyright law is advised.

It is recommended that assessment forms not be taken into the patient room, as it may become a barrier to building rapport. Due to shorter hospital stays, assessment is less formalized and is based on initial and ongoing interactions with the patient and family. These interactions will inform the direction of the therapeutic process moment-by-moment with the best interests of the patient in mind. Because a hospitalized patient can be quite ill, the therapist cannot expect that he or she will be in a similar situation or feeling the same from day to day. Informal assessment occurs each time the therapist sees a patient. More formalized assessment, particularly for those patients who may be seen long-term, is part of the hospital documentation procedures and will be completed and placed in the chart. Assessment notes are also valuable to the therapist in order to track progress across patients, and as a reminder of information for the individual patient. Depending on the hospital environment and standard charting procedures, the assessment and other documentation may be handwritten or word-processed documents, or electronically filed.

Adult Medical/Surgical Units
Music Therapy Assessment

Patient Name ______________________________ **Patient #** __________________
Admit Date: ____________________ **Estimated Length of Stay** __________

Location: Inpatient Unit: ______________ Outpatient Clinic: ______________

Referred by: __________________ **Date**: _______ **Assessment Date**: ______________

DOB __________________ **Age** ______________
Diagnosis: ____
____
____

Family Hx/Support: ____
____

Other Services: (staff name, pager #, and time of scheduled services)
PT __________________________ OT ______________________
Speech ______________________ Activity Therapy __________
Education ____________________ Groups Attending __________

Assessment Summary:
Cognitive ____
____
____
____

Communication ____
____
____
____

Motor ____
____
____
____

Social/Emotional ____
____
____
____

Self-Help Skills ____
____
____
____

Music Preferences ____
____
____
____

____
Recommendations for Music Therapy: ______________________________
____
____
____
____
MT-BC: ______________________________
Parent(s) Informed (date/method) ______________ **Blue Consult Completed/Filed** ______

Music Therapy Goals and Interventions

Due to brief hospitalization, inpatient goals are generalized to the patient population with individualized objectives. Some patients are hospitalized for longer periods of time (e.g., heart transplant), in which the treatment plan is modified to accommodate both the patient and the family over the changing needs dependent on the diagnosis, prognosis, and hospital course. Outpatient services may also be occasional and brief and may consist of sessions where the focus is on procedural support. Ongoing group music therapy sessions designed to address a particular goal for a specialized outpatient clinic can also be a part of the adult medical/surgical music therapy program of services.

Adult Medical/Surgical Music Therapy Goals

- Reduce perception of pain
- Reduce anxiety
- Provide pre-procedural and procedural support
- Improve or elevate mood/reduce depression
- Improve social-emotional support
- Increase motivation/compliance with rehabilitation or treatment regime
- Improve multisensory experiences
- Improve physiological outcomes (blood pressure, respiratory rate, heart rate, oxygen saturations)
- Improve satisfaction of hospital stay (inpatient)
- Improve quality of life

Reduce perception of pain

In large hospitals, treatment is quite specialized, and staff from varying departments may be looking only at one area of specialization with a patient. Pain is a complex issue, and the multidimensional qualities of music (e.g., timbre, dynamics, tempo, contour, etc.) make music therapy an effective non-pharmacological method of pain relief (Walker & Adamek, 2008). When a patient has mild to moderate acute or chronic pain, music therapy may be effectively used as a non-pharmacological strategy to reduce the perception of pain (Standley, 2000). Because the experience of pain takes place in mind and body, music therapy is an appropriate treatment, affecting a patient both physiologically as well as psychologically. The music therapist can approach the treatment of pain in a holistic manner by incorporating physiological, sensory, emotional/affective, cognitive, behavioral, sociocultural, spiritual/existential, and financial contributors to pain perception.

One neurologically based theory related to pain perception is the Gate Control Theory (Henry, 1995; Melzack & Wall, 1965; O'Sullivan, 1991; Wall & Melzack, 1962). This theory proposes that there are mechanisms in the brain that are able to shut out pain in certain situations, that is, serve as "gates." This gating system in the central nervous system opens and closes to either allow or block pain messages to the brain. Competing stimuli to the pain can serve to block the perception of pain. The music therapist can provide pleasant sensory stimulation (auditory, tactile, or visual) with a variety of live vocal or instrumental music making to compete with the pain so that the patient's neurological system focuses on the positive stimuli and blocks the pathway to the perception of pain.

Stress and anxiety that is manifested in the body may also contribute to pain perception. Music listening can be used to reduce anxiety associated with pain in a variety of contexts: pre and post surgery, during procedures, or when waiting for pain medications to take effect. In essence, the music therapist is offering an alternative stimulus that provides conflicting sensory input (like rubbing a place on our body when we have just hit it on something), thus providing comfort. These methods provide relief without causing injury, and are cost-effective and easily administered.

A person's thoughts, beliefs, and emotions may also affect how much pain is experienced. Patients may find that their pain is worse when they feel depressed and hopeless—feelings that may contribute to the heightened perception of pain. A patient may not find pain as troubling when the focus is on doing something that demands attention or is enjoyable. For example, Alma, a patient with multiple medical problems, reported significant pain in her abdominal area. The music therapist had provided a piano keyboard for her use. When the music therapist visited Alma, she reported no pain in her stomach while playing the keyboard for an hour. Although the physical cause of pain had remained the same, the perception of pain was quite different for Alma, as she had focused on the task of playing the keyboard for self-expression.

Providing an outlet for emotional expression may reduce fear and anxiety, which in turn may reduce the perception of pain. The use of music results in a mixture of emotions entering into a situation. Where there may be only sadness or grief expressed, with music and the skills of a music therapist, other emotions may also be stimulated and articulated through live music-based discussions, listening, and music making.

Because a person's thoughts can affect the way he or she feels and behaves, the music therapist offers cognitive strategies such as concentrating on tapping toes; thinking the melody; singing, saying, or mouthing lyrics; or remembering pleasant memories associated with music. These types of distraction require concentration, so they may be draining or fatiguing for a patient and, consequently, may be most effective for brief acute pain. The music therapist may also use imagery, cognitive reframing, music imagery, music-based discussion, and the provision of choice and control to reduce pain perception. Relaxation and breathing techniques can be taught and used in conjunction with music listening. See the Appendix of this monograph for descriptions of relaxation techniques, as well as Chapters 2 and 5 for additional information.

Pain may also be influenced by past experience and expectation. Music therapists use methods of cognitive behavioral reframing in order to reduce pain perception. For example, Margie came to the clinic once every 3 weeks to receive chemotherapy for her cancer. The day before her appointment, she would begin to feel pain and nausea, which was associated with the appointment and the expectation of chemotherapy the following day. The music therapist worked to condition Margie so that she could look forward to her appointments with positive associations, because her husband would sing love songs to her while accompanied on guitar by the music therapist in the outpatient clinic.

The **iso principle** (Shantin, 1970) is a technique commonly used by music therapists. It is a technique in which the patient's current patterns of behavior (e.g., emotional and/or physical state) are initially matched by the therapist with the musical elements, followed by a gradual transition in the music towards the intended therapeutic goal. With regards to pain management, music therapists use the iso principle by matching the intensity of the patient's pain musically (e.g., fast or loud if the pain is intense), and then modifying the music elements (e.g., slowing the tempo and dynamics) to support a transitional change in behavioral elements. For example, the music therapist can empower a patient to create a vocal or instrumental auditory image of the pain that facilitates an experiential process of healing through a predetermined format or improvisation. Moving the patient musically from pain to healing allows for a concrete opportunity to experience a shift in behavior and cognitive construct of his or her pain. Music therapists may also use suggestion to help patients relax and reduce pain perception.

Since music is social in nature and a part of all cultures, it is effectively used to reduce the pain caused by isolation or cultural stoicism. Some patients may isolate themselves because of depression or changes in their appearance, or because a family member is a strict gatekeeper. Patients may not want to ask for pain medication for cultural or religious reasons, or for fear of being labeled a complainer or someone who is never satisfied. Patients who are stoic and refuse pain medication may be using energy that could be used for healing, both in a physical and psychological manner. Using music as a vehicle for social support is common practice in music therapy, as is the presence of another caring human. The human connection with the therapist and the music can both play a role in relieving pain. Moreover, music is an integral part of religious and spiritual practices. If people are in acute pain, they may not be able to attend the service for their community of faith, even in the hospital. Spiritual music can provide a means of strength, comfort, and peace in a stressful environment.

Reduce anxiety

A patient's perception of pain can be related to his or her level of anxiety. Anxiety can affect overall recovery and personal well-being. The general hospital can be a stressful environment, filled with foreign sights, smells, sounds, unusual equipment, bustling hallways, and intimidating directions. Added to this are the fears associated with procedures, expenses, anticipation of pain, changes in appearance, separation from loved ones and normal routine, and the possibility of death. Patients may not be able to cope with this amount of stress with their normal everyday mechanisms.

Financial concerns can sometimes be a hidden source of anxiety that can contribute to a heightened sense of pain. Patients may worry and have increased anxiety due to the strain of medical expenses. Music therapists can facilitate expression of feelings regarding treatment, being a financial burden to loved ones, or simply financial frustration. The music therapist may provide an outlet to express these worries, but should then direct financial concerns to the social worker or case manager on the unit.

Music can be used to reduce anxiety, which in turn reduces the perception of pain and helps people relax, breathe more normally, and rest in order to help the mind, body, and spirit recover. In order to reduce anxiety, the music therapist may have a patient listen to music, sing or make music, or participate in music assisted relaxation (MAR) or MAR with imagery, progressive muscle relaxation, breathing or autogenic techniques, or music imagery. The approaches of music imagery can require advanced training and certification. See Chapters 5 for delineation of music imagery techniques that have appropriate application to adult patients. The music therapist may work with a patient and design an individualized music program according to patient needs and musical preferences. This can be recorded and given to the patient in order to assist the patient with follow-through after discharge. The following case example illustrates how the music therapist can direct relaxation for each individual and his or her particular needs.

Case Study Example

Nursing staff placed a music therapy referral for Mr. L, a 59-year-old male who was recovering from a surgical procedure called a CABG (Coronary Artery Bypass Graft) due to a heart attack. The music therapy directive was to increase stress management, elevate mood, and increase coping skills. After spending the first 3 days in the cardiac intensive care unit, Mr. L graduated to the main cardiac floor where he had been for 2 days awaiting discharge.

When the music therapist approached the door to Mr. L's room, he was dressed in a hospital gown sitting up in a Geri chair, a recliner that provides greater positioning support than a wheelchair. The television was on and he was talking on the telephone. Mr. L motioned to the music therapist to enter the room and quickly ended his telephone conversation. "How can I help you?" Mr. L inquired. The music therapist greeted him and told him about the nursing staff's music therapy referral. Mr. L responded by saying, "Yeah, those nurses are something, aren't they?" "Fine," he said. "Let's see how you can relax me." The music therapist smiled and responded by asking if the nurses were right in their assumption. Mr. L smiled and said, "They might have a point." He began to explain to the music therapist about his business, long hours that he worked, stressful employee dynamics, and family issues with his ex-wife. The music therapist agreed that all of those things combined could warrant the need for some relaxation. The music therapist asked, "When was the last time you had a vacation?" Mr. L laughed and said, "I'm on one now!" The music therapist inquired, "If you could go on vacation anywhere but here, meaning the hospital, where would it be?"

Mr. L closed his eyes to think and said, "Somewhere in the country, maybe near the river." The music therapist began to play a slow strum on the guitar and asked Mr. L to describe the vacation. She encouraged him to tell her about every detail, what he could see, smell, taste, hear, and feel. As Mr. L thought, the music therapist began to hum "King of the Road." Mr. L described a ranch in Texas where he spent all day fishing and all night smoking a cigar by the fire. Mr. L went into much detail as he recounted the patience he had while fishing. His thoughts wandered to his childhood and his future plans. He described swimming in the river and eating hamburgers and potato salad. Mr. L's eyes closed, and he smiled as he stopped talking. The music therapist began to sing and play "Don't Fence Me In" and asked Mr. L to think about the sentiment of the song. Mr. L appeared to listen to the lyrics throughout the duration of the song. As the song ended, Mr. L, with his eyes still closed, began to discuss the idea of freedom from responsibilities the character in the song had, the easiness of living in the country and working on a farm, and the motivation to seek out and explore new things.

Since Mr. L showed no signs of fatigue or disinterest, the music therapist continued and began a progressive muscle relaxation exercise. The music therapist began finger picking, asked Mr. L to take several deep breaths in and out, to listen to the music, and to try to relax his body. The music therapist understood that the patient was recovering from surgery and took note to avoid tensing and relaxing any of the upper body muscles to avoid disturbing the surgical area. Mr. L followed the music therapist's prompts, tensing and relaxing his muscles in his face and lower body.

As the music therapist ended, Mr. L opened his eyes and smiled. The music therapist then asked him what he thought of the experience. Mr. L shook his head and said, "I need you to come by every day to help me." The music therapist smiled and educated Mr. L how to perform the same exercises on his own. The music therapist discussed selecting recorded music that the patient enjoyed and Mr. L decided listening to Patsy Cline would be helpful. Mr. L and the music therapist discussed the progressive muscle relaxation, and she helped the patient rewrite a script that he could use, omitting body parts that were not appropriate to this type of relaxation experience during his recovery. The music therapist discussed additional relaxation techniques and suggested ways to make these experiences part of his daily routine. Mr. L committed to doing these exercises before he went to work. He stated, "Taking 10 to 15 minutes to start my day out right might make my whole day right." The music therapist smiled and agreed.

Overview: The music therapy session goal was to increase stress management and increase coping skills. The music therapist was able to help the patient meet these goals through education and participation in the progressive muscle relaxation and imagery exercise. Through his cooperation, the patient was able to experience an exercise that he could utilize each day to maintain a healthy lifestyle. Individualization of the patient's progressive muscle relaxation script supported the likelihood of his using these techniques upon discharge.

Procedural support

Music therapy is a highly effective strategy for offering support during medical procedures of all kinds. Music can offer distraction and provide a positive focus as well as a calm and pleasant environment. Both patients and staff can benefit from passive or active involvement with the music intervention. For example, Matt was having a bone marrow aspiration. This is a procedure in which a long needle is inserted into the hip to remove marrow to assess how a cancer is responding to treatment. Matt requested that the music therapist play guitar and sing during his procedure. Selecting Matt's preferred tunes helped him relax and focus on the music. Matt was medicated and was able to sing "The House of the Rising Sun" extremely loud without inhibition. This made Matt's wife and the doctor who was performing the procedure smile and relax as well. From a simple blood draw to the following extreme case example of termination of the ventilator, music can effectively reduce anxiety and stress during procedures.

Case Study Example

In a highly skilled nursing area such as the Neuro Intensive Care Unit (ICU), patients are medically fragile and undergo many complicated procedures. To avoid overstimulation, excessive exertion, and fatigue, there may be a specific schedule for procedures and treatments, including music therapy. In most intensive care units, a quiet time is implemented for this reason. Medications and procedures are all scheduled around this time of rest.

The Neuro ICU is set up like a horseshoe with a nurse's station in the middle, providing a 360-degree view of the 10 private rooms. The entrance to the patient rooms is a sliding glass door with a privacy curtain. The nurse's station is equipped with computer monitors measuring each patient's heart rate, respiration rate, and oxygen saturation level. An alarm sounds in the patient's room and at the computer monitors to alert the nursing staff of a medical concern. The unit is a secure area and requires authorization to enter. For referral therapies, the protocol is to check with the nurse assigned to the patient upon entering to discuss the appropriateness for treatment and permission to engage with the patient at that time.

A referral for music therapy came via pager for an 18-year-old male in a motor vehicle collision. The music therapist was given minimal information: *18-year-old male, in comatose state, family in distress, possible extubation, social worker already at the bedside, please see immediately.*

As the music therapist entered the Neuro Intensive Care Unit, the nursing staff informed the music therapist of the situation. The patient presented with multiple bone fractures, major organ failure, and brain damage and was in a comatose state. The patient was ventilated to sustain life; however, the music therapy referral was to assist the patient and family during the termination of life support.

The music therapist was met by the social worker as she entered the patient's room. The social worker spoke quietly and informed the music therapist of those present in the room: Patient J, mother, father, sister, brother, and the patient's girlfriend. The music therapist was also informed that Patient J's friends had been informed of the situation and were arriving shortly to say their goodbyes.

The music therapist quietly greeted the family, introduced herself, and asked what type of music J enjoyed. J's parents began to cry, and his mother stated, "I don't even know." J's sister answered, "Anything current, like rock, is his favorite." The patient's girlfriend stated, "Our song is "I'm With You" by Avril Lavigne." The music therapist began to play the requested song while J's girlfriend stroked his arm; tearful, she told him how much she loved him. The music therapist continued to play softly and quietly at the end of the bed. J's sister began to hum along and said, "We used to listen to this song when he drove me around." J's mother and father looked up at their daughter and smiled.

Three nurses entered the room, one of whom informed the family that the physician would arrive in a few minutes to assist with the procedure. There was silence from the family so the nurse repeated herself. J's mother turned to the nurse and said, "Before the machines are turned off, I'd like his friends to say goodbye." The nurse nodded and stated that she would inform the physician and would check back with the family in 30 minutes. During this conversation, the music therapist continued to play current rock music at a lower volume to maintain continuity in the sound environment, increasing the volume upon the nurse's departure.

For the next 30 minutes, J's friends arrived in groups of three; tearfully they expressed to J that they loved him, how much they would miss him, reminisced about past fun experiences, and expressed their condolences to the family. The music therapist continued to play throughout the visit. J's friends requested songs including "Blurry" by Puddle of Mudd, "In the End" by Linkin Park, "Complicated" by Avril Lavigne, "Hanging by a Moment" by Lifehouse, "Drive" by Incubus, "Drops of Jupiter" by Train, and "Kryptonite" by 3 Doors Down.

As the last of J's friends left the room, the physician arrived to once more explain the procedure to the family to be sure they clearly understood the process. The physician asked the music therapist to step out the room so that he could speak with the family privately. J's mother quickly suggested that she and her husband step out of the room to speak with the doctor, explaining, "The music should continue for J." She got out of her seat, touched the music therapist on the shoulder, and directed the physician out of J's room.

After J's parents left the room, his younger brother said aloud, "I like being here with him." J's sister and girlfriend did not respond to the younger brother's statement, so the music therapist turned to J's brother and said, "I'm sure he likes it that you are here, too. If you want to, you can say to him whatever you like." At that moment J's brother began to cry and said, "I'm sorry I was mad at you the other day; I'm not mad anymore. I love you." J's sister also began to cry and looked at her younger brother and said, "He loves you, too. Nobody is mad anymore; we just love each other."

Note: Practicing in a family-centered care mindset, the music therapist must evaluate and differentiate between the realistic situation and the therapeutic needs of the patient and family. It was an important therapeutic priority to support the younger brother in expressing his feelings, regardless of the fact that, due to the extensive brain damage of the patient, the probability of the patient actually hearing his brother's words was unlikely.

When the parents and the physician returned, J's mother quietly announced that they were going to go ahead with the procedure and sat down next to her son. She looked at the music therapist and said, "When they start, can you make sure to keep playing?" The music therapist nodded and asked if she had any songs in mind; she shook her head and simply said, "His favorites." The medical staff filed in, the nurses repositioned J in the bed, removed some equipment from his body, and proceeded to discontinue the ventilator. The machine made several sighs, at which time J's mother looked at the music therapist and requested the song "Puff the Magic Dragon." The music therapist transitioned to the requested song and continued to sing and play while the family wept and held each other surrounding J's bed.

Overview: The music therapy goal was to assist the patient and family during the termination of life support. The music therapist was able to build rapport and connect with the family members through the use of patient-preferred music and by maintaining an inconspicuous, yet supportive presence in the patient's room. The first interaction encouraged the patient's girlfriend to express her thoughts and feelings about their relationship through the request of "their" song. The patient's sister, after hearing a specific song, was able to reminisce about memories while riding in the car with the patient. During this difficult time, the youngest sibling was also able to express emotions of forgiveness and love. The patient's mother valued the presence of the music in the room and, at the end, perhaps trying to comfort her son one last time, requested a specific song.

Improve or elevate mood

Due to changes in levels of functioning, appearance, social contact, and/or support systems, patients may experience low mood or depression during hospitalization, creating such problems as fatigue, feelings of hopelessness and helplessness, somatic complaints related to depression, reduction in ego strength and self-esteem, and ineffective coping skills. Because of the brief time frame for treatment, the music therapist more commonly works toward a goal of improvement in mood rather than a reduction of depression, which is typically considered a more long-term goal.

In the acute setting, the music therapist can use music techniques in a variety of ways to effectively change or elevate a patient's mood. Combining live music with a trusting relationship normalizes and humanizes the sanitary environment. Therapists match live music making to the mood of the patient, and then gradually modify the music to elevate or change mood. Recorded music is also used, and recordings can be produced and individually tailored for use when the music therapist is unavailable or after discharge. Lyric discussion can lead to expression and validation of emotions, which can lift mood as well. With the stimulus of song lyrics, relevant positive and alternative coping strategies can be discussed as needed. Singing or playing instruments is a form of self-expression and a catalyst for discussion, which can alter frame of mind. Working together with family or visitors in active music making energizes and offers a sense of belonging and accomplishment for all involved. Songwriting provides a means for self-expression and the building of ego and self-esteem. The following case example illustrates how a music therapist can elevate mood and offer hope for the future after a patient has had a significant change in level of functioning.

Case Study Example

The music therapist was given a referral to see a 56-year-old male, Mr. G, who was hospitalized following a mild CVA (**cerebrovascular accident**). Mr. G had a history of musical experience and interest in playing the guitar. He presented with left-sided hemiparesis (weakness) and slight facial droopiness on the left. Carrying two guitars, the music therapist knocked and opened the door. Mr. G began to cry and explained that he had intended to start playing the guitar again before his stroke. With the current weakness in his hands, Mr. G stated that he was unsure if he'd be able to play.

Due to his tearful mood and expressed interest in playing the guitar, the music therapist decided to assess Mr. G's left side strength and his level of engagement with her. After asking what his music preference was, she began playing Creedence Clearwater Revival's "Have You Ever Seen the Rain." The music therapist asked Mr. G to tap in rhythm using his right hand as she began playing the guitar. Mr. G immediately found the downbeat and was able to maintain a consistent beat. As the music continued, the music therapist asked Mr. G to use his left hand (his affected side) to do the same. He was again able to find the downbeat and began tapping his leg. Using a tabletop, the music therapist then modeled a rhythm using only the fingers. As part of the assessment, the music therapist was trying to determine how much strength each individual finger was capable of performing in order to determine if Mr. G would be able to successfully play guitar chords. Understanding the severity of Mr. G's deficits allowed the music therapist to re-introduce Mr. G to playing the guitar through a series of successful approximations rather than having him be discouraged by an unsuccessful experience. For the next several minutes, the therapist varied the tempo of the guitar as the patient tapped his fingers along to simple and complex rhythms. Without any prompts, Mr. G began singing harmony.

In an effort to reduce physical fatigue, the music therapist paused the accompanied singing and inquired about the patient's current length of stay, reason for hospitalization, and family support. The patient easily engaged in conversation, answered questions, and initiated other topics of discussion. He stated that he used to play guitar 20 years ago with friends. He said, "We'd gather around the living room singing songs and drinking beer. We'd play all night, me and my buddies, but now, I'm not sure if that can still happen." The music therapist suggested that he could try with her to see how it would go. Mr. G agreed and the music therapist handed him the second guitar. He held it under his right arm and wiggled his left hand a few times. The music therapist, sensing his uneasiness and hesitancy, asked Mr. G if he remembered some of his chords. He said, "I kind of remember." She fingered a D chord and asked Mr. G if she was correct. He nodded yes and the music therapist asked if he could verbally describe what his fingers were supposed to do. Mr. G was successful at describing the exercise; however, when he tried to imitate the music therapist's hand position on the guitar, he had a difficult time. After a few corrections, Mr. G was able to replicate each hand position.

As the session continued the music therapist and Mr. G sang The Animal's "House of the Rising Sun," "Take It Easy" by the Eagles, Lynyrd Skynyrd's "Simple Man," and Creedence Clearwater Revival's "Down on the Corner." After each song, Mr. G participated in the guitar chord imitation exercise. He was able to verbally describe each finger position and form each guitar chord. During this session, Mr. G did not play one note, but in his words, "I was able to play the guitar today."

Overview: The music therapy goal was to elevate mood, increase finger dexterity, increase coping skills, and increase quality of life. During the music therapy session, the patient met these goals in the following ways:

- Elevate mood and quality of life – the patient engaged with minimal to no prompt. Based on his history of guitar playing, the patient and MT-BC instantly built rapport. The patient made eye contact, participated in conversation, expressed positive affect, showed a willingness to participate in new things, reminisced about the past, and sangalong.
- Finger dexterity – demonstrated by participating in the fingering exercises.
- Coping skills – the patient was able to express his feelings about his current abilities. The MT session gave the patient a sense of accomplishment and increased his self-efficacy. During the MT session, the patient was also given an opportunity to express imself through a familiar and comfortable modality.

Improve social-emotional support

Isolation, lack of structured or constructive time, and ineffective coping are problematic within the hospital setting. Isolation occurs for patients who may be medically isolated, or simply may not have any visitors except essential medical staff. In addition, patients may have another medical condition that in itself can be isolating, such as depression or dementia. Lack of structure or constructive use of time may result due to long periods of time when patients are waiting for medical personnel, medications, test results, or procedures. When patients are out of their regular routines, their normal coping mechanisms may not be as accessible to them. This is particularly true during a hospitalization. In each of these instances, music can be used as an outlet for expression of feelings and to provide emotional support.

The use of songwriting offers a safe environment where patients have opportunities to connect with and express their feelings at their own chosen pace. Songwriting cultivates supportive interactions between the patients and their loved ones and enables patients to maintain some degree of physical well-being. Songwriting facilitates communication among family members (Salmon, 1993; Slivka & Magill, 1986); portray patients' feelings (Bruscia, 1991; Magill-Levrault, 1993); facilitate images, dreams, and fantasies (Magill-Levrault, 1993); and, when presented as gifts, creates a lasting musical memory or memento (Bruscia, 1991; Krout, 2000; Porchet-Munro, 1993). Songwriting can be a valuable and powerful tool to aid in the expression of feelings experienced by the patient and/or family members during hospitalization.

Patients and families can experience a range of emotions, even emotions that are unexpected or unrelated to the source of hospitalization. Sometimes people merely need an opportunity to release emotion. Music-based experiences may elicit an emotion that is unexpected or close to the surface, or one one that a patient is unable to articulate. Emotional expression often comes in the form of tears that may be elicited simply by hearing a song. Tears may be accompanied with verbalization, anger, or laughter. People may even change how they are responding or interacting due to the emotional impact of the music; someone may be verbally engaged with a bright affect but change dramatically when a particular song is played/sung. The music therapist must be able to validate the patient by assuring him or her that it is a normal response to the music. One cannot just leave the room or ignore the patient if he or she is having an emotional response to the music.

Exploring the reaction to the music is the responsibility of the music therapist. Giving patients permission to acknowledge their feelings is of utmost importance and it is unethical to do otherwise. For example, in a group session, a patient requested that the group sing the folk song "Red River Valley." As the group sang the song, one patient began to cry. In an effort to validate the patient's individual experience, yet not embarrass or call undesired attention to her tears within the group context, the music therapist made a general acknowledgment of music as a powerful medium and how sometimes a song can move one to tears. The tearful patient looked up and smiled at the therapist and began to talk about how the song was a favorite of her grandfather's and shared with the group how it made her think of him. After the session, the music therapist caught up with this patient to ask how she was doing, and she asked about her grandfather. The patient spoke fondly of her grandfather, thanked the therapist for the good memory, smiled, and left the group room. This expression of emotion was unrelated to the patient's hospitalization, but the song created a strong emotional response that elicited a good memory. The validation by the therapist allowed the patient to express her emotion to the extent she desired and needed at that moment.

Unlike other settings where the therapist may have months or even years of building connections with patients, the hospital is most often a quick and sharp-edged experience for patients. The trauma of hospitalization, no matter the reason or diagnosis, is often incomprehensible to the patient and/or family, even if it is temporary. Medical personnel are focused on aspects of treatment and discharge planning. It is often the music therapist who creates a haven for expression for the patient and family, offering the mechanisms to work with their emotions, and helping to link them to the body and current medical and psychosocial aspects of care. Additionally, the immediate depth and level of emotion that a hospitalized person may unveil in the initial moments of contact with the music therapist is often remarkable. The therapist creates a shared experience with the music that can quickly develop a sense of trust and rapport with the patient. Therapists in turn should maintain good self-care in order to be available to support the emotional needs of the patients they serve (Scheiby, 2002). The following description of a one-to-one session demonstrates how the music therapist can elevate mood, assist with coping, and facilitate a life review; writing one's life events down in a permanent product, such as a song, can help put things in perspective.

Case Study Example

Upon entering a regional medical center, Mr. P was informed of his poor prognosis due to lung cancer. He was referred to music therapy in order to elevate his mood and to increase his quality of life, coping skills, and opportunities for socialization.

The music therapist approached the room and knocked on the door; Mr. P said that she could enter. As she entered the room, the music therapist introduced herself, stating that she was from the music therapy department and wished to play some music with him. Mr. P was apprehensive and stated that he did not intend to pay for the music therapy service, but reluctantly agreed that the music therapist could stay. The music therapist assured Mr. P that there was not a charge to him personally for the services and his participation was voluntary. As she spoke to him, the music therapist oriented herself to the room, found a place to stand near the bedside, and unpacked the guitar. Quickly she observed that the environment was neat; the bed was made and the shades were closed, letting only a bit of sunlight in, and the room was bare. There were no cards, balloons, gifts, or floral arrangements decorating his space. She continued the conversation by asking him what kind of music he enjoyed. The music therapist noted that Mr. P was alert and oriented, dressed in street clothes, and sitting on the bed with his feet dangling off the side. He did not turn to face the music therapist, but glanced over his shoulder, engaging in a reciprocal conversation and occasionally making eye contact.

Mr. P stated that he enjoyed Motown music and expressed hesitancy about his role in the music therapy session. To alleviate further anxiety, the music therapist decided that it was best to just start playing, and began with the Temptations' song "My Girl," using a moderate tempo and strumming pattern. As soon as the music began, Mr. P started tapping his foot to the beat, swayed gently back and forth in bed, and made consistent eye contact with the music therapist. His body language invited the music therapist to move closer to the bed. She motioned for permission to sit next to Mr. P; he shifted his body so that they were facing each other and began to hum along, so she sat next to him and continued. The music therapist associated this change in the patient's body language as an indication of rapport, a willingness to engage, and a desire to continue with the session. This simple behavioral cue essentially gave the music therapist permission to pursue further rapport building and consider additional music therapy intervention strategies.

The music therapist continued with, "The Way You Do the Things You Do." Mr. P stated, "This is my song." He continued to move slowly with the music, hummed along, and at times even sang some of the words. At the end of the song, Mr. P stated, "I'm surprised you could do my kind of music." The music therapist inquired about the patient's music history, why this particular song was "his" song, and about his current situation. Mr. P was receptive to all of the conversation topics and began a reciprocal conversation, asking music therapist where she was from, when she learned how to sing and play guitar, and why she played in hospitals.

Mr. P suggested Marvin Gaye's "I Heard It through the Grapevine." As the music therapist began to play an accompaniment pattern, she suggested Mr. P think about what he liked most about the song and why he chose it. As she began to sing, Mr. P closed his eyes, swayed to the music, sang along, and clapped his hands. At the end of the song, Mr. P opened his eyes and spoke about his upbringing, adventures and the lifestyle of his youth, lost loves, true loves, and break-ups. The music therapist asked if Mr. P would mind if she took notes in order to write a song as a gift for him. Mr. P laughed and said, "When I see it, then I'll believe it." Mr. P spoke for about an hour and ended the session by thanking the music therapist and stating that he was tired and wanted to lie down. The music therapist asked if she could return the next day to present him with a song of celebration. He laughed again and said, "Sure."

The music therapist returned to her office to write Mr. P's song. She used the song parody or piggybacking method, which uses a melody from an existing song with new lyrics. The music therapist used the melody from "The Way You Do the Things You Do" and inserted Mr. P's exact words from his story about his life.

The next afternoon, the music therapist returned to sing Mr. P's celebration of life. She knocked on the door, greeted him, announced herself, and was invited in. Mr. P was again dressed and sitting on his bed. He immediately inquired about his song. "What did you come up with?" The music therapist smiled and asked if he would like to invite some nurses to join the celebration. Mr. P agreed. Two nurses and one CNA arrived shortly and were given maracas and tambourines to play along with the therapist. Mr. P was presented with a copy of the lyrics on decorative paper. At the end of the song, Mr. P stated, "I can't believe you wrote a song about me! Let's hear it again." The music therapist sang Mr. P's song of celebration four more times, and all the while Mr. P expressed his excited disbelief and gratitude for such a gift.

Overview: The music therapy goals were to elevate Mr. P's mood, increase quality of life, increase his coping skills and increase socialization. During the music therapy session, Mr. P met these goals in the following ways:

- Elevate mood, quality of life, and socialization – at the beginning of the session, the patient displayed hesitation, closed body language, and a bit of anxiety. After the initial musical interaction, the patient began to hum and sing, displayed open body language by turning to face the music therapist, made consistent eye contact, initiated conversation, and shared ideas and personal stories.
- Increase coping skills – the concepts of self expression, self-esteem, and self-examination are all linked to the patient's ability to cope during his current situation. Through the songwriting exercise, the patient was able to look back and discuss the good and bad times that he experienced, his regrets, his accomplishments, and the perception of himself as a man.

Increase motivation and/or compliance to support motor functioning

Some patients may require a treatment plan that includes rehabilitation to support their motor functioning. For example, a patient who has experienced cardiac concerns, an orthopedic surgery, or a stroke may require physical therapy to maintain muscle strength or rehabilitate affected areas of motor functioning. Patients may begin rehabilitation during their inpatient visit, while awaiting placement in a rehabilitation facility or discharge followed by outpatient physical therapy. Due to common issues such as repetitive exercises, pain with movement, habits that are not conducive to strong motor functioning, and low mood or fatigue, patients may need some assistance with motivation in order to change or to improve their health. Compliance with a physical rehabilitation or motor strengthening regime is important to the recovery process, as weakened physical strength can hinder the healing process.

The use of music with exercise can make repetitive tasks seem easier and more interesting, provide a focus to reduce pain, or elevate mood to improve motivation.

Providing a musical structure for new routines may improve compliance during hospitalization, as well as after discharge. Co-treatment with physical or occupational therapy, or other medical staff, may support motor functioning while saving time, expense, and frustration for the patient. A specialized technique that integrates movement and music is Neurologic Music Therapy (NMT). NMT outlines specific music-based techniques to address sensorimotor concerns related to range of motion, ambulation, stamina, muscular strength, physical coordination, balance, and posture (Thaut et al., 2008). Description of these techniques is beyond the scope of this monograph. For further information, please see the Center for Biomedical Research in Music website at http://www.colostate.edu/dept/CBRM/

Sometimes an emotional reason will be the underlying cause of a patient being noncompliant with his treatment plan. As described above, music therapy can assist in the expression of feelings that may lead to a resolution to a noncompliance conflict. The following case example illustrates how rapport with the music therapist allowed for the discovery of the primary reason for noncompliant behavior, and how music therapy facilitated coping mechanisms that changed a frustrating situation for patient and staff to a constructive and positive one.

Case Study Example

Ms. R, a 92-year-old African American woman, was recovering from cardiac surgery in the Medical Surgical Intensive Care Unit (MSICU). The second day after surgery, Ms. R started to refuse to sit up in the Geri chair for any length of time during the day. The protocol for transfer from the MSICU to the main cardiac floor includes several physical requirements: sitting up in bed or in a Geri chair, standing up, and walking a few steps, if possible. After the first day of recovery, most patients are encouraged to sit up in the Geri chair for as long as they can tolerate, several times during the day. Nursing staff placed a referral for music therapy services to assist with increasing Ms. R's mood, socialization, and quality of life.

Upon entering the MSICU, the music therapist consulted with Ms. R's nurse. The nurse informed the music therapist that Ms. R had been sitting up in the Geri chair for the past 15 minutes and was adamant about returning to bed. The nurse wondered if the music therapist could assist with keeping Ms. R seated in the Geri chair for a while longer. The music therapist gathered some additional background information about Ms. R from the nurse and the hospital chart and then proceeded to Ms. R's room. The music therapist knocked on Ms. R's door, smiled and greeted her, and asked if she could come into the room. Ms. R nodded her assent and the music therapist entered. Upon approaching Ms. R, the music therapist introduced herself and explained that she had been asked to visit and was wondering if Ms. R would like to hear some gospel music. Ms. R smiled and asked if the music therapist knew "Amazing Grace." The music therapist sat down next to Ms. R, placing two maracas on the side table within Ms. R's reach. The music therapist began to play, using a moderate strumming pattern. Ms. R began to sing along without any prompts and her feet began to move to the music. The music therapist continued playing and transitioned without hesitation to "Glory, Glory, Hallelujah." Ms. R picked up the maracas and began to shake the instruments with a consistent rhythm throughout the song. Continuing the music at a slightly faster tempo, the music therapist began to sing, "Wade in the Water." Ms. R sang along without any prompts and continued to play the maracas. As the music therapist ended the songs, Ms. R opened her eyes, smiled, and stated, "It's my very own church service." The music therapist asked Ms. R where she learned all of these songs. Ms. R answered, "In church, baby, and my mother." Ms. R began to describe her humble upbringing, how her life was intertwined with all of the church functions, her mother's daily scriptures reminding her to "follow the word," the memories of singing in the church choir with all of her friends, who had all passed, and the reminders of how, if you ask, the spirit can heal you.

The music therapist asked and discussed Ms. R's reason for hospitalization, her thoughts about the process of healing and recovery, her thoughts about her own healing process, and her family and church support. The music therapist also inquired about her resistance to sitting up in the Geri chair and participating in the daily exercises. During this conversation, Ms. R disclosed her anxiety about her recovery. She stated that she was afraid of being sent home too soon, knowing that she might not be ready to go home alone. She stated that she was worried that she might fall and no one would be able to rescue her. Ms. R and the music therapist discussed her concerns and a potential plan of action to decrease her anxiety. Part of the discussion focused on the value of understanding the process and options available to Ms. R. The music therapist asked about specific family members that she could utilize as contacts, discussed the rehabilitation services usually provided before a patient is discharged, and how the social worker might be able to assist in formulating a plan and helping Ms. R after discharge. Recognizing that Ms. R was demonstrating an openness to information and was still sitting in her chair without mention of fatigue, the music therapist asked if Ms. R would like the nurse to come in and explain what was required of her before she would be able to transfer to the cardiac unit and be discharged to home. Ms. R agreed that would be helpful, so the music therapist briefly left the room to explain the request to the nurse. The music therapist returned to the room and continued to sing with Ms. R while waiting for the nurse. When the nurse arrived, she waited for the song to finish, at which point the music therapist cued both Ms. R and the nurse by stating, "Your nurse is here to give you some information about the expectations for discharge." The nurse proceeded to explain the specific protocols required before discharge from the MSICU to the main cardiac unit. Ms. R's nurse then suggested that they schedule a family meeting before Ms. R was discharged to openly discuss options for her and her family. After the nurse left, Ms. R asked to continue music.

This initial music therapy session lasted 45 minutes and Ms. R continued sitting in her Geri chair for the rest of the afternoon. After the session, the music therapist followed up with the nurse who had already made a referral to the social worker. In addition to the hospital chart note, the music therapist left a message for the unit's social worker to explain what had occurred in the session.

Overview: The music therapy session referral was to elevate mood, increase socialization, and improve quality of life. After assessing the patient, the music therapist determined that increasing coping skills was a primary patient goal.

- Elevate mood, socialization, and quality of life – the music therapist was able to use patient-preferred music and provide an opportunity to participate in musical experience that had varying levels of engagement. The patient was able to choose between passive participation via listening to the therapist sing and a range of active participation by singing with the therapist and playing the maracas that had been strategically placed in an easily accessible position. In addition, live music making facilitated a distraction from sitting upright, a position necessary for the patient's recovery from surgery and ultimately her quality of life. The extended length of time in the Geri chair supported an increased tolerance for an upright position.
- Coping skills – after building rapport with the patient, the patient revealed to the music therapist the underlying issue for her resistance to sitting in the Geri chair. Throughout the session, the patient appeared to feel as if she were in a "safe" environment, and with minimal cues from the music therapist, she began to disclose her fears and anxiety about the recovery process. In the context of the music therapy session, the patient was able to express autonomy and self-expression.

Ms. R continued music therapy sessions for the next week: two more music therapy sessions in the MSICU, and three sessions on the main cardiac unit. These sessions were varied to meet Ms. R's immediate needs. Two sessions included Ms. R sitting in her Geri chair; another session was co-facilitated with the physical therapist as Ms. R tried to stand up and walk a few steps. The fourth session involved Ms. R lying in bed exercising her legs as directed by the physical therapist. During the fifth session, Ms. R had not had much sleep the night before, so the music therapy session focused on increased relaxation.

Improve multi-sensory experiences

The hospital environment has varying degrees of stimulation—from too much audio stimulation in an open ICU bay, to quieter areas where patients may be isolated and are in need of more normalized surroundings. Using vocals, alone or in combination with vibrotactile, visually stimulating, or calming instruments or manipulatives, the music therapist is able to offer appropriate multisensory experiences that offer a wide array of possibilities for stimulation to meet the individual needs of patients.

For example, when a patient is in a comatose state due to a trauma, music therapy can effectively provide multisensory stimulation. At times, sedative medications may be used to place patients in a medically induced coma in order to keep them from harming themselves or removing necessary medical equipment, or as a necessary treatment to facilitate the healing process. Music therapists can offer coma stimulation that may help with both short- and long-term outcomes. Coma stimulation is an organized, systematic approach to providing multisensory opportunities for the patient to respond to the environment in an adaptive way. Familiar, meaningful preferred music, voices, and other stimuli that have emotional significance to the patient are usually more likely to elicit responses.

The intensive care units may have strictly limited visitation times. In addition, patients with a variety of diagnoses may have restrictions on visitation due to illness or disease that keeps them isolated from family, friends, and nearly all normal routines. Increased isolation reduces the exposure to sensory stimulation, often resulting in sensory deprivation. The music therapist can provide normalized experiences for patients who are restricted from outside visitors. In this circumstance, the relationship developed between the music therapist and the patient can become particularly important to the patient, as the majority of other interactions may be with staff and may involve care that addresses only their medical needs.

For someone who is unable to verbally communicate, a brief visit from a music therapist can provide a release of emotions in a nonverbal format. For example, John was in the ICU post surgery and his family was concerned that he had lost hope and was not making medical progress. They were hoping he would be extubated and transferred to a medical unit where they could visit more often. The family informed the music therapist of John's favorite music and asked her to visit him. On her visits to the ICU, the music therapist sang country music with guitar accompaniment. Although John was unable to speak, he made direct eye contact, raised his eyebrows, had tears flowing down his cheeks, and squeezed the therapist's hand after the music stimulation. He was able to leave the ICU after extubation in a few days, and the music therapist continued to visit John on another unit. The primary goal was changed from stimulation to mood elevation when John was able to communicate his emotions verbally and have support of his family.

Instead of creating stimulation, the music therapist may be consulted to offer suggestions or assistance to a unit to make it less stimulating. Music therapists may measure sound levels and provide ideas on how to calm an area. For individual patients, the music therapist can offer recordings and equipment such as boom boxes, MP3 players, and pillow speakers that will effectively mask unwanted environmental sounds.

Improve physiological outcomes

The literature suggests that the therapeutic use of music can effect change in physiological outcomes such as blood pressure, respiratory rate, heart rate, and oxygen saturations. Clinical outcomes have also demonstrated favorable changes in a patient's physiological responses during music therapy. However, long-term outcomes are still not well documented. Positive changes in physiological responses can be particularly relevant for the patient who is being monitored for such vital aspects of their physical well-being, such as on the intensive care and cardiac units. Blood pressure, heart rate, and oxygen saturation levels are measured by medical equipment located near the patient and monitored in the patient room and hospital staffing areas. Patients' medical monitors can be supervised from a centrally located nurses' station and/or in a smaller observation station that is a pod of several rooms being attended by a single nurse. Respiration rate may or may not be monitored by medical equipment, but it is an observable physiological response that music therapists can use to assess and observe changes during an intervention. When possible, music therapists can monitor and document changes in physiological outcomes during music therapy sessions. When a music therapist observes changes due to direct intervention, he or she should include this objective data when talking with patients, families, and staff, and use this information for documentation.

Improve satisfaction of hospital stay

The patient's perception of the hospital experience may impact his or her compliance with the treatment plan, follow-up services, or the future use of that hospital. Positive patient satisfaction can be a great concern for hospitals, particularly those in competitive markets. The addition of music therapy services can improve positive patient and family perception of the hospital experience. Previously described case examples have demonstrated how music therapy services can transform the hospital experience in remarkable ways. Music therapy services tend to be viewed as a positive and valuable service by patients. These viewpoints can improve the perception of hospitalization and treatment outcomes, thus increasing the positive public and community relations for the hospital and the specialized units.

Examination of long-term treatment outcomes for patients who have received music therapy services will provide a better understanding of the efficacy of music therapy and how it affects the perception of patient satisfaction. Hospitals market music therapy as a unique benefit to their general services. Consistently presenting information to professional and community organizations and bringing positive publicity to the institution is part of the music therapist's responsibilities.

Due to staffing levels and time constraints, follow-up services after hospitalization are sometimes difficult to provide. Providing patients with the tools while they are hospitalized can help them follow through with exercises and can assist with new ways of coping or changing behaviors upon discharge. For example, music therapists offer music recordings for pain, anxiety, exercise, and rest that can be used by patients after discharge. Many therapists are also able to provide connections to agencies or therapists in the local area of the patient. Other music therapists may be able to follow up with communication to the patient, family, clinic, or other local agency. If the patient will be receiving music therapy services at another facility, a standard discharge summary form may be applicable. The hospital may have a standard discharge summary form, or the music therapist can provide a narrative summary to be placed in the chart. A discharge summary may be a standard requirement of the hospital for all services engaged with the patient. Informal communication with team members on the unit may consist of verbal information relayed during a discharge meeting, copies of music therapy documentation sent to specific areas or staff, or an informal verbal interaction with a variety of staff that also cared for the patient.

Outcome Documentation

Budgetary restrictions demand that music therapy is a cost-effective treatment modality. Music therapists must provide measurable outcomes from treatment in order to support the cost effectiveness of music therapy. Clinical practice with an evidence-based practice mindset will support an efficacious music therapy program. Music therapy services tend to be viewed by patients as positive and valuable. These viewpoints can help improve perception of hospitalization and treatment outcomes, thus increasing the positive public and community relations for the hospital and specialized units. Moreover, music therapy programming may provide a unique marketing tool for the hospital through improved patient and family satisfaction with their hospital stay or outpatient clinic service.

While patient satisfaction and positive perceptions of music therapy services are valuable, formal documentation of clinical outcomes in the patient records is a necessary component to the viability of the medical music therapy program. Documentation in the official patient chart is a legal document that records the efficacy of treatment and contributes to programming quality assurance. Official documentation will comply with the hospital's specific format and guidelines. Documentation may be electronic or handwritten, as well as in a narrative or checklist format. In addition to the official documentation, the music therapist may wish to complete documentation records specific to the music therapy program. This is particularly vital when seeing multiple patients in a short period of time.

Music therapy program charting creates an objective record of outcomes that is easily quantifiable and simple to use. It also reflects the efforts and changes in the music therapy program. These data are important to inform how best to improve, expand, or sustain music therapy services. For example, one hospital was able to hire a full-time music therapist to expand the program through a private funding agency. Objective data outcomes regarding the number of patients referred and served, amount of time spent in direct patient contact, and progress and benefits to patients was critical to procure support from hospital administration and the private funding agency. Without these program records, the music therapists would have needed to search hospital records to create the necessary information. Program documentation allows for quick and easy access to relevant information in an efficient and timely fashion. Providing regular reports or presentations to administrators will support the continued vigor and viability of the music therapy program. Figure 4 provides an example of one approach to program documentation.

The University of Iowa Hospitals and Clinics/Children's Hospital of Iowa
Music Therapy Program Patient Intervention Tracking

Patient Name ____________________ **Patient #** __________________ **MT** __________
Unit ________________ **Room** ______________ **Page** ________ **of** ____

Goal ________________________________ **Objective** ________________________

Date										
+/–										

Date	Session Comments/Recommendations

Goal ________________________________ **Objective** ________________________

Date										
+/–										

Date	Session Comments/Recommendations

Figure 4. Music Therapy Program Patient Intervention Tracking

Conclusion

The future of music therapy with adults in the general medical/surgical area is promising. Changes in health care will require music therapists to adapt clinical practice in a proactive manner. Viewing traditional methods and areas of practice in new ways will allow for continued growth, development, efficacy, and viability of the medical music therapy program. For example, one potential area for future growth that has not traditionally been served by music therapy is the emergency room (ER). In the ER, there are often long periods of waiting and high stress for patients. There are often more patients than can adequately be seen, because many people do not have a primary care physician and must go to the ER for treatment. Music therapists could provide procedural support, lower the stress level, offer emotional support, and improve patient and staff satisfaction in a cost-effective manner.

Music therapists are often the best staff able to meet the emotional, social, spiritual, and physical needs of patients who are having difficulty with hospitalization. Music therapy used from an evidence-based perspective is cost-effective, enhances patient satisfaction, and provides unique services for coping with hospitalization. More research created and conducted by music therapists is needed within the acute hospital and outpatient settings. Many hospitalized patients have benefited from clinical practice, but having a larger body of evidence will open opportunities for hospitals to create positions where patient satisfaction, overall quality of care, and medical well-being will be enhanced with music therapy services.

References

American College of Physicians. (n.d.). *About internal medicine*. Retrieved June 8, 2008, from http://www.acponline.org/patients_families/about_internal_medicine/

Bampton, P., & Draper, B. (1997). Effect of relaxation music on patient tolerance of gastrointestinal endoscopic procedures. *Journal of Clinical Gastroenterology, 25*, 343–345.

Bruscia, K. (Ed.) (1991). *Case studies in music therapy*. Phoenixville, PA: Barcelona.

Buffum, M. D., Sass, C., Sands, L. P., Lanier, E., Yellen, M., & Hayes, A. (2006). A music intervention to reduce anxiety before vascular angiography procedures. *Journal of Vascular Nursing, 24*, 68–73.

Cadigan, M. E., Caruso, N. A., Haldeman, S. M., McNamara, M. E., Noyes, D. A., Spadafora, M. A., & Carroll, D. L. (2001). The effects of music on cardiac patients on bed rest. *Progress in Cardiovascular Nursing, 16*(1), 5–13.

Centers for Disease Control and Prevention. (1996). *Universal precautions for prevention of transmission of HIV and other bloodborne infections*. Retrieved July 3, 2008, from http://www.cdc.gov/ncidod/dhqp/bp_universal_precautions.html

Chan, M. F., Wong, O. C., Chan, H. L., Fong, M. C., Lai, S. Y., Lo, C. W., Ho, S. M., Ng, S. Y., & Leung, S. K. (2006). Effects of music on patients undergoing a C-clamp procedure after percutaneous coronary interventions. *Journal of Advanced Nursing, 53*(6), 669–679.

Chen, Y.-L., Hayden, R., Sneden-Riley, J., & Clair, A. A. (2004). *Effects of music enhanced physical therapy on treatment outcomes of persons with severe COPD*. Unpublished manuscript. The University of Kansas.

Chlan, L., Evans, D., Greenleaf, M., & Walker, J. (2000). Effects of a single music therapy intervention on anxiety, discomfort, satisfaction, and compliance with screening guidelines in outpatients undergoing flexible sigmoidoscopy. *Gastroenterology Nursing, 23*, 148–156.

Cooke, M., Chaboyer, W., Schluter, P., & Hiratos, M. (2005). The effect of music on preoperative anxiety in day surgery. *Journal of Advanced Nursing, 52*, 47–55.

DeFrances, C. J., Hall, M. J., & Podgornik, M. N. (2005). 2003 National Hospital Discharge Survey. *Advance Data from Vital and Health Statistics, 359*. Retrieved July 4, 2008, from http://www.cdc.gov/nchs/data/ad/ad359.pdf

DeFrances, C. J., Lucas, C. A., Buie, V. C., & Golosinskiy, A. (2008). 2006 National Hospital Discharge Survey. *National Health Statistics Reports, 5*. Hyattsville, MD: National Center for Health Statistics. Retrieved July 4, 2008, from http:// www.cdc.gov/nchs/data/nhsr/nhsr005.pdf

Engen, R. L. (2005). The singer's breath: Implications for treatment of persons with emphysema. *Journal of Music Therapy, 42*, 20–48.

Ferraz, C. (2003). A personal experience in the process of implementing music therapy in hospital in Brazil. *Voices: A World Forum in Music Therapy, 3*(3). Retrieved from https://normt.uib.no/index.php/voices/article/view/135/111

Good, M., Anderson, G. C., Ahn, S., Cong, X., & Stanton-Hicks, M. (2005). Relaxation and music reduce pain following intestinal surgery. *Research in Nursing & Health, 28*, 240–251.

Good, M., Stanton-Hicks, M., Grass, J. A., Anderson, G. C., Lai, H. L., Roykulcharoen, V., & Adler, P. A. (2001). Relaxation and music to reduce postsurgical pain. *Journal of Advanced Nursing, 33*, 208–215.

Hamel, M. J. (2001). The effects of music intervention on anxiety in the patient waiting for cardiac catheterization. *Intensive & Critical Care Nursing, 17*, 279–285.

Hayes, A., Buffum, M., Lanier, E., Rodahl, E., & Sasso, C. (2003). A music intervention to reduce anxiety prior to gastrointestinal procedures. *Gastroenterology Nursing, 26*, 145–149.

Heiser, R. M., Chiles, K., Fudge, M., & Gray, S. E. (1997). The use of music during the immediate postoperative recovery period. *Association of periOperative Registered Nurses Journal, 65*, 777–778.

Henry, L. L. (1995). Music therapy: A nursing intervention for the control of pain and anxiety in the ICU: A review of the research literature. *Dimensions of Critical Care Nursing, 14*(6), 295–304.

Kane, F. M., Brodie, E. E., Coull, A., Coyne, L., Howard, A., Milne, A., Niven, C. C., & Robbins, R. (2004). The analgesic effect of odour and music upon dressing change. *British Journal of Nursing, 13*(19), 4–12.

Krout, R. E. (2000). Hospice and palliative music therapy: A continuum of creative caring. In AMTA (Ed.), *Effectiveness of music therapy procedures: Documentation of research and clinical practice* (3rd ed.) (pp. 323–341). Silver Spring, MD: American Music Therapy Association.

Kshettry, V. R., Carole, L. F., Henly, S. J., Sendelbach, S., & Kummer, B. (2006). Complementary alternative medical therapies for heart surgery patients: Feasibility, safety, and impact. *Annals of Thoracic Surgery, 81*, 201–205.

Lange, R. J., & Twain, S. (2002). Forever and for always [Recorded by Shania Twain]. On *Up!* [CD]. Nashville, TN: Mercury Records.

Lazaroff, I., & Shimshoni, R. (2000). Effects of medical resonance therapy music on patients with psoriasis and neurodermatitis: A pilot study. *Integrative Physiological & Behavioral Science, 35*, 189–198.

Leardi, S., Pietroletti, R., Angeloni, G., Necozione, S., Ranalletta, G., & Del Gusto, B. (2007). Randomized clinical trial examining the effect of music therapy in stress response to day surgery. *British Journal of Surgery, 94*, 943–947.

Loewy, J. (1994). *A hermeneutic panel study of music therapy with an emotionally disturbed boy* (Doctoral dissertation, New York University, 1994). *Dissertation Abstracts International, 55*(09A), 2631.

Loewy, J. (2000). Music psychotherapy assessment. *Music Therapy Perspectives, 18*, 47–58.

Lopez-Cepero Andrada, J. M., Amaya Vidal, A., Castrol Aguilar-Tablada, T., Garcia Reina, I., Silva, L., Ruiz Guinaldo, A., Larrauri De la Rosa, J., Herrero Cibaja, I., Ferre Alamo, A., & Benitez Roldan, A. (2004). Anxiety during the performance of colonoscopies: Modification using music therapy. *European Journal of Gastroenterology & Hepatology, 16*, 1381–1386.

Lovelace, K., & Paisley, B. (2003). In my daughter's eyes [Recorded by Martina McBride]. On *Martina* [CD]. Nashville, TN: RCA Records.

Magill-Levrault, L. (1993). Music therapy in pain and symptom management. *Journal of Palliative Care, 9*(4), 42–48.

Mamaril, M. E., Windle, P. E., & Burkard, J. F. (2006). Prevention and management of postoperative nausea and vomiting: A look at complementary techniques. *Journal of Peri-Anesthesia Nursing, 21*, 404–410.

Mandel, S. E., Hanser, S. B., Secic, M., & Davis, B. A. (2007). Effects of music therapy on health-related outcomes in cardiac rehabilitation: A randomized controlled trial. *Journal of Music Therapy, 44*, 176–197.

Melzack, R., & Wall, P. D. (1965). Pain mechanisms: A new theory. *Science, 150*, 171–179.

Nicks, S. (1974). Landslide [Recorded by Dixie Chicks]. On *Home* [CD]. Columbia Records. (2003)

Nilsson, U., Rawal, N., & Unosson, M. (2003). A comparison of intra-operative or postoperative exposure to music: A controlled trial of the effects on postoperative pain. *Anaesthesia, 58*, 699–703.

O'Sullivan, R. J. (1991). A musical road to recovery: Music in intensive care. *Intensive Care Nursing, 7*, 160–163.

Padmanabhan, R., Hildreth, A. J., & Laws, D. (2005). A prospective, randomized, controlled study examining binaural beat audio and preoperative anxiety in patients undergoing general anaesthesia for day case surgery. *Anaesthesia, 60*, 874–877.

Porchet-Munro, S. (1993). Music therapy perspectives in palliative care education. *Journal of Palliative Care, 9*, 39–42.

Robison, B. (1996). Travelin' soldier [Recorded by Dixie Chicks]. On *Home* [CD]. Columbia Records. (2003)

Salmon, D. (1993). Music and emotion in palliative care. *Journal of Palliative Care, 9*, 48–52.

Scheiby, B. B. (2002). Caring for the caregiver: Trauma, improvised music and transformation of terror into meaning through community music therapy training. In J. A. Loewy & A. Frisch Hara (Eds.), *Caring for the caregiver: The use of music and music therapy in grief and trauma*. Silver Spring, MD: American Music Therapy Association.

Schiemann, U., Gross, M., Reuter, R., & Kellner, H. (2002). Improved procedure of colonoscopy under accompanying music therapy. *European Journal of Medical Research, 7*, 131–134.

Sendelbach, S. E., Halm, M. A., Doran, K. A., Miller, E. H., & Gaillard, P. (2006). Effects of music therapy on physiological and psychological outcomes for patients undergoing cardiac surgery. *Journal of Cardiovascular Nursing, 21*, 194–200.

Shantin, L. (1970). Alteration of mood via music: A study of the vectoring effect. *Journal of Psychology, 75*, 81–86.

Siegel, J. D., Rhinehart, E., Jackson, M., Chiarello L., & Healthcare Infection Control Practices Advisory Committee. (2007). *Guideline for isolation precautions: Preventing transmission of infectious agents in healthcare settings, June 2007*. Retrieved July 3, 2008, from http://www.cdc.gov/hicpac/pdf/isolation/isolation2007.pdf

Slivka, H. H., & Magill, L. (1986). The conjoint use of social work and music therapy with children of cancer patients. *Music Therapy, 6A*(1), 30–40.

Smolen, D., Topp, R., & Singer, L. (2002). The effect of self-selected music during colonoscopy on anxiety, heart rate, and blood pressure. *Applied Nursing Research, 15*, 126–136.

Society of Critical Care Medicine. (2001–2009). *History of critical care*. Retrieved June 8, 2008, from http://www.sccm.org/AboutSCCM/History_of_Critical_Care/Pages/default.aspx

Standley, J. (2000). Music research in medical treatment. In AMTA (Ed.), *Effectiveness of music therapy procedures: Documentation of research and clinical practice* (3rd ed.) (pp. 1–64). Silver Spring, MD: American Music Therapy Association.

Thaut, M. H., Thaut, C., & LaGasse, B. (2008). Music therapy in neurologic rehabilitation. In W. Davis, K. Gfeller, & M. Thaut (Eds.) *An introduction to music therapy: Theory and practice* (3rd ed.) (pp. 261–304). Silver Spring, MD: American Music Therapy Association.

Thorgaard, B., Henriksen, B. B., Pedersbaek, G., & Thomsen, I. (2004). Specially selected music in the cardiac laboratory—An important tool for improvement of the wellbeing of patients. *European Journal of Cardiovascular Nursing, 3*, 21–26.

Tse, M. M., Chan, M. F., & Benzie, I. F. (2005). The effect of music therapy on postoperative pain, heart rate, systolic blood pressures and analgesic use following nasal surgery. *Journal of Pain & Palliative Care Pharmacotherapy, 19*(3), 21–29.

Tusek, D. L., Cwynar, R., & Cosgrove, D. M. (1999). Effect of guided imagery on length of stay, pain and anxiety in cardiac surgery patients. *Journal of Cardiovascular Management, 10*(2), 22–28.

Twain, S., & Lange, R. J. (2002). Up! [Recorded by Shania Twain]. On *Up!* [CD]. Nashville, TN: Mercury Records.

Twiss, E., Seaver, J., & McCaffrey, R. (2006). The effect of music listening on older adults undergoing cardiovascular surgery. *Nursing in Critical Care, 11*, 224–231.

Uedo, N., Ishikawa, H., Morimoto, K., Ishihara, R., Narahara, H., Akedo, I., Ioka, T., Kaji, I., & Fukuda, S. (2004). Reduction in salivary cortisol level by music therapy during colonoscopic examination. *Hepato-Gastroenterology, 51*, 451–453.

Voss, J. A., Good, M., Yates, B., Baun, M. M., Thompson, A., & Hertzog, M. (2004). Sedative music reduces anxiety and pain during chair rest after open-heart surgery. *Pain, 112*, 197–203.

Walker, J., & Adamek, M. (2008). Music therapy in hospice and palliative care. In W. Davis, K. Gfeller, & M. Thaut (Eds.), *An introduction to music therapy: Theory and practice* (3rd ed.)(pp. 343–363). Silver Spring, MD: American Music Therapy Association.

Wall, P. D., & Melzack, R. (1962). On nature of cutaneous sensory mechanisms. *Brain, 85*, 331.

White, J. M. (1999). Effects of relaxing music on cardiac autonomic balance and anxiety after acute myocardial infarction. *American Journal of Critical Care, 8*, 220–230.

Wiens, M. E., Reimer, M. A., & Guyn, H. L. (1999). Music therapy as a treatment method for improving respiratory muscle strength in patients with advanced multiple sclerosis: A pilot study. *Rehabilitation Nursing, 24*, 74–80.

Zimmerman, L., Nieveen, J., Barnason, S., & Schmaderer, M. (1996). The effects of music interventions on postoperative pain and sleep in coronary artery bypass graft (CABG) patients. *Scholarly Inquiry for Nursing Practice, 10*, 153–170.

Appendix

Assessment Overview

Developed by Judy Nguyen Engel and Jennifer Jarred Peyton
for Tallahassee Memorial HealthCare Music Therapy

Therapist Personality:
Be aware of your own personality and adjust to what the patient needs (e.g if you are an extrovert and like to take charge of the conversation you may have to adjust if the patient needs you to be an active listener instead).
Do you have any nervous ticks?
Do you have a preconceived agenda for the session? Is that appropriate or necessary?
Decide what your boundaries are before you enter a patient's room (e.g., how do you feel about disclosing personal information including: religion, marriage, your family, where you live etc.).

Initial:
Find the best place to be in the environment; determine if you should sit or stand and which side of the bed you should approach from or be.
Display open body language
Look for clues in the environment (e.g. Are there any flowers or cards present? Is the room organized or disorganized? Are the lights on or off? What time of day is it and what is the patient doing? Is there anyone else at the bedside or in the room? Who are they in relation to the patient?)
Identify and adjust your demeanor based on the patient's affect/mood
Multi-task (e.g. while unpacking your materials, determine the best location for them in the environment, in relation to you and the patient/family; move furniture if necessary, all the while engaging with the patient/family)
Bring with you a presence of confidence and support to the patient
Set yourself and your patient up for success

Assessment:
Engage the patient/family with your personality.
Don't ask to just ask. Assessment should not be treated like a questionnaire; use both open and closed-ended and purposeful questions in a conversational style.
Utilize active listening techniques
Silence is OK
Top Seven Assessment Areas

- Current mood, responsiveness
- Coping skills, depression
- Family support
- Current situation/hospitalization
- Communication
- Reality orientation
- Pain

Patient Behavioral Observation:
Observe the patient's entire body for behavioral cues throughout the music session
Look for positive and negative cues; reinforce positive responses and be sensitive to negative responses (verbally or non-verbally)
Evaluate the patient's responses to develop music therapy objectives

- **Repertoire:**
  Have several songs memorized within each genre to decrease "down time" of flipping through your songbook
  Suggest one or two genres
  Find the closest genre (if a patient requests a genre you do not have)
  Give choices
  Link songs using lyrics/themes patient is discussing
  If you already know what type of music the patient prefers, don't ask again, just start playing… with a statement like "I heard you enjoy…, let me know if you know this one".

Use caution when asking patient "what is your favorite song?" Is it likely that you'll have it? Maybe, but unless you are going to go and learn it right away and come back-set yourself up for success and use the variety of a genre instead.

Note: This Overview is used to assist beginning practicum students in the early stages of their music therapy practice where music repertoire could be very limited. An experienced music therapist would probably overlook these suggestions.

Think about how you'll use music to accomplish goal/objective during session
What kind of music to choose from?
Think about the content, lyrics, possible negative/positive associations with music
Meet the patient where they are with music (iso-principle) choose finger picking, slow/ fast strum, humming, instrumental only, etc.
Plan for song choices to move closer to therapeutic goal-thinking about what you'll say when song is over; tie in patient reactions, thoughts, and statements
Flow of session: is there a need to balance music/talking, should there be more music than talking? Did you keep the session moving forward?

- **Termination:**
  Think about how to smoothly end session/establish closure/prepare for end of session
  What loose ends need to be attended to?
  Will you see patient again?
  Did you accomplish the identified patient goals? Did you identify new goals for next time?
  If this is the only session you'll have, did the patient meet his/her goals?

When making a follow-up appointment with the patient be sure to clarify whether they would like the MT-BC to wake them upon return or to let them sleep if they are sleeping.

CHAPTER 5

Cancer Care

Dawn McDougal Miller
Clare O'Callaghan

Cancer is one of the most feared diseases in every culture.
—Die-Trill, 1998, p. 857

Wholeness is never lost, it is only forgotten. . . . Being with people at such times is like watching them pat their pockets, trying to remember where they have put their soul.
—Remen, 1996, pp. 108–109

Working with cancer patients, who may be in the midst of the greatest physical and emotional challenge of their lives, is a privilege. To musically journey with people with cancer is to be willing to be present with them in the midst of their fears, anguish, tears, celebrations, sacred times, and their day-to-day tasks of survival and healing. The combination of the music and the therapeutic relationship creates the potential for patients to experience deep levels of emotional and spiritual healing. As music therapists in cancer settings, it is an honor to witness the unique ways that individuals choose to deal with the personal challenges of their cancer experience.

Within oncology inpatient units or outpatient cancer centers, music therapy can bring a sense of normalcy, wholeness, hopefulness, perspective, transcendence, or a vision of health to patients and their families and friends during their cancer treatment process. Music therapy in cancer care is the creative and professionally informed use of music in a therapeutic relationship with people identified as needing physical, psychosocial, or spiritual help. People aspiring to experience further self-awareness, thus enabling an increased life satisfaction and quality throughout the phases of their cancer experience, may also benefit from music therapy (O'Callaghan, 2001a, 2001b, 2004).

Throughout this chapter, the terms *cancer patient*, *oncology patient*, or *cancer survivor* are utilized to describe people with cancer, because the terms are consistent with the terminology that is used within a medical setting. Health care professionals, including music therapists, must always be mindful that they are working with people who have been diagnosed with cancer, and that each individual may respond to living with cancer in his or her own unique way. The cancer diagnosis is always of less importance than the recognition of the personal identity and the unique strengths of the person being treated.

The term *family members* is utilized as an umbrella term to identify spouses, partners, children, parents, extended family members, friends, and any other people (excluding medical professionals) who are significant in the patient's life. There is an increased focus on treating cancer as a family experience, as contrasted with treating cancer only as it affects the individual diagnosed with cancer (Lewis, 1999). Families also struggle with the diagnosis and its effects on those close to them. A diagnosis of cancer in a family can be perceived as a profound threat to the assumptive worlds of family members that may bring about changes in their values, priorities, self-image, and role within the family system (Lewis, 1999; Loscalzo & Brintzenhofeszoc, 1998). The family members may also feel anger and other emotions as they discover that their hopes and plans are threatened (Baxandall & Prasuna, 1993).

Potential shifting of roles traditionally performed by the person with cancer can be an added stressor in the family. Children and adolescents may develop behavioral difficulties when they are not provided opportunities to talk about feelings related to the cancer, or are expected to assume responsibilities beyond their developmental years (Ferszt & Waldman, 1997; Wellisch, 1979). Considerations for family-centered and continuity of care issues related to patients and their family members are important aspects of the services provided.

Overview of Cancer and Patients in the Hospital Setting

Cancer treatment strategy descriptions have been recorded throughout history. The origin of the term *cancer* is credited to the Greek physician Hippocrates (460–370 B.C.), who chose the Greek word *karkinos*, meaning crab, to describe cancer tumors (American Cancer Society, 2002; Cassileth, 1979). The selection of this term may have been a reflection of the crab-like fingers that can be observed in metastasized cancer tumors (American Cancer Society, 2009b). Treatment for cancer dates back to ancient Egypt, circa 160 B.C., with anecdotal reports of surgery for the removal of cancer tumors (Burke, 1999; Stahl, 1997). The development of modern cancer treatment modalities can also be traced throughout history.

The introduction of anesthesia in 1847 led to the development of modern surgical techniques between 1900 and 1930 for the removal of malignant tumors (Cassileth, 1979; Holland, 1998). Radiation therapy is one of the oldest treatments for cancer. The first reported cure using radiation therapy was in 1899 for basal cell cancer (Strohl,

1999). Descriptions of chemotherapy have been found in records of medical treatment from the 1500s, when heavy metals were used to treat a variety of cancers. The basis for modern chemotherapy agents occurred during World War I, when the effects of poisonous mustard gas exposure on soldiers were studied (Burke, 1997; Miakowski & Viele, 1999).

In the 17th and 18th centuries, cancer was believed to be contagious, and remnants of this misperception exist today. Cancer continues to be one of the most feared of all diseases (Die-Trill, 1998; Ferszt & Waldman, 1997). Old attitudes and myths about cancer and treatment persist despite new information, advances in research, and increased public cancer education. The American Society for Control of Cancer (later named the American Cancer Society) was formed in 1913, followed by the development of the National Cancer Institute in 1937 (Dolbeault, Szporn, & Holland, 1999). These organizations have worked to increase public awareness of cancer and have emphasized the importance of emotional support and educational programs.

Until the last half of the 20th century, the diagnostic and prognostic information that was given to a cancer patient was limited. In the 1950s, a survey of physicians in the United States revealed that only 10–35% disclosed the diagnosis of cancer to their patients (Fitts & Ravdin, 1953, and Oken, 1961, as cited in Die-Trill, 1998). Until the initial use of modern chemotherapy agents in the 1950s, effective cancer treatment was unknown, resulting in a diagnosis of cancer that was often perceived as a death sentence. Before the development of curative cancer treatments, the diagnosis of cancer was so frightening that it was considered cruel to reveal it to the patient, and only the family was given the prognosis and results of tests. Families often chose to hide their family member's cancer diagnosis from the rest of the community (Holland, 2002). This lack of disclosure often left the patient feeling alone and isolated (Dolbeault et al., 1999.) Within some cultures today, it is still common for the diagnosis of cancer or prognostic information to be withheld from the patient. These include cultures from parts of southern Europe, Japan, India, Pakistan, Bangladesh, Nepal, Sri Lanka, Africa, Latin America, and China (Die-Trill, 1998; Lipson, Dibble, & Minarik, 1996).

Developments in cancer care occurred in the last half of the 20th century. In the 1960s, advances in cancer treatments dramatically improved the length of survival for patients, and cancer was transformed from an incurable and fatal disease to a chronic illness of uncertain duration (Glajchen, 1999). With more patients living longer with cancer, the need for oncology psychosocial and rehabilitative care became more evident. During the 1970s, the number of oncology psychosocial and behavioral research studies increased, resulting in financial support for psychosocial studies. The first national conference on psychosocial research was held in 1975. Kubler-Ross's theories inspired a "death with dignity" thanatology movement during the 1960s, which led to the formation of the first hospice program in the United States (Holland, 2003).

Psychobiological research and the field of **psychoneuroimmunology** (PNI) rapidly developed in the 1990s. Behavioral, psychosocial, and psychopharmacological intervention trials began, and the field of **psycho-oncology** became recognized as a valid subspecialty of cancer care and research. Assessment tools and controlled research trials of new therapies began to include quality of life-based outcome measures, not just survival statistics (Sourkes, Massie, & Holland, 1998). Over the past 30 years, quality of life has become a respected measure that has been used to evaluate health care outcomes and efficacy of cancer treatments (Ferrans, 2000).

Currently, most cancer centers have a health professional available to treat the psychological issues of patients and families (Holland, 1998). Research and theoretical models within psycho-oncology have been developed. Today there is an increased number of cancer survivors, well-informed cancer patients, open disclosure of diagnosis for a majority of cancer patients, valid assessment tools, less emphasis on fatalism of cancer, and a stronger dialogue between physicians and patients regarding treatment options and decisions.

A majority of oncology care has shifted from inpatient to ambulatory care settings; this trend will continue to increase (Knobf, Pasacreta, Valentine, & McCorkle, 1998; Martin & Xistris, 2000). Inpatient oncology admissions are reserved for patients who require intensive monitoring after surgery, have had drastic changes in physical conditions, have onsets of acute pain or nausea, or are acutely ill. In 2000, throughout the U.S., almost 75% of all surgical procedures were performed in the ambulatory setting (Frogge & Cunning, 2000). Most cancer patients in the U.S. currently receive chemotherapy treatments in ambulatory care settings or 24-hour observation units (Goodman, 2000). Currently, there are very few individuals who require inpatient hospitalization for chemotherapy. Some chemotherapy regimes administered prior to bone marrow and stem cell transplants are administered in the outpatient setting (Goodman, 2000). In the U.S. between 1987 and 1997, the inpatient length of stay decreased by 23% and the average patient acuity level, as determined by the case mix index, increased by 12% (Bartley, 1999, as cited in Krumm, 2000).

Due to medical and technological advances, there have been improvements in the delivery of oncology treatments. Technological advances have made surgical procedures less invasive, resulting in shorter recovery times. New developments in **antiemetic** medications and chemotherapy regimes have decreased the severity of oncology patients' side effects, such as nausea and vomiting. Some patients are even able to return to work the day after chemotherapy treatment. The duration of protective isolation for patients who are **immunocompromised** as a result of chemotherapy has decreased with the development of colony-stimulating factors (CSFs) that stimulate **hematopoiesis** (Camp-Sorrell, 2000). The administration of chemotherapy has also improved due to developments in designs of **Vascular Access Devices** (VADs), such as **peripherally inserted central catheters** (PICCs), tunneled catheters, and **implantable ports** (Camp-Sorrell, 1997). Certain chemotherapy regimes are now administered through VADs with portable ambulatory pumps, greatly decreasing the amount of time patients may have to spend at the outpatient cancer center.

These developments in the delivery of medical care have brought a new set of issues to cancer patients. Patients must find a way to manage the stresses of a time-consuming treatment schedule while experiencing the side effects of cancer treatments. They are challenged to balance their cancer treatment with the day-to-day responsibilities of family, home, and work. The shift to ambulatory care has also made a difference in the approach of interdisciplinary oncology staff members. Patients are not available 24 hours a day on the inpatient unit, so time to provide psychosocial support and education may be limited. Patients may have to independently seek out the resources that can be provided by psychosocial oncology support teams, and patients must value the professional support enough to commit to juggling the extra appointment times with their already demanding schedule of doctors' appointments, laboratory tests, and chemotherapy or radiation therapy treatments.

The music therapist serving patients diagnosed with cancer has adapted and changed to best address the well-being of the patient in light of the advancing treatment modalities and methods. It has been suggested that music may have helped to re-focus patient care on the whole person rather than on an impersonal, research-oriented and technology-driven hospital environment (Bellamy & Willard, 1993). Some early music therapists serving cancer patients volunteered to bring music into the hospital setting. For example, in 1973, Lucanne Magill brought music to cancer patients while she was an employee in patient relations in the Diagnostic Radiology Department at Memorial Sloan Kettering Cancer Center (MSKCC) in New York. Ten years later, she became a full-time music therapist in the Supportive Care Program within the hospital's Pain Service (L. Magill, personal communication, April 28, 2001). This was at a time when music therapy programs serving patients with cancer started to emerge throughout the Western world. Music therapy programs continue to provide a continuity of care across the treatment process to include inpatient and outpatient services, as well as palliative and hospice care (Bellamy & Willard, 1993; Haghighi & Pansch, 2001; Holland & Holmes, 2000; Lane, 1993; Lee, 1995; Martin, 1989; Miller, 1992; O'Brien, 1999; O'Callaghan & Colegrove, 1998; Rykov & Salmon, 1998).

Common Current Characteristics

Cancer is considered a fundamental biological challenge in that an organism's own cells attempt to destroy itself (Yarbro, 2000). It is characterized by differentiated body cells that change and experience uncontrolled reproduction at the molecular level. These changes result in the loss of normal cell regulation, characteristics, and functions. The abnormal cells can penetrate and destroy nearby tissue and spread (**metastasize**) through the bloodstream or lymphatic system to other parts of the body. Solid tumors grow and put more pressure on adjacent structures, invading, obstructing, and destroying surrounding tissue (Baxandall & Prasuna, 1993; Commonwealth Department of Human Services and Health, 1994; Gribbon & Loescher, 2000; Miakowski & Viele, 1999; Thomas, 1997; Workman & Visovsky, 1999; Yarbro, 2000). If cancer metastasizes or recurs in another part of the body, it is still identified by the primary site of origin. Metastasis is the major cause of all cancer-related deaths (Gribbon & Loescher, 2000). Although cancer is classified according to organ systems, it is really a disease of the cells. In Taber's Cyclopedic Medical Dictionary, cancer is defined as "an imprecise term used to describe an estimated 200 different kinds of malignant **neoplasms**" (Thomas, 1997, p. 293) that differ according to where they originate within the body, symptomatology, and prognosis.

The development of a malignant tumor from a single cancer cell requires a series of conditions to occur over time in a susceptible host. These conditions include exposure to environmental events or to substances that mutate genetic content, enhanced expression of genetic changes, insufficient immune function, and other host factors (Workman & Visovsky, 1999). Physical, chemical, or biological agents that damage genes causing cancer are called **carcinogens**. Physical stimuli include ultraviolet and nuclear radiation, chemical stimuli include tobacco and alcohol usage, and biological stimuli include viral agents such as the human papilloma and hepatitis B viruses (Burton, 1998). Over 300 agents have been identified as causes of human cancer (Burton, 1998). Research studying oncogenes indicates that the development of some cancers can be genetic due to the inheritance of a mutated cancer predisposition gene (Burton, 1998; Vaux, 2001). More than half of cancer-related deaths in the U.S. can be attributed to dietary factors and exposure to tobacco smoke (Trichopoulos, Li, & Hunter, 1996). Host characteristics that have been shown to influence cancer susceptibility include age, sex, genetic predisposition, ethnicity, race, and socioeconomic factors (Reid, 2000).

The National Cancer Institute (n.d.a) calculates the impact of cancer deaths in mortality rates, as well as years of life a person loses due to death from cancer. From this perspective, cancer was responsible for more years of life lost in 2003 than any other cause of death (National Cancer Institute, n.d.b). In the United States, the most prevalent types of cancer for men include prostate, lung and bronchus, colon, urinary bladder, non-Hodgkin's lymphoma, melanoma of the skin, kidney and renal, oral cavity, leukemia, rectal, and pancreatic. For women, the most prevalent types of cancer include breast, lung and bronchus, colon, uterine corpus, non-Hodgkin's lymphoma, melanoma of the skin, thyroid, kidney and renal, leukemia, ovarian, pancreatic, rectal, and urinary bladder (American Cancer Society, 2007). Overall, death rates related to a cancer diagnosis in the U.S. are declining, with the exception of cancers of the esophagus, liver, and thyroid. The survival rate is lowest for African Americans, followed by Caucasians (National Cancer Institute, n.d.b). More than 50% of patients diagnosed with cancer are cured with conventional medical treatment (Rossman, 2003).

Most Common Types of Cancer
(most to least rate of incidence)
(American Cancer Society, *Cancer Facts and Figures*, 2007)

Male	Female
prostate	breast
lung and bronchus	lung and bronchus
colon	colon
urinary bladder	uterine corpus
non-Hodgkin's lymphoma	non-Hodgkin's lymphoma
melanoma of the skin	melanoma of the skin
kidney and renal pelvis	thyroid
oral cavity	kidney and renal pelvis
leukemia	leukemia
rectum	ovary
pancreas	pancreas
	rectum
	urinary bladder

Patients on adult oncology units have diseases with a wide spectrum of prognoses—from curable, chronic, rapid deterioration, to death. Treatment aims vary from **curative** to **palliative care**. Although palliative care grew out of hospice care, it is no longer synonymous with care for the dying (Doyle, Hanks, & MacDonald, 1998). Palliative care aspects can be relevant throughout the cancer illness trajectory (Doyle et al., 1998) but are especially pertinent when efforts are being made to prolong the lives of those whose illnesses cannot be cured, as well as during the final phase of life.

Phases of the Disease Continuum

The cancer experience can be divided into the following phases that make up the disease continuum: diagnosis, treatment, remission, survivorship, recurrence or progression of disease, advanced disease, and terminal stage (Ferszt & Waldman, 1997; Loscalzo & Brintzenhofeszoc, 1998). These phases can serve as a helpful framework with which to identify the complex issues and problems that may be experienced by a person with cancer and to select appropriate treatment goals and interventions (Burns, 2002; Ferszt & Waldman, 1997). The phases of the cancer disease continuum and corresponding issues are discussed below. They are also discussed in further detail, along with music therapy goals and techniques, in the chart *Music Therapy in Adult Cancer Care: Across the Cancer Continuum*, located in the Appendix to this chapter.

Diagnosis

Following diagnosis, people with cancer often experience shock, numbness, disbelief, anger, fear, panic, and depression (Ferszt & Waldman, 1997; Greer, 1997). A diagnosis of cancer can be emotionally taxing as the individual negotiates the meaning of the illness at personal, social, and cultural levels (Greer, 1997). The first 100 days following a diagnosis of cancer can be particularly challenging and may be dominated by life and death concerns, acute emotional distress, and anxiety about health and physical symptoms (Weisman & Worden, 1976). Existential questions that challenge one's spirituality or philosophical beliefs may arise following a cancer diagnosis (e.g., "Why me?" "What is the purpose of my life?" "Is there a God?" "Is there life after death?") (Grey, 1994; Lewis, 1999; Musick, Koenig, Larson, & Matthews, 1998), which may stem from a common longing for a sense of grounding, purpose, or meaning in life.

Finding purpose or meaning within the experience of cancer may be enough of a motivation for a patient to continue to endure the rigor of surgery, chemotherapy, and radiation therapy treatments, finding reasons for living fully each day (Jones & Butman, 1991, as cited in Thompson & Holland, 2003). It is important to recognize that spirituality does not always involve traditional religious beliefs, attitudes, or behaviors. Spirituality refers to an individual's "personal search for meaning and purpose in life," while religion "refers to beliefs and practices associated with organized religious groups" (Fitchett & Handzo, 1998, p. 790).

Many types of spiritual needs may coexist in one person and may encompass situational (e.g., purpose, hope, and social presence), moral-biographical (e.g., forgiveness, peace, and reconciliation), and religious (e.g., clergy visits) dimensions (Kellehear, 2000), which may impact how the diagnosis is viewed. Adherence to a set of rigid religious beliefs has also been shown to cause distress for some people in their struggle with the existential issues of the cancer experience. However, religious beliefs may provide strength to persons with cancer in four ways: secondary control, in which the patient relinquishes control of the situation to God or a Higher Power; provision of spiritual worldview, in that the individual's world view influences how cancer and treatment are perceived; participation in a spiritual community that provides important aspects of social support; and coping with death and dying. A spiritual or religious connection to something bigger than one's self may help a person to put his or her life in order, to have a greater tolerance towards the difficulties of the illness, and to understand one's own meaning of death (Musick et al., 1998).

Events within the cancer trajectory, such as surgery, chemotherapy, and radiation therapy, may be perceived by patients as crisis events, in addition to the end of active treatment, remission, and survivorship (Loscalzo & Brintzenhofeszoc, 1998). The overall experience of adapting to and living with cancer may constitute a psychosocial transition, not just a series of crisis events. Psychosocial transitions are "characterized by deep personal reflection, cognitive-emotional searching, and existential questions" (Lewis, 1999, p. 321). Both crisis and psychotherapeutic interventions may be effective with patients during the different phases of their disease continuum.

The prevalence of cancer-related psychological disorders such as anxiety and depressive states may persist for years, even when there is no longer evidence of disease

(Breitbart, Chochinov, & Passik, 1998). In addition to psychological disorders, which can be diagnosed using *DSM-IV-TR* guidelines, many cancer patients may experience psychological distress. Some cancer centers utilize a patient self-reported distress scale, such as the Distress Thermometer, to measure a patient's levels of distress (Holland, 2003). *Distress*, as defined by the National Comprehensive Cancer Network's Distress Practice Guidelines Panel, is

> an unpleasant emotional experience of a psychological (cognitive, behavioral, emotional), social, and/or spiritual nature that may interfere with the ability to cope effectively with cancer and its treatment. Distress extends along a continuum, ranging from common normal feelings of vulnerability, sadness, and fears, to problems that can become disabling, such as depression, anxiety, panic, social isolation, and spiritual crisis. (National Comprehensive Cancer Network, 2001, p. 89)

Psychosocial needs vary and change across the phases of the cancer trajectory, and each cancer survivor may react in his or her own unique way.

Treatment

Treatment in outpatient cancer centers, inpatient hospital admissions, or both, is often essential for a chance of cure. Coping with physical changes and side effects becomes a primary focus for patients in active treatment. Coping becomes an even greater challenge due to (a) the illness and its related problems such as pain or the side effects of treatments (which are sometimes life-threatening in themselves), and (b) life as it is altered by the illness (Blumberg, Flaherty, & Lewis, 1980).

Coping styles and coping strategies are models that attempt to describe the process a person experiences while adjusting to the challenges encountered with the diagnosis and treatment of cancer (Folkman & Greer, 2000; Lazarus & Folkman, 1984). *Coping style* describes an individual's long-term manner of coping used throughout life to handle a variety of difficult situations. Coping styles are related to a person's overall disposition and pre-existing personality factors, such as optimism or pessimism and introversion or extroversion (Lazarus & Folkman, 1984). *Coping strategies* are shorter term and are used by individuals for specific situations. There are three broad categories of coping strategies: problem-focused, emotion-focused, and meaning-focused (Barsevick, Much, & Sweeney, 1997; Folkman & Greer, 2000) (Table 6).

Problem-focused strategies involve "defining the problem, generating alternative solutions, weighing the alternatives in terms of their costs and benefits, choosing among them, and acting" (Lazarus & Folkman, 1984, p. 152). Problem-focused coping strategies may be directed internally or toward the environment. Cancer patients often utilize problem-focused strategies during their active treatment phase. When using a problem-focused strategy, cancer patients may seek information about treatment options, or adapt their work schedules or daily routines in order to combat the fatigue resulting from cancer treatments. Problem-focused coping strategies may increase the patient's sense of participation and perceived ability to change the outcome (Barsevick et al., 1997).

Emotion-focused coping strategies include a wide range of strategies, including lessening or increasing the degree of emotional distress (Lazarus & Folkman, 1984). Patients more often use emotion-focused coping strategies in the post-treatment phase. During this phase, patients have more time and energy and are able to turn from the tasks of surviving the rigors of active cancer treatment to those of experiencing the emotions that arose from their cancer experience.

Meaning-focused strategies are used when patients seek out an understanding of the meaning within their cancer experience and realize what impact cancer has had on their life. Meaning-focused strategies may occur later in the post-treatment and survivorship phase and within the palliative care phase.

Table 6
Coping Strategies Commonly Used by People with Cancer

Strategy	**Successful**	**Unsuccessful**
Anger	Ability to identify source of anger Able to express and/or resolve anger Maintain sense of self within expression of anger	Depression, passivity, or aggression
Humor	Used to reduce tension or stress Used to decrease social distance	Masks feelings Avoidance of all emotions
Depression	Normal response to diagnosis of cancer	Persistent, pervasive feelings of loss Suicide
Anxiety	Gradual understanding Initially protective	Ignoring or refusing reality
Denial	Allows for a gradual processing of information, at a pace that the patient can manage	Minimizing or ignoring all diagnostic or prognostic information Refusing to make treatment decisions
Hopefulness	Comforting and sustaining Belief that healing will happen and treatments will be effective Motivator to continue treatments	Limits choices Inability to mobilize energy Refusal to accept reality of diagnosis

(Adapted from Barsevick, Much, & Sweeney, 1997; Rainey, 1984)

Post-treatment and survivorship

Although patients may feel relieved to have completed the rigors of their treatment schedule, the end of active treatment can bring a time of new fears and emotions. Patients may feel more anxiety because they are no longer receiving active treatments to control any remaining cancer cells or tumor growth. They may also feel overwhelmed by fears of the cancer returning. Patients may experience periods of heightened anxiety and emotional distress, especially during the days or weeks when they have to wait to hear the results of routine tests to monitor for signs of cancer recurrence. The time period from diagnosis to active treatment often moves so rapidly (days to a few weeks) that patients are able to focus only on making treatment decisions, before having to cope with the physical symptoms of the active treatment process. During this time, patients may not have the energy or internal strength needed to experience and process the emotions brought about by their cancer diagnosis and treatment experience. Once their active treatment has been completed, patients may finally have the time, energy, and strength to focus on their emotions and to wrestle with the existential questions that arose as a result of their cancer diagnosis and treatment.

Although individuals differ in their personal constructions of what cancer means, three common themes include loss of personal control, threat to survival, and threat to self-image (Greer, 1997). Health professionals may be surprised to find that some cancer survivors, in their post-treatment and survivorship phases, will identify the benefits, positive changes, and even the perceived blessings that cancer has brought into their lives. Other cancer survivors make lifestyle changes based upon the messages they have learned from their body and their experience of cancer.

Recurrence, advanced disease, and palliative care

The news that a patient's cancer has recurred or advanced may trigger a time period filled with more emotional angst and anxiety than during the initial diagnosis (Ferszt & Waldman, 1997). The patient's familiarity with the health care system may alleviate some anxiety associated with future treatments. Cancer support professionals can address issues of emotional support and expression, stress management, and symptom management with patients in this phase of their disease continuum (Burns, 2002).

If the patient's cancer becomes significantly more advanced to the point where curative treatments may no longer be effective, the focus of treatment may turn to palliative care. It should be noted that a thorough review of hospice and palliative care issues and the related music therapy literature is beyond the scope of this chapter; however, a summary of this phase has been provided to support the clinician's understanding of relevant issues.

Palliative care, as a phase of cancer treatment, has been divided into four Tasks of Mourning (Worden, 1991) to delineate and explain the grief and loss issues that might be experienced by a person experiencing a terminal illness. The process of grieving and healing is complex and difficult to represent in a model (Niemeyer, 2002), so an adaptation of the Tasks of Mourning attempts to describe the complexity of the active process that may be experienced by a person who has been given the news that his or her cancer has moved into a terminal phase (E. Holland, personal communication, January 1997; Miller & Pansch, 1997; West, 1994). The four palliative care tasks are (1) acknowledge the reality of the loss, (2) experience and express the pain of grief, (3) optimize quality of life in a "new reality" with heightened awareness of one's own mortality, and (4) withdraw from life while reinvesting energies for the transition. Underlying all of the tasks is a fifth task of personal "meaning-making" within the experience of living and dying with a terminal illness (E. Holland, personal communication, January 1997). This model can help the clinician recognize the complexity of the grieving process and the issues related to a patient's terminal diagnosis (Niemeyer, 2002) in order to better design relevant music therapy treatment goals and interventions.

The Tasks of Mourning model differs from stage theory models (Kessler & Kubler-Ross, 2005; Kubler-Ross, 1997) in that the tasks are not regimented and or necessarily sequential. They may be worked on in any order, or simultaneously within the same time frame. There is no expectation of completion. The therapist must meet a person where he or she is, without judgment or expectations for closure or resolution. To facilitate a sense of continuity of life, family members and friends of the deceased could be encouraged to develop a sense of continuity with the life of the person who died through a meaningful, symbolic connection (Niemeyer, 2002).

Common Medical Treatment Modalities

In order to have an understanding of the symptoms and issues that might be addressed within music therapy sessions, it is important for music therapists working with oncology patients to have an awareness of the main types of cancer treatment modalities and the corresponding side effects. Medical treatments vary according to the nature of the illness and a patient's ability to tolerate the treatments. The most common medical treatments include surgery, radiotherapy or radiation therapy, and chemotherapy or pharmacotherapy.

The majority of cancer patients will receive some form of surgery during the course of their cancer trajectory (Burke, 1999). Surgery is the most frequently used and most successful cancer treatment method currently available (Frogge & Cunning, 2000); however, if cancer metastasizes or recurs, a surgical cure is less likely. Surgery may be used for many different reasons in oncology treatment, including diagnosis, staging, prevention, treatment, reconstruction, insertion of therapeutic or supportive devices, and in the treatment of oncologic emergencies. The majority of cancer patients receive a combination of treatment modalities, rather than surgery alone (Stahl, 1997).

Chemotherapy is one of the most common and well-known cancer treatments (Knobf et al., 1998). Chemotherapy is a systemic treatment that prevents cancer cells from multiplying, invading, and metastasizing to distant sites (Miakowski & Viele, 1999). It can be used to achieve curative, life-extension, or palliative goals in the treatment of cancer patients (Knobf et al., 1998). Over 50 chemotherapeutic drugs are used to treat a wide variety of cancers (Burke, 1997). They can be used as single agents or in combination chemotherapy treatment regimes.

Many misconceptions still exist about chemotherapy. Chemotherapy may be viewed as experimental rather than conventional treatment, and patients may feel anxious if they have heard negative accounts regarding the side effects of chemotherapy. Side effects still do occur, but their severity, such as nausea and vomiting, have decreased with advances in chemotherapy regimes and new developments in medications used to treat chemotherapy side effects. Emotional distress and anxiety have been shown to be prevalent in patients receiving chemotherapy (Knobf et al., 1998).

Common Chemotherapy Side Effects
(Camp-Sorrell, 2000; Knobf, Pasacreta, Valentine, & McCorkle, 1998; Miakowski & Viele, 1999)

Alopecia – hair loss
Myelosuppression – a decrease in the total number of circulating blood cells that may cause impaired *immunocompetence*, fatigue, and increased potential for infections, bleeding, and injuries (Burke, 1997). Types of myelosuppression experienced by cancer patients are:
- granulocytopenia - a decrease in the total number of white blood cells
- neutropenia - a decrease in the number of *neutrophils*
- anemia - a decrease in the number of red blood cells
- thrombocytopenia - a decrease in the number of platelets (Rieger, 1997)

Nausea and vomiting
Mucositis – sores and/or inflammation of mucous membranes in mouth, nasopharynx, esophagus, rectum, and anus
Anorexia – loss of appetite (*In this context, anorexia is used to describe a symptom of cancer treatment, not to be confused with the DSM-IV-TR diagnosis of Anorexia Nervosa.*)
Hemorrhagic cystitis – bladder infection or pain due to urinary elimination of chemotherapy
Diarrhea or constipation
Weight changes
Nutritional deficiency, and/or fluid and electrolyte disturbances
Taste alterations
Decreased cardiac output
Impaired respiration (rate, rhythm, depth)
Impaired sensory/motor function and/or neuropathy
Altered sexuality patterns and/or sexual dysfunction – related to body image changes, decreased libido, fatigue, alopecia, and other physical chemotherapy side effects
Infertility
Sterility (temporary or permanent)
Alterations in developing fetus
Anxiety
Depressed mood state
Intellectual function, concentration, reaction time, and short-term memory – impaired with some chemotherapy regimes (Knobf et al., 1998); some cancer patients have used the term *chemo brain* to describe neurological side effects

Over 60% of oncology patients will receive radiation at some point during the course of their cancer trajectory (Iwamoto, 1997; Strohl, 1999). Radiation therapy can be used for curative, life-extending, or palliative treatment goals. It involves the use of high-energy ionizing radiation doses to target cancer cells in a specific anatomical area (Iwamoto, 1997). Radiation therapy is administered by a large highly technological machine requiring the patient to be alone in a room with thick lead or concrete walls where the radiation cannot be seen or felt. This environment can cause the patient to feel apprehensive (Greenberg, 1998; Strohl, 1999). In addition, patients may have unrealistic fears of being radioactive or may believe that radiation treatments will be similar to the effects of radiation resulting from war or nuclear accidents (Strohl, 1999).

Common Physical Symptoms of Radiation Therapy
(Iwamoto, 1997)

Skin reactions localized to treatment sites
Fatigue
Anorexia – loss of appetite (*In this context, anorexia is used to describe a symptom of cancer treatment, not to be confused with the DSM-IV-TR diagnosis of Anorexia Nervosa.*)
Mucositis – inflammation of mucous membranes in mouth, nasopharynx, or esophagus
Cystitis – bladder infection
Taste changes
Xerostomia – dry mouth
Cough
Diarrhea
Nausea and vomiting

Other medical treatments include biologic therapy and hormonal therapy. **Biologic therapy**, also known as **biotherapy** or **immunotherapy**, is designed to alter the body's immune system to fight the cancer (American Cancer Society, 2009b; National Cancer Institute, 1997). Biotherapy has begun to be recognized as the fourth treatment modality for cancer patients, in addition to surgery, chemotherapy, and radiation therapy (Abernathy, 1997). Hormone therapy is frequently implemented following surgery for more advanced types of breast cancer (American Cancer Society, 2009a). Medical treatments have varying side effects, depending on the nature, duration, and site of treatment. Bone marrow or peripheral stem cell transplantation can be used to replace bone marrow that has been destroyed by radiation therapy or high-dose chemotherapy as part of the transplant treatment protocol.

Oncologists, nurse practitioners, oncology nurses, and clinical nurse specialists play a large role in educating patients about their cancer, treatment, and side effects, as well as providing symptom management and psychosocial support. In doing so, they often refer patients to other health professionals such as clinical dieticians for maintenance of nutritional needs, occupational therapy for maintenance or rehabilitation of daily living functions, speech therapy to address swallowing and verbal or nonverbal communication issues, and physical therapy to promote maintenance or improvement of mobility.

Social workers, psychologists, counselors, psychotherapists, licensed marriage and family therapists, and psychiatrists may assist with psychosocial and adjustment problems resulting from pre-existing problems. Social workers assist with legal and financial issues, as well as accommodation needs. The spiritual care department supports the emotional and spiritual dimensions of patients and their families' well-being. Care coordinators for specific types of cancer, such as breast cancer coordinators or lung cancer coordinators, may also help to manage a patient's care.

Some modalities, such as cancer support groups and cognitive-behavior therapy, were once considered to be complementary therapies but have since become mainstream in current supportive oncology medical treatment. Complementary therapies are used to supplement or complement conventional cancer treatment (Cassileth & Chapman, 1996). The purpose of complementary therapies is to encourage states of physical, mental, and social well-being; to facilitate the normal healthy state of homeostasis (balance); and to focus on an absence of disease (Freeman & Lawlis, 2001). Complementary therapies are designed to enhance a sense of mental and physical well-being, quality of life, hopefulness, coping, and adaptation (Doan, 1998; Richardson, Sanders, Palmer, Greisinger, & Singletary, 2000). Many complementary therapies also have physiological effects on the neuroendocrine and immune systems (Post-White & Bauer-Wu, 2005).

Complementary therapies are more commonly included than alternative therapies within conventional cancer care delivery systems (Doan, 1998). Cancer patients frequently report the use of at least one complementary or alternative therapy as part of their cancer treatment (Richardson et al., 2000). An alternative therapy is one that would be promoted as a substitute for conventional medicine and may be invasive and biologically active (Vickers & Cassileth, 2001). It could be considered a complementary therapy if it was used to complement medical treatment instead of substitute for conventional medical treatment. Music therapy would rarely, if ever, be defined as a strictly alternative therapy.

The National Center for Complementary and Alternative Medicine (NCCAM) classifies music therapy as a complementary and alternative medicine (CAM) mind-body intervention. Complementary and alternative medicine, as defined by the NCCAM, is a group of "diverse medical and health care systems, practices, and products that are not presently considered to be part of conventional medicine" (NCCAM, 2004a). Within many cancer centers and oncology units, patients and staff members often recognize music therapy as a complementary or an integrative therapy. A better classification for music therapy might be integrative medicine or an integrative therapy, which, as defined by NCCAM, combines "mainstream medical therapies and CAM therapies for which there is some high-quality scientific evidence of safety and effectiveness" (NCCAM, 2004b).

Music Therapy and Cancer Care

Psychoneuroimmunology (PNI) is the physiological science of mind-body interactions. It provides a framework in which complementary and integrative therapies such as music therapy may be selected, carried out, and evaluated (Post-White & Bauer-Wu, 2005). PNI examines interactions among behavior, neural and endocrine function, and the immune processes of adaptation (Ader, 1996, as cited in Post-White & Bauer-Wu, 2005). The immune system acts as the body's defense against infectious and malignant disease (Bauer, 2000). Because cancer diagnosis and treatments are associated with changes in the immune system, and music therapy is considered to be a mind-body intervention, a basic understanding of PNI theories and research is important for music therapists working within cancer care.

An ever-increasing number of PNI-based research studies have examined the physiological mechanisms of the relaxation response, the improvement in physical and psychological symptoms, and overall improvement in quality of life measurements of patients (Bauer, 2000; Richardson et al., 1997). In addition to studies that have demonstrated significant improvements in quality of life measurements, several quantitative research studies have demonstrated significant positive effects of psychological modalities and mind-body interventions in decreasing the incidence of cancer recurrence and prolonging survival in cancer patients (Cunningham et al., 2000; Fawzy et al., 1993; Richardson, Shelton, Krailo, & Levine, 1990; Spiegel, Bloom, & Yalom, 1981). These studies found that the addition of one or more of the following interventions to the patient's cancer care treatment plan had a positive impact on survival: individual counseling, cancer support groups, psycho-educational groups, guided imagery, meditation, relaxation, and stress management techniques.

Other less promising research results did not find a link between psychosocial factors and the length of survival or remission rate of cancer patients (Cassileth, Walsh, & Lusk, 1988). More PNI-based research needs to be pursued to determine the effects of stress-reducing interventions on immune system parameters and health outcomes, such as survival, in cancer patients (Post-White & Bauer-Wu, 2005). While there is no proven link between the use of complementary therapies and cancer cure (Vaux, 2001), PNI-based research suggests exciting possibilities for the use of music in supporting healthier immune responses (Burns, Harbuz, Hucklebridge, & Bunt, 2001; Rider, Floyd, & Kirkpatrick, 1985).

Many quantitative research studies have demonstrated effects of music listening, active and receptive music interventions, music-assisted imagery, or the Bonny Method of Guided Imagery and Music (BMGIM) on measures of the immune system and/or adrenocorticol systems of healthy subjects (Bartlett, Kaufman, & Smeltekop, 1993; Bittman et al., 2001; Burns et al., 2001; Hucklebridge et al., 2000; Kuhn, 2002; McCraty, Atkinson, Rein, & Watkins, 1996; McKinney, Antoni, Kumar, Tims, & McCabe, 1997; Rider & Achterberg, 1989; Rider et al., 1985; Rider, Mickey, Weldin, & Hawkinson, 1991; Tsao, Gordon, Maranto, Lerman, & Murasko, 1991; Uedo et al., 2004). Quantitative and qualitative research studying the efficacy of music on physiological and psychological outcomes of people with cancer is emerging. Similar to the non-music-related PNI research, studies with music demonstrate inconclusive outcomes.

Salivary IgA (s-IgA) is a measurement of front line immune system defense. Two studies using music-based interventions with healthy participants showed increased levels of s-IgA (Kuhn, 2002; Rider et al., 1990). Additional studies have examined the benefits of music therapy on measurements of the immune system of cancer patients using s-IgA or salivary cortisol as a dependent variable (Burns et al., 2001; Lane, 1991; Miller, 1992). Salivary cortisol is a glucocorticoid steroid that is secreted by the adrenocortical system as a response to stress. Increases in s-IgA and decreases of salivary cortisol are indicative of better management of the stress response. The outcomes of these studies have demonstrated mixed results.

Group relaxation induction, followed by 25 minutes of live relaxation music, demonstrated significant increases from pre- to post-session levels of s-IgA levels. S-IgA levels were not significant following participation in an active improvisation music therapy intervention (Burns et al., 2001). The researchers proposed that the effects of the physical exercise within the active improvisation may have had an effect on the s-IgA levels during the improvisation intervention. No significant differences were found in measurements of salivary cortisol after either intervention (Burns et al., 2001). Individual 30-minute music therapy sessions also found significant increases in levels of s-IgA (Lane, 1991). While not significant, a subsequent study indicated a trend toward increases in s-IgA and decreases in salivary cortisol measurements, perhaps due to the patients' responses of singing or crying within the music therapy intervention (Miller, 1992).

In addition to immune system response changes, music presented live has also demonstrated significant increases in cancer patient self-reported positive mood states (Lane, 1991; Miller, 1992), as well as improved vigor, self-expression, relaxation, and reduced anxiety, stress, and boredom (Bailey, 1983; O'Brien, 1999). While the focus of music therapy is on the therapeutic relationship, components of straightforward applications of music are also evident in cancer care (Beck, 1991; Zimmerman, Pozehl, Duncan, & Schmitz, 1989). Pertinent research reflects varied philosophical orientations, providing different lenses through which the use of music in cancer care can be examined.

Studies using taped music conditions and involving people living with cancer in various settings (e.g., inpatients or outpatients) have revealed reports of reduced pain (Beck, 1991; Zimmerman et al., 1989), anxiety (Frank, 1985; Sabo & Rush Michael, 1996; Weber, Nuessler, & Wilmanns, 1996), perceived nausea (Standley, 1992), tension and energetic arousal, and improved well-being and immunological responses (Burns et al., 2001). Incorporating live and taped music in sessions was also found to increase relaxation and comfort levels in inpatients who completed structured questionnaires (Boldt, 1996).

A music therapy study (Burns et al., 2001) used quantitative methodology to evaluate the effectiveness of the Bonny Method of Guided Imagery and Music (BMGIM) for people with cancer (McKinney, 2002). Ten individual BMGIM sessions were provided to cancer survivors in their post-treatment phase. While the outcomes were not statistically significant, individuals who participated in BMGIM sessions scored higher on mood scores and quality of life scores than the individuals in the control group. The quality of life scores continued to improve 6 weeks after sessions were completed.

Two recent studies have examined the effects of music therapy on bone marrow transplant (BMT) patients. Twenty-three bone marrow transplant patients were provided with 45-minute music therapy sessions twice weekly, which incorporated a relaxation imagery intervention. Comparisons were made with a non-randomized control group of 19 patients. Sessions typically began after transplantation and continued to the day of discharge from the BMT unit. Patients receiving music therapy reported significant decreases in self-reported pain and nausea ratings (Sahler, Hunter, & Liesveld, 2003). A second study randomized bone marrow transplant patients from two U.S. cancer centers into either music therapy or standard care groups. Patients completed the Profile of Mood States at baseline and every 3 days during intervention. The music therapy group received three to seven music therapy sessions during their inpatient stay. Results indicated that the music therapy group scored 28% lower on the combined anxiety/ depression scale, and 37% lower on the total mood disturbance scale than the control group (Cassileth, Vickers, & Magill, 2003).

Clark et al. (2006) investigated the effect of a music listening intervention, provided by a music therapist, on distress (anxiety, depression, and treatment-related distress) and symptoms (fatigue and pain) over the time that 63 patients experienced radiation therapy. Patients were randomized into "usual care" ($n = 28$) or the intervention group ($n = 35$), which included the therapist providing the participant with relaxation techniques, and a custom-made audio recording based on the participants' music preferences. Patients were told to listen to the recording at any time, especially when they felt increased pain, fatigue, anxiety, or depression, except in the treatment bunker during their 5 or 6 weeks of treatment. The music group experienced significantly reduced anxiety, although there were no significant differences in depression, pain, or fatigue over time.

In a randomized study of hospice home care patients diagnosed with terminal cancer, those receiving routine care with music therapy experienced increased quality of life. This increased over time with more music therapy sessions. Those receiving routine hospice services, without music therapy, experienced lower quality of life, decreasing over time (Hilliard, 2003).

Combined quantitative and qualitative designs, including the use of semistructured interviews, focus groups, and informal discussions, elicited descriptions of how improvisational music therapy allowed people with cancer at a "cancer help centre" to identify and express emotions, achieve new awareness, and develop group cohesion (Bunt & Marston-Wyld, 1995). In another mixed study examining the Bonny Method of Guided Imagery and Music with cancer survivors, music therapy also had a positive effect on mood and life quality (Bonde, 2005).

Focus group transcripts were also deductively analyzed for the three "mood tones" of the UWIST (University of Wales Institute of Science and Technology) psychological test (tension, hedonic, and energetic), following separate music improvisation and music relaxation sessions. These findings were reinforced by the UWIST test results, that relaxation increased well-being and decreased tension and energy arousal, and that improvisation increased well-being and energy levels and reduced tension (Burns et al., 2001).

The relevance of music therapy in a cancer hospital—that is, What did the music therapy do and did it help?— has also been examined using the constructivist research paradigm. Written interpretations were gathered in five studies from five sources: patients who participated in music therapy, patients who overheard music therapy, visitors, staff, and the music therapist-researcher. Thematic analyses findings from the five data groups indicated predominantly positive experiences characterized by respondents' affective, contemplative, and imagined moments in music therapy. Responses included revisiting memories and depictions of transporting to new places, thoughts, and/or physical sensations, as well as feelings of "aliveness" and expanded consciousness. Many staff and visitors also stated that music helped them while they were with the patients (O'Callaghan, 2004, 2005, 2007; O'Callaghan & Hiscock, 2007; O'Callaghan & McDermott, 2004).

Two phenomenological studies on hospice inpatients, with cancer, included innovative phenomenological research designs. Forinash (1990) transcribed 10 taped sessions with 10 different patients. Her observations and reflections were condensed through a three-stage process of reflection, finally depicting her perception of how a music therapist accompanies terminally ill cancer patients on a journey. Hogan (1999a) also used a three-stage distillation process to reach a final research statement, based on transcribed semistructured interviews with 9 hospice patients with cancer discussing their music therapy experiences. Participants reported that music therapy was a positive experience at emotional, social, spiritual, and physical levels. The meaning of a music therapy community cancer support group for the 10 participants was explored using an interpretive arts-informed methodology. The group selected various music therapy methods and depicted their experiences as a profound, nonverbal connection to themselves and each other, as well as a connection with something beyond themselves. Feelings of empowerment, control, and other long-lasting effects (e.g., decreased pain, elevated mood) arose from improvised music making (Rykov, 2006, 2008).

Twenty hospice multidisciplinary team members have also described their perceptions of music therapy interviews. They described music therapy as a valued and supportive modality, noting that it addressed holistic patient care needs, and elicited favorable environmental effects, spiritual support, and bereavement assistance. There was some concern expressed, however, that occasionally patients found elicited emotions distressing (O'Kelly & Koffman, 2007).

Music Therapy Treatment Process for Adults in Cancer Care

Cancer patients may be receptive to music therapy interventions at the following times in their disease continuum:

- when undergoing diagnostic testing;
- after a recent diagnosis;
- when making treatment decisions;
- prior to or while receiving treatments that have the potential to cause adverse symptoms, especially chemotherapy and radiation therapy;
- at the beginning of the post-treatment and survivorship phase (for as long as deemed necessary);

- if experiencing advanced disease, recurrence, or a shift in their overall treatment paradigm;
- throughout the palliative care phase (Post-White & Bauer-Wu, 2005).

The approach used in music therapy will be dependent on the patient's physical, psychosocial, emotional, and spiritual status, and the hospital or outpatient cancer center contextual factors. Such factors include the physical layout, staff attitudes to music therapy, and music therapy time limitations and physical resources. In addition, the approach will also be influenced by the music therapist's professional and personal background, including his or her philosophical orientation and clinical experience. Regardless, the components of the treatment process remain consistent.

Referral

Music therapy referrals for adult cancer patients come from a variety of sources. Staff on the oncology units or cancer centers, such as nurses, chaplains, social workers, oncology psychologists or therapists, oncology clinical nurse specialists, and oncologists can make a referral. Referrals may sometimes emerge from interdisciplinary team rounds. For example, music therapy may be specifically mentioned, or the music therapist may assess the patient's need for music therapy based on specific patient care planning issues. Moreover, the music therapist, in reviewing the unit census, may generate appropriate referrals based on the patient's diagnosis, age, length of hospitalization, and reason for admission. Not all patients are appropriate for a music therapy referral, or, based on case load availability, they will have to be prioritized. The music therapist will be alert to patients who are experiencing pain, confusion, agitation, delirium, or a shift in comfort. In such cases, music therapists might visit the patient and introduce themselves and the concept of music therapy. This is a process referred to as case-finding (O'Callaghan & Colegrove, 1998).

Patient Issues Appropriate for Music Therapy Referral

- Anxiety
- Pain
- Depression
- Emotional or spiritual issues (of patient or family)
- Family and/or primary caregiver stress
- Anxiety regarding upcoming medical procedure (e.g., bone marrow aspiration or a new treatment regime)
- Changes in physical status or treatment paradigm
- New long-term care facility placement
- Body image concerns
- Difficulty with range of motion or rehabilitation from surgery
- Lengthy hospitalization
- Need for recognition or celebration of event (e.g., a birthday)
- Protective isolation lasting for more than a few days
- Agitation
- Confusion
- Change in level of responsiveness
- Imminent death

Patients and families may choose to make a self-referral. In this situation, the patient, family member, or other significant person has observed or heard of music therapy, or the therapist on the oncology unit or in the hospital, and requests the service. Music therapists are encouraged to try out various modalities for securing referrals and determine what technique is most appropriate in the setting.

A written referral form should be carefully assessed for its value, contribution, and practicality of use. Formal written referral forms can be less effective and time-restrictive for staff, but demonstration and education on the value of music therapy within the cancer unit can be quite effective. The reason for the referral and the referral source can be included within the initial progress note, as in the S.O.A.P. progress note examples provided in the Outcome Measures section of this chapter (see page 264).

For example, at the Peter MacCallum Cancer Centre (Australia), the music therapist was invited to provide services for 16 hours a week, serving 110 patient beds across five units. A referral form was attempted, but it quickly became evident that the same few staff members completed it, while others found it took too much time. Rather than continue to advocate for a written referral, in consultation with senior nursing staff, it was discontinued. Research to assess the relevance of the program (O'Callaghan & McDermott, 2004) satisfied nurse managers' requirements for establishing music therapy's efficacy. Over time, verbal music therapy referrals increased through personal contact with the music therapist or through telephone messages.

At Park Nicollet Health Services (Minnesota), a form was initially utilized to educate the staff with regards to appropriate referrals. Oncology nurses are often protective of their patients and may not refer their patients to a treatment modality they do not understand or trust. During the first year, the music therapist presented inservices to various departments within the cancer program and participated in oncology interdisciplinary rounds. The staff began to understand the purpose and goals of music therapy as they observed sessions and noted patient feedback. After a year, the form was no longer utilized or necessary.

Assessment Procedure

Music therapists may use varying assessment modalities, with or without accompanying written documentation. Music therapists can approach patients in three ways:

1. The therapist and patient both have awareness of needs that they feel music therapy could address. For example, the therapist may have received a referral for pain reduction from a staff member who already discussed this option with the patient.
2. The therapist has identified an issue that he or she feels music therapy could address, for example, through a team meeting or reading the patient case history.
3. The therapist has no pre-existing knowledge of the patient.

In all scenarios, the therapist maintains an open mind when introducing himself or herself to a patient, and considers the ways that musical properties function and how the therapeutic relationship may assist the patient through the cancer illness and treatment experience. Therapists need to consider the difference between approaching patients who have already agreed to music therapy and approaching patients to offer an invitation to consider the service. Asking patients about their musical backgrounds before they have agreed to music therapy services may not be appropriate; however, it may be helpful information as the therapist considers an appropriate music therapy technique to offer the patient. When looking in or entering a patient's room, the music therapist must first assess whether it is a good time to present the service. If the patient appears busy, tired, or distracted, the therapist may provide a quick introduction and offer to return later. Distressed patients may be offered assistance, including the procuring of another staff member.

Considerations for Therapist Approach to Patient

Prior to a session, the therapist needs to strive to be fully present for each patient by demonstrating a nonjudgmental attitude with acceptance of the patient's cancer-related choices and condition, and by preparing to listen deeply to each patient. In order to do this, it may be helpful for the therapist to develop a ritual of clearing himself/herself of any personal agenda and distractions.

Before beginning a session, one therapist pauses outside the door of a patient's room and has the following routine:

- She reviews the patient's background information: name, age, diagnosis, and reason for referral to music therapy
- She takes a deep breath, inhaling energy and strength, and exhaling and clearing personal thoughts, busy routine, or lingering impressions/reflections of a previous session. At times, she whispers a brief prayer and reminds herself to be open and present for the patient.
- Only then does she enter the room and immediately begins the process of assessment, looking for cues about the patient's energy level, or the patient's needs of the day, which might be able to be addressed by music therapy.
- She decides how to introduce music therapy to the patient.

Treatment Goals

Prior to setting treatment goals, the music therapist must be aware of the patient's current treatment paradigm. Determining congruence between the patient's mode of treatment (e.g., curative, chronic, palliative, etc.) and the prognostic information provided by the oncologist informs the music therapist in how to support the patient in his or her own healing process. Some techniques may be more or less appropriate or effective depending on the patient's treatment paradigm. Goal areas described include psychosocial aspects, physical aspects, and neuropsychological aspects.

Psychosocial aspects

Emotional expression is a common goal in music therapy sessions with oncology patients. Other goals include music as a cue for relaxation, an expression of spirituality, an aid in cognitive processing, a distracter, and a catalyst for socialization. Most music therapists prefer to use primarily live music interventions in oncology settings (Kruse, 2003) in order to adapt and modify the musical stimuli in response to the patient. The goal of music therapy for cancer patients is frequently related to reducing psychophysiological stress, pain, anxiety, as well as feelings or experiences of isolation (Guzzetta, 1988). The human voice in song expression can be a source of nurturance, as well as an extension of the therapist or patient, providing for enhanced communication. Songs can be viewed as a vehicle through which emotions and cognition are stimulated, resulting in enabled communication (Magill Bailey, 1984, 1985).

Song selections made by cancer patients and families can encompass central themes that often differ, depending on when they are engaged in music therapy. During the contact phase, song themes may reflect the environment and outside world. In the early sessions, music therapists encourage patients and families to choose songs the therapist can use to identify and work moods, needs, and concerns. During the awareness or acceptance phase, hope, pleasure, reminiscence, relationships, needs, desires, feelings, loss, and death may be reflected through song themes. During the final resolution phase, song themes may reflect peace. In later sessions, the therapist can introduce song material with musical and personalized elements to guide patients through these stages (Magill Bailey, 1984). Each patient and family uniquely process a cancer diagnosis, so some may not reach acceptance or resolution. The music therapist must always respect and accept patients' individual choices about their treatment process, regardless of the music therapist's personal beliefs or emotions. It is important to be aware that allowing patients and families to choose their own songs, especially in early sessions, may elicit associated cognitive and emotional experiences (Magill Bailey, 1984); however, the music therapist should not minimize the patient's and family's autonomy.

Music therapy has been identified as a modality that can enhance cancer patients' quality of life by increasing their self-esteem, expression of emotion, and ability to communicate feelings to loved ones through songs, thereby facilitating relaxation and reduced tension and isolation (Bellamy & Willard, 1993). Music therapy can also motivate by supportive musical (including current and past musical interests) and social interactions on the units among patients, staff, and families. In addition, music therapy can support patients' spiritual needs, offering hope, comfort, and a connection with their higher power (Bellamy & Willard, 1993).

Music to stimulate memories for cancer patients and their families can have positive benefits. These include improved communication, self-esteem, dignity, self-worth, sense of purpose, identity, and ethnic and cultural affirmation. Reminiscence through music therapy has enhanced insight, pleasure, comfort, personal conflict resolution, acceptance of death, and spiritual growth (Beggs, 1991; Forrest, 2001; Hogan, 1999b; Lloyd-Green, 1994; Magill Bailey, 1984; O'Callaghan, 1984). Regret and disappointment can elicit considerable guilt. Such feelings that have emerged during music therapy sessions have been resolved through the music and life review process (Lloyd-Green, 1994; O'Callaghan, 1984). The literature challenges the acceptability of life review with older adults (Coleman, 1986, 1994; Garland, 1994; Thornton & Brotchie, 1987); however, one study showed that, for adults with cancer, memories or affects elicited were not harmful when the music therapist used preferred music (O'Callaghan & McDermott, 2004).

Physical aspects

Music therapy can help patients with cancer feel comfortable enough to communicate concerns that may affect other targeted domains (Munro, 1988) and motivate patients to continue toward "normal" life. Pain is a major physical concern for patients with cancer. It has been suggested that 70% of cancer patients experience severe pain at some time during the course of their illness. Seventy-five percent of those with advanced cancer have pain, and 25% of people with cancer die in severe pain (Breitbart, Passik, & Pane, 1998). Cancer pain may result from tumor growth, metastases, or side effects of cancer treatments such as surgery, chemotherapy, radiation, or procedures. Current pain management techniques can control almost 95% of cancer pain (Du Pen & Panke, 1997). Effective pain management can reduce anxiety and increase relaxation. Although it is difficult to isolate the value of any one intervention because patients use many different management approaches simultaneously (e.g., pharmacological, physical, etc.) (Magill Bailey, 1983), the use of music therapy in cancer pain management has also been advocated (Magill Bailey, 1983; Magill-Leverault, 1993; O'Callaghan, 1985, 1996b).

Theoretical rationales for pain reduction in music therapy include a direct physiological response to music stimuli that can alter neural components of pain sensation, and a cognitive and emotional change aligned with increased self-awareness that can alter perception of pain (Magill Bailey, 1983, 1986; Magill-Leverault, 1993; O'Callaghan, 1985, 1996b). Music therapy techniques used in pain management include live song and guitar music, songwriting, recording of patients' and families' music making, and patient-selected recorded music (Magill Bailey, 1983), as well as relaxation techniques and music-focused guided imagery. Specific music techniques and musical elements can alleviate the cycle of fear and anxiety that exacerbate pain, diverting attention to pleasing sensations (Magill Bailey, 1983, 1986). The music therapist promotes greater comfort and meaningful experiences by integrating prior experiences with the patient's current abilities (Magill Bailey, 1986).

Patients with acute pain or acute anxiety may find familiar music with a strong rhythmical pulse beneficial, but they may also prefer unfamiliar music without prior connotations (nor risk-aversive associations with their favorite music later). If pre-recorded music is used, the patient can be given headphones and encouraged to use the volume control to find their own volume comfort level. The therapist may also instruct the patient to use the volume level as a way to manage the changes in pain perception. For example, the patient can be instructed to increase the volume of the music as the pain increases. The use of headphones allows the music to be the primary focus for the patient, thus increasing the patient's sense of control in an effort to decrease the perception of pain. A decreased perception of pain may be related to a reduction in the responsiveness of neural pain receptors based on the Gate Control Theory of pain management (O'Callaghan, 1996b). However, this method is not recommended for long periods of time due to contraindications to the patient's hearing.

Receptive music experiences can also support management of chronic pain and issues of anxiety, boredom, or decreased consciousness, as well as support those in need of a healing environment. In this case, recorded music may best be played through speakers into the room to create a healing sound environment. Music for the purpose of reducing chronic pain or generalized anxiety can be unfamiliar and therefore sedative in nature.

It is important to note that, when a patient is in acute pain, especially at extreme levels, the extrasensory musical stimuli may not help and could possibly compound the pain experience. In this circumstance, the patient may be less likely to engage in music therapy sessions (O'Callaghan & Colegrove, 1998). The primary goal is to increase the patient's sense of control and to decrease the perception of the pain. While there is a limited understanding as to how music therapy can decrease the perception of pain for a patient with cancer, there are four theoretical perspectives that may support such a change. These perspectives include a psychological relationship between the music and pain, a psychophysiological theory, spinal mechanisms involved in pain modulation, and the role of endorphins (O'Callaghan, 1996b).

Neuropsychological aspects

Cancer may affect neural areas, which can result in cognitive, motor, and/or sensory losses for the patient. Cerebral areas and neural pathways for language and musical function are relatively independent (Elbert, Pantev, Weinbruch, Rockstroh, & Taub, 1995; Schlaug, Jancke, Huang, & Steinmetz, 1995; Sergent, Zuck, Tenial, & MacDonald, 1992; Zatorre, Evans, & Meyer, 1994). Therefore, when working with people who have a brain impairment, targeting music and language skills simultaneously may stimulate greater areas of preserved neural function than language or music used alone. A multisensory music therapy approach may also enhance supportive communications between neurologically impaired, severely ill patients and their families, friends, and caregivers (O'Callaghan, 1993, 1999b). Case studies have indicated that cancer patients with cognitive, motor, and sensory impairment may experience increased self-esteem and joy as they sing and interact with families during music therapy sessions. Families may find comfort in meaningful modes of communication established through sharing music and memories (O'Callaghan, 1993, 1999b). In fact, songs written with clients and families may provide comfort for the family following the patient's death (Rykov, 1999).

Communication and musical skills are helpful in promoting active participation during music therapy sessions among people experiencing brain impairment (O'Callaghan, 1989; O'Callaghan & Turnbull, 1987, 1988). These skills are regarded as relevant for a variety of patients with advanced neurological conditions affecting cognition (Magee, 2000), including cancer (O'Callaghan & Brown, 1989). When working with brain-impaired palliative care patients, music therapists draw on the evocative power of familiar music and the fact that long-term memories are relatively preserved (Bright, 1988; Butler & Lewis, 1982). Patients often sing lyrics or hum well-known music even when they cannot speak in complete sentences due to **aphasia** or word-finding difficulties (Clair, 1996; Sparks, Helm, & Albert, 1974). Some family members have commented that their loved one's cognitive deterioration is harder to cope with than their physical deterioration. Through music, families have an alternate means of forming an emotional connection with their loved ones. When a patient is severely affected by the disease, the family may find comfort in playing the patient's favorite music (O'Callaghan, 1996a). Language and music offer expanded opportunities for patients with brain impairments to experience positive, aesthetic experiences.

Considerations for Effective Practice

When working in adult cancer care, the music therapist must take into account several aspects prior to and during the implementation of treatment strategies. Consideration must be given to the selection of music, the therapeutic process in relation to the stages of cancer, aspects of family-centered care, contraindications, and the patient setting. Instruments, sheet music, CD players, CDs, or an MP3 player accompany most music therapists as they visit hospitalized patients individually or in a group setting (Bellamy & Willard, 1993; Lane, 1993; Munro, 1988; O'Brien, 1999; O'Callaghan, 2001b). Some music therapists may have a visual aid or "musical menu" available to offer patients a format with which to consider various music therapy techniques. For example, the musical menu may include representations for the use of recorded music for relaxation or energizing, the use of music for painful medical procedures, scheduling music therapy sessions with family visits, learning to play a musical instrument, song composition, development of a music-focused relaxation recording, patient song selection, listening to the therapist sing (Lane, 1993) and guided imagery and music (Burns, 2001; Hale, 1992; Munro, 1988; Pickett, 1987).

Selection of music

The choice of songs is particularly important if the patient is wrestling with painful emotions. Thoughtful selection of music based on the therapist's assessment of the patient's issues is essential, rather than random selection based on the music therapist's available repertoire. A specific song may be chosen to represent and match the patient's mood to facilitate the desired goal, or the song may be selected to provide an opportunity for the patient to transition to other emotions within the treatment phase.

Cancer affects people of all ages, cultures, spiritual beliefs, and walks of life. Therefore, it is necessary for the medical music therapist to have a wide repertoire of music, both instrumental and vocal, that is sedative in nature and representative of a variety of genres and eras. A vast variety allows the music therapist to effectively use the functions of music to address the therapeutic needs of the patients. Several music therapy programs have developed lists of songs that are most requested by their patients. Some programs have created compilation songbooks and corresponding lyric books (made in accordance with copyright laws), which include songs from a wide variety of musical genres that are most often requested by patients. The selection of songs for each music therapy program will vary in order to reflect regional and cultural differences.

The lyrics can be an important consideration during song selection, and the therapist should not select song lyrics with the goal of "fixing" the patient's emotional state, or as an attempt to answer the unanswerable questions that may arise from the patient's state of emotional angst.

> The music used for therapy . . . is selected according to how well it will serve therapeutic aims; nor is the purpose of therapy always to help the client relax, cheer up, or feel better in some immediate sense, as it may be to help the client traverse an elaborate and potentially difficult process of inner healing. (Abrams, 2001, p. 1)

It is often enough for the therapist to select music that relates to the sadness or grief the patient is expressing and to be present for the patient if the music stirs up difficult emotions. It is not the job of the music therapist (nor any interdisciplinary team member) to provide the patient with "answers" to spiritual questions, or to attempt to answer existential questions that may arise from the individual's search for meaning within the cancer experience. The therapist can support the patient's process of wrestling with questions without attempting to provide answers or solve the patient's problems. In her book *Kitchen Table Wisdom*, Rachel Naomi Remen (1996) writes:

> I suspect that the most basic and powerful way to connect to another person is to listen. Just listen. Perhaps the most important thing we ever give each other is our attention. And especially if it's given from the heart. When people are talking there's no need to do anything but receive them. . . . Most times caring about it is even more important than understanding it. (p. 143)

Within the first few music therapy sessions, the therapist often encourages the patient or family member to initiate the selection of songs. The goal of using a specific song may initially be obvious to the patient, or it may become evident as the patient hears the lyrics of the song or responds to specific elements in the music, such as harmony, rhythm, pulse, tempo, timbre, or tonality. The patient could identify with the songwriter, using the song to project his or her feelings, discuss a memory related to the song, share a story about the song's meaning and relevance to his or her life, or relate the song to an aspect of facing the challenges of cancer. If a patient requests songs that are not in the music therapist's repertoire, the music therapist can offer options of songs with similar characteristics, or learn the song. Sometimes the patient can sing the melody and enough of the words that the music therapist can provide an accompaniment or gain enough familiarity with the song in order to locate it and learn it for another session.

Brief Outline of a Music Therapy Session

1. After a brief discussion of the patient's music preferences, the patient and/or therapist select song(s).
2. The patient participates in receptive music listening experience or active music-making experience, such as singing with the therapist.
3. If the patient appears to have an emotional response to the music (observable through a patient's tears or changes in affect and body position), the therapist can provide some type of acknowledgment of the patient's emotional expression through a verbal reflection and/ or empathic nonverbal reaction (e.g., a small nod and maintenance of eye contact). It is crucial for the therapist to communicate (nonverbally and/or verbally) his/her willingness to be present and open as the patient expresses emotions of sadness, anger, or other intense emotions. If the patient cries while hearing the music (a regular occurrence in oncology music therapy sessions), it is important for the therapist to acknowledge the patient's emotional response. If the patient's emotional response is not acknowledged, the patient may not feel that he or she has permission to experience or express intense emotions within the therapeutic relationship. If the therapist is able to communicate a willingness to be present for the person in the midst of his or her emotional, spiritual, or physical pain or angst, the patient may later be able to express the emotions directly and openly, musically and/or verbally, within the context of the music therapy session and the therapeutic relationship. Some patients may not feel comfortable processing their emotions verbally.
4. The therapist asks a series of open-ended questions to allow the patient to further express emotions and/or put a verbal component to them.
5. The therapist utilizes various counseling models (see below). These models may guide the level or depth of the questions/statements the therapist selects. An important consideration when working with families and/or patients is that they do not have to experience actual music for a music-based counseling experience. Through talking about music, imaging and remembering music experiences, therapeutic consequences may also emerge. It is possible that verbally reflecting on thoughts and emotions elicited during music experiences could thwart a therapeutic response. Hence, therapists need to consider when not to reflect, question, or probe, and allow for contemplative moments of silence.
6. The therapist must be careful not to "fix" or "solve" the patient's problems or unanswerable questions.

Religious songs should be utilized only with respect to a patient's spiritual belief systems and religious background, and with awareness that the diagnosis of cancer or a change in the patient's medical status may cause a feeling of anger toward a higher power. As a result, the patient may reject the religious songs that he found comforting in the past. For the patient experiencing complicated emotions, offering only traditional religious music may leave him or her feeling that it is not permissible to express anger or question faith issues within the therapeutic setting. If the patient selects religious music, the therapist has an assurance that it is safe to proceed with religious songs and discussion of topics that relate to the therapeutic intent and needs of the patient.

Because spiritual issues can be brought to the forefront within the oncology setting, music therapists may find that patients frequently request spiritually or religious-oriented music. The inclusion of the large amount of religious-oriented songs in the Appendix of this chapter is a reflection of the songs that are regularly requested in music therapy sessions with oncology patients. The inclusion of songs of earlier time periods in the chart is a reflection of the large number of older adult oncology patients served by music therapy, due to an increased incidence of cancer with age.

Therapeutic process

The **iso principle** can be an effective framework within a music therapy session; however, the therapist might want to consider that this principle may need to be carried over a series of sessions. An expectation for a cancer patient to express grief and then modulate to hopefulness within a single music therapy session is not realistic, nor may it ever happen. Music therapy can be an important part of the patient's process of expressing intense emotions and finding meaning within the cancer experience. The length and number of music therapy sessions are limited, so it is important for the therapist to empower patients to connect with their own support resources. Encouraging patients to identify and experience their personal sources of support can be an important goal addressed within the music therapy session.

Awareness of the developing therapeutic relationship and the patient's overall comfort level with the therapeutic process is an important consideration. Often, medical patients have had little or no previous experience with psychotherapy (Short, 2002) and may be initially uncomfortable discussing insights or experiencing emotions within the therapeutic process. Initial inquiries from the therapist in the first music therapy session may be different than the communication that occurs when the therapeutic relationship has been securely established. The interventions and the selection of music can be designed for work at a deeper emotional level once the therapeutic relationship has been established. If the patient has a change or decline in physical status, the patient may have reduced defenses and decreased coping ability. The therapist may need to use a more supportive approach and comforting music. Music therapists may find that some patients with cancer are very open to freely expressing their emotions and insights within a single music therapy session after experiencing so much emotional turmoil in their cancer experience. In this case, a therapeutic relationship may form and deepen more quickly than within other music therapy settings.

The cancer trajectory challenges the music therapist to understand the stages of cancer, treatment approaches, and the patient's desired direction for treatment. For example, a patient who is in the midst of aggressive treatment may be concerned about fatigue, energy management, stress reduction, immune system enhancement, or anxiety about upcoming treatment regimes. Familiarity with the literature on palliative and hospice care is helpful for medical music therapists working in cancer care. Although many of the interventions may seem similar, music therapists in the oncology setting need to be aware that over 50% of people diagnosed with cancer will be in complete remission after treatment and are considered "cured" of their cancer (Rossman, 2003).

Cultural aspects

Music therapists need to be mindful of a patient's culture and how therapeutic techniques may need to be modified based on these cultural considerations (Dileo & Magill, 2005; Dileo & Starr, 2005). Culture includes a broad range of factors that include age, disability, ethnicity, socioeconomic status, sexual orientation, indigenous heritage, national origin, gender (Hays, cited in Dileo & Starr, 1995), and religious or spiritual orientation. Although generalizations cannot be made about working with individuals from varying cultures, general issues for consideration arise. These include the nature of hierarchical family relationships in the patient's support network, varying religious and spiritual traditions, and how therapy self-disclosure and information sharing may be regarded in the particular culture (Dileo & Starr, 2005). In addition, it is essential to understand the cultural implications of body language. For example, some groups believe it is impolite to look an elder in the eye.

Contraindications

Music therapists need to be aware of aversive possibilities associated with their medium (O'Callaghan, 1996b). For example, when considering how many musical choices to offer patients with memory loss, one should consider the extent of their cognitive decline. Questions should be structured to ensure that patients use their recall abilities to their maximum potential, thereby supporting a successful experience. To encourage and maintain arousal among patients experiencing **adynamia**, familiar music should be used. People with disinhibition also need a great deal of structure in sessions to reduce the potential for tangential experiences (O'Callaghan, 1993; O'Callaghan & Brown, 1989).

Contraindications for music therapy in cancer care can occur when coping skills are severely diminished (Bailey, 1985), patients are in acute and severe pain, and patients do not like music (Magill Bailey, 1983). Patients who are barely coping with emotions related to their cancer diagnosis or to changes in their condition may appropriately refuse music therapy services because they do not have enough physical stamina or energy to be emotionally available at the time.

When facilitating relaxation exercises, music therapists should understand that the techniques of tensing and releasing muscles used in progressive muscle relaxation can increase a cancer patient's pain, particularly if the pain is a result of metastases to the bone. Relaxation techniques involving deep breathing may be uncomfortable or impossible for lung cancer patients or other patients with **dyspnea**. Fast and highly rhythmical pieces sometimes exacerbate pain (Magill Bailey, 1983). Other contraindications include **musicogenic epilepsy** and musically induced catastrophic reactions, both possible in people with neural damage. Patients may also experience altered and unpleasant musical perception following neural involvement of cancer (O'Callaghan, 1996b). Music therapists need to be cautious that when patients perform musically, they may either experience heightened feelings of achievement and power, or the reinforcement of a "disabled" identity if their abilities are not what they were in the past (Magee, 1998). Appropriate assessment will help the therapist to provide a positive outcome.

Some patients have wondered whether hearing specific songs while receiving chemotherapy treatments may trigger a strong memory of the chemotherapy and an adverse physical response when hearing the song at a later time. While some patients can find that specific music listened to during aversive treatments can elicit unpleasant reactions when the music is heard later, others do not report this experience. Music therapists may invite patients to consider whether they want to risk such aversive associations with preferred music before selecting what they use during their treatments.

Family-centered care

Family members also may have a significant role in music therapy. Studies have confirmed that family members also experience a myriad of emotions during the time of initial diagnosis and their process may parallel that of the person with cancer (Glajchen, 1999). It is essential that family members be included as active participants in the patient's care plan and process. Therapists may work with families to improve life negotiations or adaption and to allow for the positive expression of the patient's and significant other's perceptions. Also, music therapists help promote positive communication and memory sharing, and affirm the value of each other by including thoughts and feelings not previously shared. When family relationships are maladaptive due to longstanding difficulties, family therapy may be useful. Music-based counseling may be co-facilitated with a professional skilled in counseling family relationships.

Case Example of Family Involvement in a Music Therapy Session

The music therapist was referred to see an oncology inpatient that, as a result of the conditions of her malignant tumor, had a strong odor. Although family members visited regularly, they spent most of their time away from the patient, down the hall in the lounge, because they had difficulty being in the physical environment of the patient's room. Many attempts to decrease the odor in the room had been implemented by the nursing staff, including aromatherapy interventions and adjustments in the patient's medications. The family members continued to be extremely uncomfortable, remaining mostly in the lounge and focusing on the negative aspects of care, such as the strong odor and the impersonal institutional conditions of the hospital environment. When the music therapist arrived at the patient's room, the patient and one of her adult daughters were present and they agreed to participate in music therapy. During the first song, the patient smiled, sang, and moved her feet in a familiar pattern of dance steps. During the second song, the daughter became tearful and ran out of the room. The therapist was concerned, but continued to play and sing. In a few minutes, the daughter returned down the hall from the lounge, escorting her sister and her father to the patient's room. The patient and her entire family participated in a 30-minute music therapy session, singing, laughing, crying, and discussing memories of music and dancing, and sharing stories of important music-related family events. At the end of the session, the family selected recordings of the patient's favorite types of music from the music listening library, and played the music for her many times during the 3 days before she was discharged. During those 3 days, the family was able to remain with the patient in her room when they were visiting. Both the family and nursing staff reported that the music therapy session had made the key difference in the family's ability to remain in the room during their visits, and the family reported that the music therapy session had allowed them to provide much more support to their mother and participate in her treatment plan.

Cancer center outpatient settings

Flexibility and adaptability are key qualities for the music therapist working in outpatient cancer center environments. The time and location of music therapy sessions may need to be varied or adjusted due to changes in patients' treatment schedules. A patient's physical status and level of fatigue should always be considered when determining the duration of sessions and the selection of interventions. The identity of the patient with cancer as the primary client is less defined than it is in other settings, because within cancer care, it may be appropriate for the therapist to work with the patient, the family, and the caregivers (Sourkes et al., 1998).

A private room in the outpatient cancer center, such as a family consultation room or a room specifically dedicated for counseling or music therapy sessions, will increase the accessibility of music therapy services for patients. The room should be able to accommodate a stereo system and a recliner. Ideally, it should have enough floor space for a cushioned relaxation mat and for placement of music therapy equipment for patients to play and an electric keyboard and guitar. A room designated for music therapy sessions allows patients to meet with the music therapist at times other than during their chemotherapy treatments. Some patients request to have music therapy sessions before or after laboratory tests or appointments with their oncologist, before radiation therapy appointments, or during the week prior to their chemotherapy treatment. A private room designated for music therapy establishes what some patients have called a "sacred space to focus on healing" within the cancer center.

It also may be helpful for music therapy services to be available at regular times for patients receiving chemotherapy in the outpatient cancer center setting. Patients who wish to receive music therapy can request to have their treatments scheduled during the designated music therapy times. Other patients may learn of music therapy through educational or personal interactions or exposure to the music therapist occurring during the cancer center's scheduled music therapy hours. With the establishment of a regular music therapy schedule, oncology patients and staff members begin to identify music therapy as an integral part of treatment at the cancer center. If patients are unable to schedule treatment at the regularly scheduled music therapy times, the music therapist can offer to schedule sessions before, during, or after patients' scheduled chemotherapy. Inclusion of music therapy education tools such as brochures and posters within the informational materials of the cancer center's support and education programs is necessary to inform patients of the availability and potential benefits of music therapy services.

Intervention Strategies

A variety of music-based techniques are appropriate for cancer care in the hospital setting. Music therapists use these techniques across populations, diagnoses, and settings. Multiple techniques can often overlap in the session. Descriptions of some techniques appropriate to the adult hospital patient can be found in the Appendix of this monograph.

Clinical Techniques Using Music Cited in 88 Clinical Reports From Greatest to Least
(Krout, 2000)

Clinical Technique	*N* of Reports Including Technique
Music listening	42
Improvisation	26
Singing	26
Songwriting	26
Music playing	21
Song choice	19
Music listening and imagery for relaxation	12
Lyric analysis	9
Guided Imagery and Music (Bonny Method)	7
Musical life review	6
Creative arts therapies (body movement, writing, painting, and clay work)	4
Music and drawing/painting	3
Therapeutic touch	3
Art therapy with music therapy	2
Creation of tape as music legacy	2
Music therapy and verbal social work techniques	2
Hypnosis	1
Meditation	1
Milieu and environmental therapy	1
Multimodalmusic therapy	1
Music therapy combined with occupational, speech, and language therapy	1
Pediatric group music therapy	1
Stimulation protocol	1
Toning	1

Specific to music therapy and cancer care, the chart *Music Therapy in Adult Cancer Care: Across the Cancer Continuum*, outlines the various cancer phases paired with music therapy interventions. This chart is found in the Appendix to this chapter and is not meant to be a used as a "cookbook" approach to music therapy, but rather as a guide or starting place for the music therapy clinician new to working within cancer care.

Every person with cancer responds to the experience of cancer in an individual way. A process of ongoing and constant assessment is key in order for the therapist to determine the appropriate goals and interventions for each patient. The sample music therapy goals and techniques that have been listed in the continuum chart found in the Appendix to this chapter represent only a limited sample of a wide variety of those that might be effective. These examples, listed in *Music Therapy in Adult Cancer Care: Across the Cancer Continuum*, have been drawn from the authors' years of clinical practice and have been used with oncology patients as they actively meet the challenges that may occur in each phase of the cancer continuum. The song titles referenced in the Discography in the Appendix of this chapter have also been pared down to include only a small number of songs that have been requested by patients and are relevant to the treatment issues within each phase of the continuum. There are an infinite number of songs that could be used in each category.

In utilizing the *Music Therapy in Adult Cancer Care: Across the Cancer Continuum*, the music therapist is not meant to exclude other music therapy goals, techniques, songs, or types of music. The therapist designs the goals and interventions to meet an individual patient's specific needs, goals, and belief systems, as well as the patient's music preferences. In addition to assessing the patient's needs, the music therapist utilizes creativity and intuition to guide the selection of music and adaptations of the technique. Music therapy in cancer care is truly a combination of art and science. Detailed descriptions of clinical interventions in the Resources section of this monograph will focus on implementation specific to both inpatient and outpatient cancer care in the hospital setting, with an understanding that a variety of treatment approaches may be utilized by music therapists in cancer care.

Music Therapy Treatment Approaches Utilized in Hospice, Palliative, and Cancer Care
(Krout, 2004)

- The Bonny Method of Guided Imagery and Music (Bruscia, 1991)
- Cognitive behavioral methods (Hilliard, 2003)
- Improvisation-based methods (Lee, 1995)
- Music therapy as milieu (Aasgaard, 1999)
- Medical music therapy (Aldridge, 1996)
- Music-based collage (Munro, 1984)
- Musically supported counseling (Porchet-Munro, 1993)
- Life review (Beggs, 1991)
- Physioacoustic therapy (Butler & Butler, 1997)
- Psychodynamic (Bruscia, 1991)
- Psychospiritual music therapy (Salmon, 2001)
- Receptive approaches such as music listening (Curtis, 1986)
- Supportive eclectic music therapy for grief and loss (Bright, 2002)
- Songwriting (O'Callaghan, 1999a)

New music therapy clinicians may find the medical adult cancer setting to be challenging. It requires a vast musical repertoire, knowledge of the many types of cancer, related cancer treatment issues within the cancer trajectory, a focus on patients' immediate experiences and responses, and spontaneity in the utilization of techniques and materials. Typically, it is not appropriate for the therapist to have a pre-planned session agenda or utilize preconceived interventions for a session, because the needs of the medical patients may change or vary from day to day, hour to hour, and even moment to moment. Ongoing assessment is of utmost importance, and the clinician must have the ability to objectively observe patient responses and adapt the music or technique appropriately (Barry & O'Callaghan, 2008).

Throughout the music therapy session, the therapist needs to truly listen to the patient and family. New clinicians may be too focused on thinking ahead about what to say or which song to use next. In doing so, they may miss important cues from the patient. When the therapist listens attentively and mindfully and is fully present with the client, the direction of open-ended questions, reflective statements, appropriate song selection, and intervention strategies will be based upon the content, context, and emotions of what the patient has presented. This sense of "knowing" can also be referred to as *practice wisdom* (Scott, 1990). Practice wisdom can be described as an implicit understanding of knowledge that is gleaned from reflective examination of practice by the experienced professional. The professional recognizes the competence required to respond to patient needs, particularly in situations that are atypical, uncertain, unique, or conflicted (Schön, 1991).

Practice wisdom is also applicable to music therapy and related fields. Clinical data mining research methodology, which is derived from the social work discipline (Epstein, 2001), informed O'Callaghan's (2005) examination of her practice wisdom, which included her perceptions of the relevance of her music therapy program at Peter Mac, an Australian comprehensive cancer center. Part of the thematic statement findings included:

> Music therapy offered patients, staff, and visitors opportunities for a "music space," characterized by the experience of altered intra-awareness or transient, musically inspired communities, although these may have been experienced simultaneously. "Music space" denotes a time where the value of music is recognized, even emancipated, in an otherwise clinical hospital environment. Music spaces are a fluid, changing entity, characterized by people creatively expressing their musical, psychosocial, cognitive, motor, and spiritual beings, either on their own or through supportive and enlightening interactions with others. They may also be a place where people are just simply able to "be," whatever that means for them. (O'Callaghan, 2005, pp. 226–227)

O'Callaghan (2005) found that writing and analyzing her clinical reflexive journal was a "self dialogic" process that both uncovered and extended her practice wisdom. An oncologic music therapy student used a comparable method to extend her professional development (Barry & O'Callaghan, 2008).

Underlying knowledge of the patient's treatment paradigm and relevant music therapy goals will also help to provide the framework for which the therapist can select the interventions. A music therapist may desire further training and practice to increase his or her comfort level with various counseling techniques, such as the use of open-ended probes (Gardstrom, 2001). Integrating these skills and insights into practice, combining intuition and knowledge, and learning to trust the therapeutic process can be a huge step in the development of a medical music therapy clinician.

Patients with cancer are often educated and informed individuals who appreciate explanations of the potential benefits of music therapy. Discussions might include an explanation of the psychoneuroimmunology research that supports the effects of music on the immune system and adrenocortical system, descriptions of the theories of pain management, and the role of music within the pain management process, as well as explorations of an individual patient's personal use of music within the process of healing. Medical music therapists must stay abreast of the latest research and theories related to music therapy, music medicine, the expanding body of popular literature written about music in medicine, and evidence-based practices in related fields. If appropriate, the music therapist can utilize this information as tools to educate and motivate patients. This may be the one of the more important aspects of being a music therapist in cancer care. Education serves to motivate and empower patients to utilize techniques learned in music therapy within their overall treatment and healing process.

Receptive and Active Music Interventions

Music therapists working with adults in oncology settings may find that a large number of interventions utilized with patients are receptive versus active music-making interventions. Several researchers have examined the differences between these two types of interventions with cancer patients. Both receptive and active music experiences allow for group cohesion, increased mood ratings, less tension, and an overall sense of well-being (Burns et al., 2001; Waldon, 2001). Receptive music experiences (e.g., listening) may be more relaxing for patients, and active music experiences (e.g., improvisation) may help the patient feel more energetic (Burns, Sledge, Fuller, Daggy & Monahan, 2005).

Music listening, particularly live music performed by the therapist, is the most often used intervention when working with patients with a terminal illness (Gallagher & Steele, 2001; Krout, 2000; Mramor, 2001). Within adult oncology settings, receptive music experiences are extremely effective and are often chosen and preferred by patients over active music-making experiences.

Reasons for Receptive Interventions with Oncology Patients

- Acute and ever-changing physical status of inpatients.
- Restrictions on active participation due to patients' IV tubing placement or patients' minimal amounts of physical energy.
- Limited number of music therapy sessions that may occur. With short inpatient stays, it is not uncommon for patients to have only one music therapy session. This makes it difficult to develop the level of therapeutic relationship necessary to provide the context for introduction of unfamiliar musical experiences with adult clients.
- Space limitations of the physical environment in medical settings.
- Patients' reluctance to try new or unfamiliar experiences when in the midst of the emotions of their own health crises.
- Patients' initial resistance to engage in active music-making experiences, due to the patients' interpretation that some activities may not appear to be age-appropriate.
- Patients not recognizing the relevance of active music-making interventions within their overall cancer treatment plan.
- Desire of patients to focus on learning and experiencing the relaxation response, and thus requesting receptive music therapy experiences, which naturally facilitate this response.
- Process that some cancer patients go through of redefining the priorities in their life. If active music making is not a priority for a patient, it may not happen within a music therapy session in the adult oncology setting.

Music environmental therapy

Music environmental therapy has been defined as "a systematic process of using music to promote health in a specified environment inside or outside of institutions" (Aasgaard, 1999, p. 34). Live instrumental music that is primarily sedative in nature and played in the hallways or group treatment spaces can transform a sterile oncology environment into a healing environment. It can create a sense of a healthy environment that fosters self-growth, creativity, and connectedness among the people. Music environmental therapy can also involve patients and hospital staff through such experiences as vocal choirs, bell choirs, concerts, and music paired with other creative arts (Aasgaard, 1999). Music therapy in open areas of hospital oncology units may even support the emergence of transient communities (O'Callaghan, 2007).

Besides music therapists, highly skilled volunteers can also be trained to provide music environmental therapy. Excellent musicianship, paired with exceptional observational and interpersonal skills, is essential for the individual who provides the music. When deciding when and where to play, the therapist or trained musician should assess the existing environment and continue to make periodic evaluations of the effect music has on those nearby. Care should be taken to close doors of the rooms of patients who do not wish to hear the music. If the music does not appear to enhance the environment or if it has a negative effect on any person within the auditory environment, then the intervention should be stopped or the musician should move to another corridor or treatment area.

Music environmental therapy can be contraindicated for patients and staff on units such as an oncology intensive care unit, where the patients are in critical medical conditions. Patients and staff members can easily confuse environmental music or music performances with more traditional music therapy. The music therapist must be very clear about the musical difference and the intention between music therapy and music environmental therapy.

Music that is representative of specific religious traditions should be avoided in music environmental therapy, unless the therapist has prior knowledge of the backgrounds of all patients who might be within the acoustical environment and plays a variety of music to represent the diversity of patient backgrounds. Staff members particularly enjoy and request environmentally oriented music and often comment that it has positive effects on the atmosphere of the unit. If used thoughtfully and considerately, music environmental therapy can serve as an excellent marketing tool for music therapy (Lane, 1993). As a result of hearing the hallway music, many patients and family members request individual music therapy sessions in their rooms, and oncology staff members hear the music and often stop to give the music therapist specific patient referrals.

Active music-making interventions

Active music-making interventions may be more appropriate and well received by cancer patients who do not have an acute medical status and are able to participate in multiple music therapy sessions. Active music-making interventions often emerge from receptive music interventions, such as music listening. A patient may begin to spontaneously and voluntarily sing with the music therapist. Music therapists have found that when adult medical patients are invited to sing with the music therapist before any music has been played, patients may quickly decline, responding with a negative comment about their ability to sing. When their singing is a spontaneous response to the music, and not a specific request by the therapist prior to the commencement of the music, patients may continue to sing with the therapist throughout the session. Nonverbal or verbal encouragement from the therapist and assurance that the patient's singing ability is not being evaluated encourage patients to continue singing with the therapist.

The music-based life review can be an extremely effective intervention for a patient in palliative care. The therapist may choose to use this intervention for the purpose of exploring a patient's loss history. This may have an influence on the patient's response to a cancer diagnosis by providing a vehicle for the patient to reflect on past times when he or she faced adversity and solutions arising as a result. A newly diagnosed cancer patient in a curative treatment mode may not benefit from the life review technique, as his or her life is not nearing an end. A detailed description of the musical life review technique can be found in the Resources section of this monograph.

Another aspect that may be incorporated into the music-based life review technique is an exploration of the patient's history of losses (Sourkes et al., 1998). The patient can be asked to select songs that represent losses in his or her life, ranging from earliest childhood memories to the present time, including losses such as termination of relationships, loss of employment, geographical separations, deaths of significant people and pets, and the loss of the patient's hopes, aspirations, or dreams (Loscalzo & Brintzenhofeszoc, 1998). Questions the music therapist may use to facilitate the discussion include "What were most stressful aspects of each loss experience?" and "What type of support was positive, deleterious, or lacking altogether?" One patient requested to hear a song she had played at her violin recital and reflected that her biggest regret was selling her instrument and never again having the opportunity to play the violin.

A patient's previous experiences in dealing with loss can affect how he or she will face the changes that occur as a result of the cancer experience. Another patient requested to hear songs that her mother used to play and sing throughout the patient's childhood. After hearing and singing the songs, the patient tearfully revealed that her mother had died from the same type of cancer as the patient's own cancer diagnosis. The history of cancer within the family and the health outcomes of that family member will affect the impact of the diagnosis on the patient (Sourkes et al., 1998).

The musical life review has been used to describe the memories patients discuss, which are triggered as they listen to music with or without cueing by the music therapist (Lloyd-Green, 1994). This review could also include more structured methods of recorded musical profiles, where patients' musical selections and life stories are put on audio recording (O'Callaghan, 1984) or a video recorded musical performance and life review interview (Beggs, 1991).

Relaxation, guided imagery, and the Bonny Method of Guided Imagery and Music

There is much confusion in the literature regarding the distinctions between relaxation techniques, guided imagery, music imagery, and the Bonny Method of Guided Imagery and Music (BMGIM). Relaxation techniques differ from imagery techniques. Relaxation techniques include progressive muscle relaxation, deep breathing, and autogenic relaxation, providing patients with specific cues for physical relaxation. The goal of a relaxation technique is to help patients learn and experience a *relaxation response*, a term coined by Dr. Herbert Benson (1975) in the 1960s to describe "a physical state of deep rest that changes the physical and emotional responses to stress" (Mind Body Medical Institute, 2010).

Professionally administered relaxation training has been found to be superior to audiotaped and paraprofessionally administered relaxation training in reducing anxiety symptoms. Relaxation and guided imagery techniques provided by a professional therapist reduced emotional distress and increased food intake in cancer patients undergoing chemotherapy (Carey & Burish, 1987).

Imagery techniques incorporate visual, auditory, **gustatory**, **olfactory**, kinesthetic, or emotion-based images. Within music therapy sessions, imagery techniques may be used for the purpose of facilitating physical relaxation, experiencing emotions, enhancing immune system parameters, or exploring insights and spiritual issues. Imagery techniques include therapist-directed techniques, such as directed imagery; guided imagery; music imagery; music-focused imagery; and interactive imagery techniques, such as the Bonny Method of Guided Imagery and Music, and Interactive Guided Imagery.

Imagery Techniques

Therapist Directed: Directed imagery, guided imagery, music imagery, music-focused imagery, guided imagery and music

Interactive Imagery: Bonny Method of Guided Imagery and Music, Interactive Guided Imagery

Pre-recorded and live music for relaxation and imagery exercises. The music that is utilized by music therapists for relaxation and imagery techniques may be pre-recorded or provided by the therapist. While there is still little understanding of the differential benefits between recorded music and therapist-provided live music, several studies suggest that the overall impact of live music may be more powerful than that of recorded music (Bailey, 1983; Cassileth et al., 2003; Finnas, 2001; Saperston, 1995). These studies, however, did not specifically assess music for relaxation interventions. One study that did compare live versus recorded music as an independent variable for relaxation did not report a level of significance in the effects between the two (Burns et al., 2001).

For relaxation and imagery exercises, the music therapist will often improvise music while providing verbal relaxation cues to the patient. The use of live improvised music allows the therapist to immediately adapt the music to the patient's physical responses and to pace it according to the patient's respiration rate and volume, release of muscle tension, and changes in position. By improvising live music, the therapist can produce and play a continuous selection of relaxation music, without taking time to search through or turn pages in music books or leaving large gaps of silence between music selections.

Some medical patients have had little or no previous experience with structured relaxation or imagery experiences (Short, 2002) and may be initially hesitant to participate. In this case, it can be helpful for the therapist to improvise relaxation music that incorporates elements or characteristics of the patient's preferred music. Qualities of New Age music, hymns, popular or country ballads, waltzes, classical music, jazz, pentatonic music, or metered or non-metered music can be included within an improvisation. Another important advantage to using live music is the therapist's ability to spontaneously create and combine the music with spoken or sung cues to guide the physical response of relaxation. The lyrics, accompaniment music, and patient cues are matched so that each contribution complements and enhances the rhythm and pacing of the other.

Recordings that are compilations of music selections with relaxing qualities are currently on the market. One of the advantages of using pre-recorded music is to guarantee that the music was specifically composed, performed, mixed, and remixed to achieve a high-quality end product. The use of pre-recorded music also ensures a predictable product, and with prior knowledge of the specific recording, the therapist can utilize the elements of the music as a focus for the relaxation or imagery cues. It is especially important for the therapist to place the relaxation cues to coordinate with the underlying rhythm, tempo, and phrasing of the music, rather than try to verbalize over the music.

The pacing of cues will vary with the selection of music and with the responses of individual clients. It is helpful for the therapist to have carefully listened to the music, both in a relaxed state to experience the sedative qualities of the music, and in an upright state to analyze the musical elements that support or detract from the experience of relaxation. Reading a pre-written script may not necessarily be the most effective way for a music therapist to implement a relaxation session. The therapist should strive to incorporate the unique images of each individual to facilitate the needs of the patient. However, when first using relaxation and imagery techniques, a pre-written script may help the music therapist develop confidence and pacing. The possibilities for personalizing sessions for individual oncology clients are endless. Once the therapist's comfort level has increased, the pre-written script can be set aside or modified for the individual patient. Helpful illustrations of music relaxation and imagery sessions can be found in Grocke and Wigram (2007).

The use of pre-recorded music may also allow patients to use their own familiar relaxation music. Once the routine of relaxation has been established and the sequence of relaxation cues is learned, the use of pre-recorded music may empower patients to use relaxation techniques with their own music at home, without the therapist to provide the music and cues. Some patients will learn the sequence of relaxation techniques and adapt it to different recordings of music, changing the music to reflect changes in their emotional or energy state that day. Others will continue to use the same recording of music but will change their relaxation exercise sequence, or vary the type of relaxation method to reflect changes in their body. Perhaps the biggest advantage for the therapist in using recorded music is that it does not require the therapist to manage the details of spontaneously composing a personalized relaxation script for the patient, while simultaneously having to improvise high-quality live music specifically designed to facilitate the patient's relaxation response.

Music-focused or music-assisted relaxation or imagery techniques are not the same as using music as a background for scripted relaxation or imagery exercises. Music-focused relaxation techniques incorporate relaxation cues that include a reference to the elements of the music. Music therapists may suggest to the patient to "breathe with the phrases of the Native American flute," or they may ask, "Do the sounds of the cello resonate in any part of your body?" Relaxation cues that encourage patients to connect the elements of music to their physical state may make a huge difference in the way that patients experience the music. Training in the Bonny Method of Guided Imagery and Music (BMGIM) can be helpful for music therapists seeking to understand and learn more advanced techniques of connecting the relaxation and imagery process to the elements of the music applicable the hospital setting.

Interactive imagery and specific immune system enhancement imagery

In contrast with the process of directed guided imagery where the client listens to the verbal cues given by the therapist, the process of interactive imagery involves the client in a relaxed state, dialoging with the therapist or facilitator. Interactive imagery allows the client to immediately report what he or she is experiencing during the process of the imagery session, and allows the therapist to adjust the interventions accordingly. Based on the patient's description of a relaxing scene or image, the therapist can improvise live music to support the imagery process. Images do not necessarily have to be visual. Patients with cancer may report visualizing images, experiencing strong emotions, becoming aware of kinesthetic or energy sensations, or exploring messages that come from their body or their cancer, relayed from within their unconscious. The use of interactive imagery techniques ensures that the therapist is working with the individual patient's images and process.

Two examples of methods that use interactive imagery techniques are the Bonny Method of Guided Imagery and Music (BMGIM) and Interactive Guided Imagery. BMGIM has specifically defined parameters within a wide range of imagery methods. BMGIM is "a process that involves a client who is willing and able to explore his/her inner process, through carefully selected music, in an altered state of consciousness, with a trained BMGIM therapist" (Ventre, 2002, p. 29). The pure form of BMGIM is comprised of nine characteristics, presented below (Bruscia, 2002).

Characteristics of the Bonny Method of Guided Imagery and Music
(Bruscia, 2002)

1. An individual form, one client and the guide (therapist). Group sessions are not included in the definition of the pure form of BMGIM.
2. An exploration of consciousness with the intent of healing, psychotherapy, self-development, and spiritual work.
3. Spontaneous imaging that is not scripted or directed by the facilitator.
4. An expanded state of consciousness, through an initial relaxation induction.
5. Pre-designed programs of classical music that facilitate the imagery process.
6. Interaction with the guide throughout the imagery experience.
7. The use of non-directive, non-analytical, music-based interventions.
8. A client-centered orientation.
9. Inclusion of the following components within each session: preliminary conversation, relaxation induction, guided or interactive music-imagining experience, return to normal state of consciousness, and postlude discussion.

Confusion in the use of these terms continues to exist within music therapy and other related psychotherapy fields. Typically, the terms *guided imagery, directed imagery, music-facilitated, music-focused,* or *music-assisted imagery* have been used to describe music and guided imagery techniques that are not associated with the Bonny Method of Guided Imagery and Music, whereas individual and group variations of the Bonny Method have been referred to as GIM or BMGIM. A continuum of practice for music and imagery identifies three levels of music and imagery practice: supportive, re-educative, and reconstructive. All pure forms of BMGIM are considered reconstructive. Music therapists trained in BMGIM will utilize all three levels of music and imagery practice in order to accommodate the changing emotional and physical states of cancer patients (Summer & Chong, 2006).

To utilize the more advanced technique of interactive imagery, advanced training and certification in one of these methods is highly recommended. Certification in BMGIM through the Association for Music and Imagery (www.ami-bonnymethod.org), involves an extensive training process, comparable to the process of completing a master's degree, with coursework in music psychotherapy, imagery, therapeutic elements of music, and the facilitation of images through specifically designed programs of classical music. Training and certification in the method of Interactive Guided Imagery is through the Academy for Guided Imagery. Interactive Guided Imagery (IGI) is a method that was developed by Martin Rossman and David Bressler, in which the guide assists clients "in learning to access and utilize the insights and solutions in their own unconscious" (Academy for Guided Imagery, 2004). IGI includes training in specific imagery techniques, such as "evocative imagery" and the "inner advisor" or "inner healer" (Rossman, 2003). Music therapists should note that coursework for the Interactive Guided Imagery certification does not incorporate extensive information on utilizing music to facilitate the imagery process.

BMGIM sessions with patients who have cancer may address different issues than BMGIM sessions with clients who do not have health issues. When an individual's functional or physical status has been compromised as a result of cancer treatment, the therapist must be mindful of using a supportive approach in combination with more structured and predictable music (Burns, 2002; Summer & Chong, 2006). Programs may need to include music that is restful, healing, and nurturing. BMGIM techniques may be modified when working with terminally ill clients due to their limited amount of emotional and physical stamina and decreased ability to concentrate (West, 1994). Significant topics that have emerged in BMGIM sessions with terminally ill clients have included lessons from the illness, transcendent images, pain management, and preparation for death (Skaggs, 1997).

When patients are no longer in a physically or emotionally vulnerable state (e.g., during the survivorship phase), the therapeutic process and music programs may advance. Music therapists have found BMGIM to be extremely meaningful for patients within their post-treatment and survivorship phases who wish to explore issues of meaning arising from their cancer experience. Within BMGIM sessions, patients have explored questions such as, "How will my life be different, knowing what I know now from my cancer experience?" "How can I begin to live out this new sense of purpose I feel as a result of surviving cancer?" and "Do I want to continue to go through my life the same way now, with these attitudes, behaviors, and ways of being that are not healthy?" Spiritual issues and transcendent images of healing may also frequently occur within BMGIM sessions with oncology clients.

Some cancer patients request imagery sessions to focus on specific immune system enhancement. This might include visualizing increases in neutrophils or white blood cells in order to increase resistance to infection, or imagining the natural killer cells targeting specific cancer cells. A mental rehearsal of the chemotherapy or radiation therapy process with the goal of exploring the individual patient's unique images of healing can be very helpful in relieving the patient's anxiety about upcoming unfamiliar treatment regimes. Within the **psychoneuroimmunology** field, it is recognized that multiple processes have a role in the immune system's regulation of cancer, and targeting a single immune response for research study or for cancer treatment is unlikely to be effective (Moynihan, 2003, as cited in Post-White & Bauer-Wu, 2005). This may also be applicable for imagery techniques in cancer care. Since the mechanisms of the immune system and the etiology of cancer are not yet completely understood, perhaps the best approach to enhance the healing process is to trust the wisdom found in the messages of the body of each individual, without trying to direct specific immune system mechanisms.

Outcome Measures

Requirements for paperwork and documentation in medical settings are extensive due to internal and external compliance regulations. Insurance companies, accreditation organizations, and quality assurance committees may require documentation in the patient's chart in order to validate the occurrence of the session. Documentation is increasingly computerized within the medical setting. Outcome measures are often reflected in the documentation format of the selected facility. The American Music Therapy Association's Standards of Clinical Practice (AMTA, 2007) recommend that documentation include a confirmation of the physician's order and a discharge summary when appropriate.

Measurement tools may incorporate perceptions from the music therapist, patients, visitors, or staff. Standardized tools may include structured "tick box" or discursive formats, kept in either the music therapist's files and/or the patient's hospital records, whichever most appropriately adheres to legal and facility-based regulations. Therapists may also write narrative progress notes in patient records. In busy hospital units or cancer centers, shorter notes are more likely to be read by team members. Time spent writing assessment and outcome measures, progress notes, and discharge summaries must be balanced with consideration for the patient load expectations during hospital admissions.

Example of Narrative Summary

Music Therapy: Mr. X has an extensive musical history, learning the trombone as a child and playing in jazz and town bands over the past few decades. Grief expressed over loss of playing ability through facial nerve damage as a result of tumor invasion. Distressed at uncertainty of prognosis and how he will respond to treatment. Misses comfort and support derived from individual and social performances. Agreed to meet during current admission to explore other instruments he may play (keyboard and guitar). Music therapy aims to support and provide opportunity for Mr. X's continuing expression of feelings related to illness and treatment effects, through live music sharing and discussion.

The Subjective, Objective/Observable data, Assessment, and Plan or S.O.A.P. note format is a common documentation format utilized in medical settings that may be used to document music therapy progress notes in the patient's medical chart. It is important for music therapists to document in a format that is compatible with that which is used within their health care system. To further coordinate care with the interdisciplinary team, music therapists should also add the primary music therapy goals to the patient's interdisciplinary care plan.

Music Therapy Progress Note: Outpatient Cancer Center
(SOAP note format, with inclusion of narrative music therapy information that was assessed within this initial music therapy session)

S: Patient discussed recent cancer diagnosis, surgery, upcoming chemotherapy treatment, and concerns of balancing work and family responsibilities throughout cancer treatment. Patient reported feeling "somewhat anxious" about the "unknowns" of her upcoming first chemotherapy treatment and its potential side effects. Patient stated that her favorite types of music were light rock, popular music, and light jazz, and that she had played tenor saxophone in band through high school. Patient reported listening to music on the radio every night to fall asleep, but had no experience with structured relaxation or imagery exercises. Patient requested to try "a sample" of the following music-focused relaxation techniques, including: deep breathing, progressive muscle relaxation, autogenic relaxation, peaceful place imagery, and immune system enhancement imagery, and patient requested "soft, relaxing piano music." After relaxation exercise, patient discussed experiencing images of being "surrounded with support" of her family, friends, and the people praying for her from her church, and discussed how these images had brought tears to her eyes when she experienced overwhelming feelings of hope, connection, and support. Patient related that she was "surprised" that she felt "more relaxed but also more energetic" after the relaxation exercise.

O: The Breast Cancer Nurse Coordinator referred the patient to music therapy to address fears and anxiety related to upcoming chemotherapy treatment regime. At beginning of session, patient rated herself as a "5" on a 0 to 10 scale, of most relaxed to most stressed. During music-focused relaxation exercise, patient closed her eyes and her respiration rate deepened and slowed. The tension in her arms, shoulders, legs, and face appeared to decrease. Patient was tearful two times during imagery part of exercise. After relaxation exercise, patient reported feeling "very relaxed" and rated herself as a "1" on the 0 to 10 scale.

A: Patient able to achieve and sustain the relaxation response throughout 25-minute relaxation and imagery exercise. The imagery process allowed patient to identify and experience personal resources of emotional and spiritual support that she can draw upon during her cancer treatment. Patient increased her awareness of energy management and relaxation techniques to utilize during chemotherapy treatment.

P: Patient provided with relaxation recordings, education on therapeutic use of music, potential benefits based on related music therapy research studies, and written instructions for use of music and relaxation exercises at home to complement management of chemotherapy side effects. Patient given a "homework assignment" to find a quiet space and time to utilize music-focused relaxation techniques at home for 10–20 minutes, several days each week. Patient requested to have music therapy during her outpatient chemotherapy treatments and was given options for scheduling another music therapy relaxation/imagery session prior to next chemotherapy treatment.

Music Therapy Progress Note: Inpatient Oncology Unit
(SOAP note format, with inclusion of narrative music therapy information that was assessed within this initial music therapy session)

S: Upon arrival of the music therapist, patient unresponsive to verbal cues. Patient's husband, daughter, son, and daughter-in law discussed patient's rapidly changing condition, stating, "Only two days ago she was walking and talking with us. This has gone so quickly. It is such a shock." Patient's family reported that patient has enjoyed listening to music in the past, and she and her husband attended many performances of Broadway musicals and concerts. Patient has a history of routinely listening to music, including hymns, Broadway musicals, and "Lorie-Line type" piano music. At end of session, patient's family expressed gratitude for music therapy session, stating "Thank you so much. This really helped us to have a much needed cry, and gave us a way to say our goodbyes."

O: The oncology chaplain referred the patient and family to music therapy for emotional and spiritual support during dying process. Patient's eyes slightly open, rolled upward during most of session. Patient demonstrated labored **Cheyne-Stokes** breathing. During music selections, patient's respirations deepened, became more regular, and slowed to tempo of music. Patient's family selected some of patient's favorite songs, including "On Eagle's Wings," "Wind Beneath My Wings," and "Amazing Grace." During 90% of session, patient's family members were tearful. They took turns sitting next to patient, stroking her face and arms, and putting their arms around each other. At end of last song, as therapist continued to play music instrumentally, patient's husband leaned over patient, hugged her, and tearfully began saying his goodbyes, thanking her for their 45 years of marriage, reminiscing about good memories, and telling her, "It's ok to let go when you're ready (to die)." For a few moments, patient opened eyes and looked directly at her husband, then closed them again.

A: Music therapy provided catalyst for emotional expression and support, spiritual support, structure for reminiscence, and vehicle/ritual for family to say goodbye to dying patient. Music therapy provided comfort, relaxation, and support for patient during the transitional process of dying.

P: Continue music therapy sessions 2–3×/week until patient's death. Continue to offer emotional and spiritual support, music for comfort, transitioning, support for dying process, and further assistance to family in planning of memorial service. Coordinate care plan with oncology chaplain. Upon request, patient's family was provided with two hymn books as resources for planning the memorial service.

Within medical settings, evidence-based outcomes are becoming standard to the medical model. Within the history of Western medicine, the outcomes of survival and tumor response have been used to measure the efficacy of cancer treatments (Barsevick et al., 1997). Quality-of-life measures are now becoming more prevalent as accepted research outcomes (Ferrans, 2000; Sourkes et al., 1998). Research in music therapy is limited in its examination of long-range outcome measurements, such as the impact of music therapy on survival rates. Home-based hospice music therapy has not been found to extend patients' longevity; however, it may significantly improve their life quality (Hilliard, 2003). Behavioral observation and patient's verbal self-report have been documented as the most common methods of data collection and measurement of effectiveness of music therapy (Krout, 2000).

Methods of Data Collection/Measurement of Effectiveness Cited in 88 Clinical Reports
(Krout, 2000)

Method	*N* of Reports Including Method
Behavioral observation	88
Verbal self-report	73
Content analysis of patient lyrics	6
Content analysis of improvised music	4
Ground theory analysis	2
Amount of pain medication administered	1
Automated event recording	1
Content analysis of patient creative writing	1
Physiological measurement	1
Survey of music therapists	1

Music therapists can ask patients to report measures such as their perceived pain, anxiety, stress level, muscle tension, energy level, fatigue, or emotions on a quantified Likert scale. While utilization of a rating scale for anxiety or other factors has not been standardized and validated in research, it can still be utilized as a numeric data collection tool by which the patient can report specific changes when administered before and after music therapy interventions. Medical settings utilize a self-report pain scale to measure a patient's pain in order to obtain statistics of patient outcomes regularly monitored by nursing staff.

Patients who are alert and oriented are familiar with being asked to rate their pain on a scale and they easily grasp the concept of giving a rating for other outcome factors. However, not all patients have the cognitive ability or a level of consciousness to understand these scales. For patients who are expressing emotional anguish or spiritual angst of their cancer crisis within the music therapy session, the scale may be cumbersome. The patient's needs must come before the music therapist's desire for quantitative measurements. Furthermore, by focusing the patient's attention on his or her pain or discomfort, one may mitigate the therapeutic effects of the music therapy experience in order to have a quantified measurement of session outcomes. For an indepth discussion of the considerations of outcome measurements, please review *Music Therapy Research and Practice in Medicine* by David Aldridge (1996).

Conclusion

Throughout the United States, the trend at the turn of the century indicated that the majority of all surgical procedures were performed in the ambulatory setting (Frogge &

Cunning, 2000). A majority of oncology care has shifted from inpatient to ambulatory care settings (Knobf et al., 1998; Martin & Xistris, 2000). The expectation is that this trend will continue to increase, making ambulatory and home care the primary health care settings, with hospitals mainly serving intensive care needs (Goodman, 2000).

There are numerous reasons for the shift of a majority of oncology care from the inpatient to the outpatient setting. Changes have been driven by the economics of today's competitive health care market (Camp-Sorrell, 2000; Martin & Xistris, 2000). Managed care has pushed for more efficient health care delivery systems, and medical care is being provided in the least restrictive and most cost-effective environment. Technological and medical advances have also decreased the need for inpatient admissions for cancer treatment, further solidifying the growth of outpatient services.

These changes reflect only initial trends in the future delivery of oncology treatment and services. Music therapists working in oncology settings will have to continue to adapt their approaches, methods, and marketing strategies in order to meet the needs of oncology patients. The majority of music therapists (73–79%) provide services to inpatients before, during, or after chemotherapy treatments, while only 38–45% report working with outpatients before, during, or after chemotherapy treatments (Kruse, 2003). Since the majority of chemotherapy treatments and surgical procedures are now being given in the outpatient setting and this trend is expected to continue, music therapists must find creative ways to integrate music therapy within oncology ambulatory care settings.

It is vital that music therapists have an awareness of current treatment trends as well as shifts in service delivery that may be integrated into the medical setting. To address such changes, music therapists should continue to provide educational programs to both patients and staff regarding developments in music therapy programming and updates of music therapy research literature in cancer care. Music therapists should coordinate patient treatment plans and foster relationships with many interdisciplinary oncology team members, including the other cancer support services staff, psychologists, oncology counselors, social workers, chaplains, outpatient IV therapy nurses, clinical nurse specialists, pharmacists, chronic and acute pain specialists, breast cancer (or other cancer-specific) treatment coordinators, surgeons, oncologists, and nurse practitioners—all who may act as potential referral sources. It is important for music therapists to explore ways to work within the pre-existing resources of their health care system.

One way to coordinate music therapy services with current resources is to incorporate music therapy documentation into the patient computerized integrated medical record and care plan. Another way is to utilize the outpatient clinic's main scheduling system for patients to conveniently access and schedule outpatient music therapy sessions. Increased involvement of music therapy within pre-existing cancer support groups or specific music therapy-based stress management groups can facilitate greater access to music therapy services for more oncology outpatients. Patients may be more receptive to attending a limited psychoeducational series, which may include a focus on music therapy/stress management topics, rather than attending an ongoing weekly support group. Finding solutions to shifting trends in cancer care creates additional ways to promote music therapy as a valid and effective cancer support service that can independently benefit patients or be integrated with other treatment modalities.

As the number of oncology patients who are treated in home care settings continues to increase, expansion of music therapy within oncology home care services is another way to increase the availability of music therapy services to oncology patients. Currently, home care is the most rapidly growing sector of health care, with the acuity level of home care patients increasing as a result of decreases in hospital length of stay (Yuska & Nedved, 2000). Excellent models for providing music therapy services in home care settings already exist within music therapy home hospice programs (Hilliard, 2005; Magill, 2009). Oncology home care patients may require more detailed assessments, education, longer but less frequent visits, and education of therapeutic techniques or resources that can be utilized independently by the patient at home (Yuska & Nedved, 2000). Ideally, a team of music therapists would be available to provide a continuity of care for patients as they move across the continuum of oncology programs within the health care system, including inpatient oncology, surgery, outpatient cancer centers, oncology home care, inpatient hospice, and home care hospice.

Music therapists must develop and expand music therapy clinical practice based upon a combination of knowledge, intuition, practice wisdom (O'Callaghan, 2005; Schön, 1991; Scott, 1990), music therapy and music medicine theories, qualitative and quantitative research, evidenced-based practice, and documented health care outcomes. Evidenced-based research in music therapy must be built upon issues that arise from clinical practice and examine relevant and current treatment issues in cancer care. Across disciplines, care providers are presented with the increasing challenge of integrating knowledge from a variety of sources, such as clinical practice and behavioral, epidemiological, and basic science research, into evidence-based practice in an effort to provide specific interventions for preventing cancer (Loescher & Reid, 2000) and improving treatment.

Grassroots efforts have led to an increasingly regarded valuable service and expansion of music therapy programs. Funding for programs, however, will remain a challenge as long as music therapy remains a non-essential service that is paid for by philanthropic funding. To promote continued expansion, music therapists need to diplomatically challenge premises on which limited resources are allocated to patient treatment and care. Listeners are often moved, audibly crying when learning about music therapy and the impact it has on individuals with cancer. Continued education of the public, professional, and medical associations will create funding and support for programs and positions. High-quality services and the documentation of evidence-based outcomes, as well as published clinical research, will create a stronger foundation on which to further develop and enhance clinical practice in cancer care. It is a privilege to musically journey with patients and their significant others through the vulnerable time of life-threatening illness experiences. It is clinical practice that will continually sustain the quest for continued expansion of music therapy in cancer care.

References

Aasgaard, T. (1999). Music therapy as milieu in the hospice and paediatric oncology ward. In D. Aldridge (Ed.), *Music therapy in palliative care: New voices* (pp. 29–42). London: Jessica Kingsley.

Abernathy, E. (1997). Biotherapy. In C. Varricchio (Ed.), *A cancer source book for nurses* (7th ed.) (pp. 122–138). Atlanta, GA: American Cancer Society.

Abrams, B. (2001). Music, cancer, and immunity. *Clinical Journal of Oncology Nursing, 5*(5), 1–3.

Academy for Guided Imagery. (2004). *What is the difference between visualization, guided imagery, hypnosis, NLP, and interactive guided imagery?* In *Interactive Guided Imagery: The process.* Retrieved November 17, 2004, from http://www.academyforguidedimagery.com/faqs.php#10

Aldridge, D. (1996). *Music therapy research and practice in medicine: From out of the silence.* London: Jessica Kingsley.

American Cancer Society. (2002). *What is cancer? Origin of the word cancer.* Retrieved November 1, 2004, from http://www.cancer.org/docroot/CRI/content/CRI_2_4_1x_What_Is_Cancer.asp?sitearea=

American Cancer Society. (2007). *Cancer facts and figures 2007.* Retrieved July 5, 2007, from http://www.cancer.org/docroot/stt/stt_0.asp

American Cancer Society. (2009a). *Hormone therapy.* Retrieved June 30, 2009, from http://www.cancer.org/docroot/CRI/content/CRI_2_4_4X_Hormone_Therapy_5.asp

American Cancer Society. (2009b). *Immunotherapy.* Retrieved June 30, 2009, from http://www.cancer.org/docroot/ETO/eto_1_3_Immunotherapy.asp

American Music Therapy Association. (2007). Standards of clinical practice. *AMTA member sourcebook 2007* (pp. 18–22). Silver Spring, MD: Author.

American Psychiatric Association. (2000). *Diagnostic and statistical manual of mental disorders–Text Revision* (*DSM-IV-TR*) (4th ed., text rev.). Washington, DC: Author.

Bailey, L. (1983). The effects of live versus tape recorded music in hospitalized cancer patients. *Music Therapy, 3*(1), 17–28.

Bailey, L. (1985). The role of the music therapist. In *Cancer Pain: Syllabus of the post-graduate course* (pp. 275–280). New York: Memorial Sloan Kettering Cancer Center.

Barry, P., & O'Callaghan, C. (2008). Reflexive journal writing: A tool for music therapy student clinical practice development. *Nordic Journal of Music Therapy, 17*(1), 55–66.

Barsevick, A. M., Much, J., & Sweeney, C. (1997). Psychosocial responses to cancer. In S. L. Groenwald, M. Goodman, M. H. Frogee, & C. H. Yarbro (Eds.), *Cancer nursing principles and practice* (4th ed.) (pp. 1393–1411). Sudbury, MA: Jones and Bartlett.

Bartlett, D., Kaufman, D., & Smeltekop, R. (1993). The effects of music listening and perceived sensory experiences on the immune system as measured by interleukin-1 and cortisol. *Journal of Music Therapy, 30,* 194–209.

Bauer, S. M. (2000). Immunology. In C. H. Yarbro, M. H. Frogge, M. Goodman, & S. L. Groenwald (Eds.), *Cancer nursing principles and practice* (5th ed.) (pp. 35–47). Sudbury, MA: Jones and Bartlett.

Baxandall, S., & Prasuna, R. (1993). *The courage to care.* Melbourne, Australia: David Lovell.

Beck, S. L. (1991). The therapeutic use of music for cancer related pain. *Oncology Nursing Forum, 18*(8), 1327–1337.

Beggs, C. (1991). Life review with a palliative care patient. In K. Bruscia (Ed.), *Case studies in music therapy* (pp. 611–616). Phoenixville, PA: Barcelona.

Bellamy, M. A., & Willard, P. B. (1993). Music therapy: An integral component of the oncology experience. *International Journal of Arts in Medicine, 11*(1), 14–19.

Benson, H. (1975). *The relaxation response.* New York: William Morrow.

Bittman, B. B., Berk, L. S., Felten, D. L., Westengard, J., Simonton, O. C., Pappas, J., et al. (2001). Composite effects of group drumming music therapy on modulation of neuroendocrine-immune parameters in normal subjects. *Alternative Therapies, 7*(1), 38–47.

Blumberg, B., Flaherty, M., & Lewis, J. (1980). *Coping with cancer: A resource for the health professional.* Bethesda, MD: National Cancer Institute.

Boldt, S. (1996). The effect of music therapy on the psychological well-being, physical comfort, and exercise endurance of bone marrow transplant patients. *Journal of Music Therapy, 33*(3), 164–188.

Bonde, L. O. (2005). *The Bonny Method of Guided Imagery and music with cancer survivors: A psychosocial study with focus on the influence of music therapy on mood and quality of life.* Unpublished doctoral dissertation, Aalborg University, Denmark.

Breitbart, W., Chochinov, M., & Passik, S. (1998). Psychiatric aspects of palliative care. In D. Doyle, W. G. C. Hanks, & N. MacDonald (Eds.), *The Oxford textbook of palliative medicine* (2nd ed.) (pp. 933–954). Oxford, England: Oxford University Press.

Breitbart, W., Passik, S., & Pane, D. (1998). Psychological and psychiatric interventions in pain control. In D. Doyle, W. G. C. Hanks, & N. MacDonald (Eds.), *The Oxford textbook of palliative medicine* (2nd ed.) (pp. 437–454). Oxford, England: Oxford University Press.

Bright, R. (1988). *Music therapy and the dementias: Improving the quality of life.* St. Louis, MO: MMB Music.

Bright, R. (2002). *Supportive eclectic music therapy for grief and loss. A practical handbook for professionals.* St. Louis, MO: MMB Music.

Bruscia, K. E. (1991). *Case studies in music therapy*. Phoenixville, PA: Barcelona.

Bruscia, K. E. (2002). The boundaries of Guided Imagery and Music (GIM) and the Bonny method. In K. E. Bruscia & D. E. Grocke (Eds.), *Guided Imagery and Music: The Bonny method and beyond* (pp. 37–61). Gilsum, NH: Barcelona.

Bunt, L., & Marston-Wyld, J. (1995). Where words fail, music takes over: A collaborative study by a music therapist and a counselor in the context of cancer care. *Music Therapy Perspectives, 13*, 46–50.

Burke, C. C. (1999). Surgical treatment. In C. Miaskowski & P. Buchsel (Eds.), *Oncology nursing, assessment and clinical care* (pp. 29–58). St. Louis, MO: Mosby.

Burke, M. B. (1997). Chemotherapy. In C. Varricchio (Ed.), *A cancer source book for nurses* (7th ed.) (pp. 103–121). Atlanta, GA: American Cancer Society.

Burns, D. S. (2001). The effect of the Bonny method of Guided Imagery and Music on the mood and life quality of cancer patients. *Journal of Music Therapy, 38*, 51–65.

Burns, D. S. (2002). Guided Imagery and music (GIM) in the treatment of individuals with chronic illness. In K. E. Bruscia & D. E. Grocke (Eds.) *Guided Imagery and Music: The Bonny method and beyond* (pp. 171–186). Gilsum, NH: Barcelona.

Burns, D. S., Sledge, R. B., Fuller, L. A., Daggy, J. K., & Monahan, P. O. (2005). Cancer patients' interest and preferences for music therapy. *Journal of Music Therapy, 42*(3), 185–199.

Burns, S. J., Harbuz, M. S., Hucklebridge, F., & Bunt, L. (2001). A pilot study into the therapeutic effects of music therapy at a cancer help center. *Alternative Therapies, 7*(1), 48–56.

Burton, R. (1998). *Cancer control into the 21st century.* Dean's lecture, Faculty of Medicine and Health Sciences, University of Melbourne (1997) (pp. 1–15). Melbourne, Australia: Anti-Cancer Council of Victoria.

Butler, C., & Butler, P. J. (1997). Physioacoustic therapy with cardiac surgery patients. In T. Wigram & C. Dileo (Eds.), *Music vibration and health* (pp. 197–204). Cherry Hill, NJ: Jeffery Books.

Butler, R. N., & Lewis, M. I. (1982). *Aging and mental health: Positive psychosocial and biomedical approaches.* St. Louis, MO: C. V. Mosby.

Camp-Sorrell, D. (1997). Vascular access devices and ambulatory pumps used in cancer treatment. In C. Varricchio (Ed.), *A cancer source book for nurses* (7th ed.) (pp. 185–199). Atlanta, GA: American Cancer Society.

Camp-Sorrell, D. (2000). Chemotherapy: Toxicity management. In C. H. Yarbro, M. H. Frogge, M. Goodman, & S. L. Groenwald (Eds.), *Cancer nursing principles and practice* (5th ed.) (pp. 444–486). Sudbury, MA: Jones and Bartlett.

Carey, M. P., & Burish, T. G. (1987). Providing relaxation training to cancer chemotherapy patients: A comparison of three delivery techniques. *Journal of Consulting and Clinical Psychology, 55*, 732–737.

Cassileth, B. R. (1979). The evolution of oncology as a sociomedical phenomenon. In B. R. Cassileth (Ed.), *The cancer patient: Social and medical aspects of care* (pp. 3–15). Philadelphia: Lea & Fibiger.

Cassileth, B. R., & Chapman, C. C. (1996). Alternative and complementary cancer therapies. *Cancer, 77*, 1026–1034.

Cassileth, B. R., Vickers, A. J., & Magill, L. A. (2003). Music therapy for mood disturbance during hospitalization for autologous stem cell transplantation: A randomized controlled trial. *Cancer, 98*, 2723–2729.

Cassileth, B. R., Walsh, W. P., & Lusk, E. J. (1988). Psychosocial correlates of cancer survival: A subsequent report 3 to 8 years after cancer diagnosis. *Journal of Clinical Oncology, 6*, 1753–1759.

Clair, A. A. (1996). *Therapeutic uses of music with older adults.* Baltimore: Health Professionals Press.

Clark, M., Isaacks-Downton, B. M., Wells, N., Redlin-Frazier, S., Eck, C., Hepworth, J. T., et al. (2006). Use of preferred music to reduce emotional distress and symptom activity during radiation therapy. *Journal of Music Therapy, 63*(3), 247–265.

Coleman, P. (1986). *Ageing and reminiscence processes.* Chichester, England: John Wiley and Sons.

Coleman, P. (1994). Reminiscence within the study of ageing. In J. Bornat (Ed.), *Reminiscence reviewed: Evaluations, achievements, perspectives* (pp. 8–20). Buckingham, England: Open University Press.

Commonwealth Department of Human Services and Health. (1994). *Better health outcomes for Australians: National goals, targets and strategies for better health outcomes into the next century.* Canberra, Australia: Australian Government Publishing Service.

Cunningham, A. J., Edmonds, C. V. I., Phillips, C., Soots, K. I., Hedley, D., & Lockwood, G. A. (2000). A prospective, longitudinal study of the relationship of psychological work to duration of survival in patients with metastatic cancer. *Psycho-oncology, 9,* 323–339.

Curtis, S. L. (1986). The effect of music on pain relief and relaxation of the terminally ill. *Journal of Music Therapy, 23*(1), 10–24.

Die-Trill, M. (1998). The patient from a different culture. In J. C. Holland (Ed.), *Psycho-oncology* (pp. 857–866). New York: Oxford University Press.

Dileo, C., & Magill, L. (2005). Songwriting with oncology and hospice adult patients from a multicultural perspective. In F. Baker & T. Wigram (Eds.), *Songwriting: Methods and clinical applications for music therapy clinicians, educators and students* (pp. 226–245). London: Jessica Kingsley.

Dileo, C., & Starr, R. (2005). Cultural issues in music therapy at end of life. In C. Dileo & J. Loewy (Eds.), *Music therapy at the end of life care* (pp. 85–94). Cherry Hill, NJ: Jeffrey Books.

Doan, B. D. (1998). Alternative and complementary therapies. In J. C. Holland (Ed.), *Psycho-oncology* (pp. 817–827). New York: Oxford University Press.

Dolbeault, S., Szporn, A., & Holland, J. C. (1999). Psycho-oncology: Where have we been? Where are we going? *European Journal of Cancer, 35,* 1554–1558.

Doyle, D., Hanks, G. W. C., & MacDonald, N. (1998). Introduction. In D. Doyle, G. W. C. Hanks, & N. MacDonald (Eds.), *Oxford textbook of palliative medicine* (2nd ed.) (pp. 1–9). Oxford, England: Oxford University Press.

Du Pen, A. R., & Panke, J. T. (1997). Common clinical problems. In C. Varricchio (Ed.), *A cancer source book for nurses* (7th ed.) (pp. 174–184). Atlanta, GA: American Cancer Society.

Elbert, T., Pantev, C., Weinbruch, C., Rockstroh, B., & Taub, E. (1995). Increased cortical representation of the fingers of the left hand in string players. *Science, 270,* 305–307.

Epstein, I. (2001). Using available clinical information in practice-based research: Mining for silver while dreaming of gold. In I. Epstein & S. Blumenfield (Eds.), *Clinical datamining in practice-based research* (pp. 15–32). Binghamton, NY: Haworth Social Work Practice Press.

Fawzy, F. I., Fawzy, N. W., Hyun, C. S., Elashoff, R., Guthrie, D., Fahey, J. L., et al. (1993). Malignant melanoma. Effects of an early structured psychiatric intervention, coping, and affective state on recurrence and survival 6 years later. *Archives of General Psychiatry, 50,* 681–689.

Ferrans, C. E. (2000). Quality of life as an outcome of cancer care. In C. H. Yarbro, M. H. Frogge, M. Goodman, & S. L. Groenwald (Eds.), *Cancer nursing principles and practice* (5th ed.) (pp. 243–258). Sudbury, MA: Jones and Bartlett.

Ferszt, G. C., & Waldman, R. (1997). Psychosocial responses to disease and treatment. In C. Varricchio (Ed.), *A cancer source book for nurses* (7th ed.) (pp. 245–252). Atlanta, GA: American Cancer Society.

Finnas, L. (2001). Presenting music live, audio-visually or aurally—Does it affect listeners' experiences differently? *British Journal of Music Education, 18*(1), 55–78.

Fitchett, G., & Handzo, G. (1998). Spiritual assessment, screening, and intervention. In J. C. Holland (Ed.), *Pyscho-oncology* (pp. 790–808). New York: Oxford University Press.

Folkman, S., & Greer, S. (2000). Promoting psychological well-being in the face of serious illness: When theory, research and practice inform each other. *Psycho-oncology, 9,* 11–19.

Forinash, M. (1990). *The phenomenology of music therapy with the terminally ill.* Unpublished doctoral dissertation, New York University, New York.

Forrest, L. C. (2001). Addressing issues of ethnicity and identity in palliative care through music therapy practice. *The Australian Journal of Music Therapy, 11,* 33–37.

Frank, J. M. (1985). The effects of music therapy and guided imagery. *Oncology Nursing Forum, 12*(5), 47–52.

Freeman, L. W., & Lawlis, G. F. (2001). *Complementary and alternative medicine: A research based approach.* St. Louis, MO: Mosby.

Frogge, M. H., & Cunning, S. M. (2000). Surgical therapy. In C. H. Yarbro, M. H. Frogge, M. Goodman, & S. L. Groenwald (Eds.), *Cancer nursing principles and practice* (5th ed.) (pp. 272–285). Sudbury, MA: Jones and Bartlett.

Gallagher, L. M., & Steele, A. L. (2001). Developing and using a computerized database for music therapy in palliative medicine. *Journal of Palliative Care, 17,* 147–154.

Gardstrom, S. C. (2001). Practical techniques for the development of complementary skills in musical improvisation. *Music Therapy Perspectives, 19,* 82–87.

Garland, J. (1994). What splendour, it all coheres: Life-review therapy with older people. In J. Bornat (Ed.), *Reminiscence reviewed: Perspectives, evaluations, achievements* (pp. 21–31). Buckingham, England: Open University Press.

Glajchen, M. (1999). Psychosocial issues in cancer care. In C. Miaskowski & P. Buchsel (Eds.), *Oncology nursing, assessment and clinical care* (pp. 305–317). St. Louis, MO: Mosby.

Goodman, M. (2000). Chemotherapy: Principles of administration. In C. H. Yarbro, M. H. Frogge, M. Goodman, & S. L. Groenwald (Eds.), *Cancer nursing principles and practice* (5th ed.) (pp. 385–443). Sudbury, MA: Jones and Bartlett

Greenberg, D. B. (1998). Radiotherapy. In J. C. Holland (Ed.), *Psycho-oncology* (pp. 269–276). New York: Oxford University Press.

Greer, S. (1997). Adjuvent psychological therapy for cancer patients. *Palliative Medicine, 11*, 240–244.

Grey, A. (1994). The spiritual component of palliative care. *Palliative Medicine, 8*, 215–221.

Gribbon, J., & Loescher, L. J. (2000). Biology of cancer. In C. H. Yarbro, M. H. Frogge, M. Goodman, & S. L. Groenwald (Eds.), *Cancer nursing principles and practice* (5th ed.) (pp. 17–34). Sudbury, MA: Jones and Bartlett.

Grocke, D., & Wigram, T. (2007). *Receptive methods in music therapy: Techniques and clinical applications for music therapy clinicians, educators, and students.* London: Jessica Kingsley.

Guzzetta, C. E. (1988). Music therapy: Hearing the melody of the soul. In B. C. Dorsy, L. Keegan, C. E. Guzzetta, & L. G. Kolkmeier (Eds.), *Holistic nursing: A handbook for practice* (pp. 263–288). Rockville, MD: Aaper.

Haghighi, K. R., & Pansch, B. (2001). Music therapy. In *Complementary therapies in end-of-life care* (pp. 53–68). Alexandria, VA: National Hospice and Palliative Care Organization.

Hale, S. E. (1992). Wounded woman: The use of Guided Imagery and Music in recovering from a mastectomy. *Journal of the Association for Music and Imagery, 1*, 99–106.

Hilliard, R. E. (2003). The effects of music therapy on the quality and length of life of people diagnosed with terminal cancer. *Journal of Music Therapy, 40*, 113–137.

Hilliard, R. E. (2005). *Hospice and palliative care music therapy: A guide to program development and clinical care.* Cherry Hill, NJ: Jeffrey Books.

Hogan, B. (1999a). A phenomenological research project. In R. Rebollo Pratt & D. Erdonmez Grocke (Eds.), *MusicMedicine* (Vol. 3, pp. 242–252). Melbourne, Australia: University of Melbourne.

Hogan, B. (1999b). Searching for the rite of passage. In D. Aldridge (Ed.), *Music therapy in palliative care: New voices* (pp. 68–81). London: Jessica Kingsley.

Holland, C. A., & Holmes, M. (2000). A study exploring a supportive group of therapies with women undergoing chemotherapy treatment for gynaecological cancers. *Psycho-oncology: Journal of the Psychological, Social and Behavioural Dimensions of Cancer, 9*(5), S5.

Holland, J. C. (1998). Societal views of cancer and the emergence of psycho-oncology. In J. C. Holland (Ed.), *Psycho-oncology* (pp. 3–15). New York: Oxford University Press.

Holland, J. C. (2002). History of psycho-oncology: Overcoming attitudinal and conceptual barriers. *Psychosomatic Medicine, 64*, 206–221.

Holland, J. C. (2003). Psychological care of patients: Psycho-oncology's contribution. *Journal of Clinical Oncology, 21*(Suppl. 23), 253s–265s.

Hucklebridge, F., Lambert, S., Clow, A., Warburton, D. M., Evans, P. D., & Sherwood, N. (2000). Modulation of secretory immunoglobulin A in saliva: Response to manipulation of mood. *Biological Psychology, 53,* 25–35.

Iwamoto, R. R. (1997). Radiation therapy. In C. Varricchio (Ed.), *A cancer source book for nurses* (7th ed.) (pp. 91–102). Atlanta, GA: American Cancer Society.

Kellehear, A. (2000). Spirituality and palliative care: A model of needs. *Palliative Medicine, 14,* 149–155.

Kessler, D., & Kubler-Ross, E. (2005). *On grief and grieving: Finding the meaning of grief through the five stages of loss.* New York: Scribner.

Knobf, M. T., Pasacreta, J. V., Valentine, A., & McCorkle, R. (1998). Chemotherapy, hormonal therapy, and immunotherapy. In J. C. Holland (Ed.), *Psycho-oncology* (pp. 277–288). New York: Oxford University Press.

Krout, R. E. (2000). Hospice and palliative music therapy: A continuum of creative caring. In American Music Therapy Association (Ed.), *Effectiveness of music therapy procedures: Documentation of research and clinical practice* (3rd ed.) (pp. 323–411). Silver Spring, MD: American Music Therapy Association.

Krout, R. E. (2004). A synerdisciplinary music therapy treatment team approach for hospice and palliative care. *Australian Journal of Music Therapy, 15,* 33–45.

Krumm, S. L. (2000). Hospital care. In C. H. Yarbro, M. H. Frogge, M. Goodman, & S. L. Groenwald (Eds.), *Cancer nursing principles and practice* (5th ed.) (pp. 1632–1640). Sudbury, MA: Jones and Bartlett.

Kruse, J. (2003). Music therapy in United States cancer settings: Recent trends in practice. *Music Therapy Perspectives, 21,* 89–98.

Kubler-Ross, E. (1997). *On death and dying.* New York: Touchstone.

Kuhn, D. (2002). The effects of active and passive participation in musical activity on the immune system as measured by salivary immunoglobulin A (SIgA). *Journal of Music Therapy, 39,* 30–39.

Lane, D. (1991). *The effect of a single music therapy session on hospitalized children as measured by salivary immunoglobulin A, speech pause time, and a patient opinion Likert scale.* Unpublished doctoral dissertation, Case Western University, Cleveland, OH.

Lane, D. (1993). Music therapy: Gaining an edge in oncology management. *The Journal of Oncology Management, 2*(1), 42–46.

Lazarus, R. S., & Folkman, S. (1984). *Stress, appraisal, and coping.* New York: Springer.

Lee, C. A. (Ed.). (1995). *Lonely waters: Proceedings of the international conference, Music therapy in palliative care, Oxford, 1994.* Oxford, England: Sobell.

Lewis, F. M. (1999). Family issues in cancer care. In C. Miaskowski & P. Buchsel (Eds.), *Oncology nursing, assessment and clinical care* (pp. 319–331). St. Louis, MO: Mosby.

Lipson, J. G., Dibble, S. L., & Minarik, P. A. (1996). *Culture and nursing care: A pocket guide.* San Francisco: UCSF Nursing Press.

Lloyd-Green, L. (1994). *Life review in palliative care—A viable interventional modality in music therapy.* Paper presented at the 18th Conference of the Australian Music Therapy Association, Brisbane.

Loescher, L. J., & Reid, M. E. (2000). Dynamics of cancer prevention. In C. H. Yarbro, M. H. Frogge, M. Goodman, & S. L. Groenwald (Eds.), *Cancer nursing principles and practice* (5th ed.) (pp. 135–149). Sudbury, MA: Jones and Bartlett.

Loscalzo, M., & Brintzenhofeszoc, K. (1998). Brief crisis counseling. In J. C. Holland (Ed.), *Pyscho-oncology* (pp. 662–675). New York: Oxford University Press.

Magee, W. (1998, April). *Singing my life: Playing my self. Song based and improvisatory methods of music therapy with individuals with neurological impairment.* Paper presented at the Fourth European Congress of Music Therapy, Leuven, Belgium.

Magee, W. (2000). A response to the review of music therapy in palliative care—New Voices [Letter]. *British Journal of Music Therapy, 14*(2), 93–94.

Magill, L. (2009). The meaning of the music: The role of music in palliative care music therapy as perceived by bereaved caregivers of advanced cancer patients. *American Journal of Hospice and Palliative Care Medicine, 26*(1), 33–39.

Magill Bailey, L. (1983). Music therapy as an intervention in pain management. *New York-New Jersey Cancer Nursing Regional Committee, Handbook on Interventions in Pain Management, 2*, 39–46.

Magill Bailey, L. (1984). The use of songs in music therapy with cancer patients and their families. *Music Therapy, 4*(1), 5–17.

Magill Bailey, L. (1985). Music's soothing charms. *American Journal of Nursing, 11*, 1280.

Magill Bailey, L. (1986). Music therapy in pain management. *Journal of Pain and Symptom Management, 1*(1), 25–28.

Magill-Levreault, L. (1993). Music therapy in pain and symptom management. *Journal of Palliative Care, 9*(4), 42–48.

Martin, J. A. (Ed.). (1989). *The next step forward: Music therapy with the terminally ill.* New York: Calvary Hospital.

Martin, V. R., & Xistris, D. (2000). Ambulatory care. In C. H. Yarbro, M. H. Frogge, M. Goodman, & S. L. Groenwald (Eds.), *Cancer nursing principles and practice* (5th ed.) (pp. 1641–1660). Sudbury, MA: Jones and Bartlett.

McCraty, R., Atkinson, M., Rein, G., & Watkins, A. D. (1996). Music enhances the effect of positive emotional states on salivary IgA. *Stress Medicine, 12*, 167–175.

McKinney, C. (2002). Quantitative research in Guided Imagery and Music (GIM): A review. In K. E. Bruscia & D. E. Grocke (Eds.), *Guided Imagery and Music: The Bonny method and beyond* (pp. 447–466). Gilsum, NH: Barcelona.

McKinney, C. H., Antoni, M. H., Kumar, M., Tims, F. C., & McCabe, P. M. (1997). Effects of Guided Imagery and Music (GIM) therapy on mood and cortisol in healthy adults. *Health Psychology, 16*, 390–400.

Miakowski, C., & Viele, C. (1999). Cancer chemotherapy. In C. Miaskowski & P. Buchsel (Eds.), *Oncology nursing, assessment and clinical care* (pp. 83–106). St. Louis, MO: Mosby.

Miller, D. M. (1992). *The effect of music therapy on the immune and adrenocortical systems of cancer patients*. Unpublished master's thesis, University of Kansas, Lawrence.

Miller, D. M., & Pansch, B. (1997, November). *Going home: A rationale for music therapy in hospice*. Presentation at the annual conference of the American Music Therapy Association, Los Angeles, CA.

Mind Body Medical Institute. (2010). *The relaxation response*. Retrieved June 14, 2010, from http://www.massgeneral.org/bhi/basics/rr.aspx

Mramor, K. M. (2001). Music therapy with persons who are indigent and terminally ill. *Journal of Palliative Care, 17,* 182–187.

Munro, S. (1984). *Music therapy in palliative/hospice care*. St Louis: MMB Music.

Munro, S. (1988). Music therapy in support of cancer patients. *Recent Results in Cancer Research, 108,* 289–294.

Musick, M. A., Koenig, H. G., Larson, D. B., & Matthews, D. (1998). Religion and spiritual beliefs. In J. C. Holland (Ed.), *Psycho-oncology* (pp. 780–789). New York: Oxford University Press.

National Cancer Institute. (n.d.a). *Cancer trends progress report, 2005 update, Mortality*. Retrieved on July 5, 2007, from http://progressreport.cancer.gov/doc_detail.asp?pid=1&did=2005&chid=26&coid=229&mid

National Cancer Institute. (n.d.b). *Cancer trends progress report, 2005 update, Persons-years of life lost*. Retrieved on July 5, 2007, from http://progressreport.cancer.gov/doc_detail.asp?pid=1&did=2005&chid= 26&coid=230&mid=#estimate

National Cancer Institute. (1997). *Cancer treatment*. U.S. National Institutes of Health. Retrieved from http://www.cancer.gov/cancertopics/treatment

National Center for Complementary and Alternative Medicine. (2004a, May 26). *What is complementary and alternative medicine?* Retrieved November 5, 2004, from http://nccam.nih.gov/health/whatiscam/

National Center for Complementary and Alternative Medicine. (2004b, May 26). *What is integrative medicine?* Retrieved November 5, 2004, from http://nccam.nih.gov/health/whatiscam/

National Comprehensive Cancer Network. (2001). Distress management practice guidelines. *Cancer Control, 8*(6, Suppl. 2), 88–93.

Niemeyer, R. A. (2002). Meaning reconstruction: A theory of bereavement resolution. In D. K. Meagher (Ed.), *The Thanatology Newsletter, 8*(2), 6–9.

O'Brien, E. (1999). Cancer patients' evaluation of a music therapy program. In R. Rebollo Pratt & D. Erdonmez Grocke (Eds.), *MusicMedicine* (Vol. 3, pp. 285–300). Melbourne, Australia: Faculty of Music, University of Melbourne.

O'Callaghan, C. (1984). Musical profiles of dying patients. *Australian Music Therapy Association Bulletin, 7*(2), 5–11.

O'Callaghan, C. (1985). *Music therapy in cancer pain care.* Paper presented at the 11th Conference of the Australian Music Therapy Association, Melbourne.

O'Callaghan, C. (1989). Isolation in an isolated spot: Music therapy in palliative care in Australia. *The next step forward: Music therapy with the terminally ill.* New York: Calvary Hospital.

O'Callaghan, C. (1993). Communicating with brain-impaired palliative care patients through music therapy. *Journal of Palliative Care, 9*(4), 53–55.

O'Callaghan, C. (1996a). Music and wellbeing: Music therapy and palliative care. *Annual Journal of the New Zealand Society for Music Therapy*, 4–19.

O'Callaghan, C. (1996b). Pain, music creativity and music therapy in palliative care. *The American Journal of Hospice and Palliative Care, 13*(2), 43–49.

O'Callaghan, C. (1999a). Lyrical themes in songs written by palliative care patients. In D. Aldridge (Ed.), *Music therapy in palliative care: New voices* (pp. 43–58). London: Jessica Kingsley.

O'Callaghan, C. (1999b). Recent findings about neural correlates of music pertinent to music therapy across the life span. *Music Therapy Perspectives, 17*(1), 32–36.

O'Callaghan, C. (2001a). Bringing music to life: A study of music therapy and palliative care experiences in a cancer hospital. *Journal of Palliative Care, 17*(3), 155–160.

O'Callaghan, C. (2001b). *Music therapy's relevance in a cancer hospital researched through a constructivist lens.* Unpublished doctoral dissertation, Department of Social Work and Faculty of Music, University of Melbourne, Australia.

O'Callaghan, C. (2004). Identifying comparable therapeutic foundations between "musical re-play" and improvisation: Cancer research inspires a hybrid perspective. *Nordic Journal of Music Therapy, 13*(2), 127–142.

O'Callaghan, C. (2005). Qualitative data-mining through reflexive journal analysis: Implications for music therapy practice development. *Journal of Social Work Research and Evaluation, 6*(2), 219–231.

O'Callaghan, C. (2007). Music therapy inspired transient ward communities in oncology. In J. Edwards (Ed.), *Music in health care: International perspectives to inform theory and practice* (pp. 1–16). Cambridge, England: Cambridge Scholars Press.

O'Callaghan, C., & Brown, G. (1989). *Facilitating communication with brain impaired people: The impact of music therapy.* Paper presented at the National Association for Loss and Grief 6th Biennial Conference, Melbourne, Australia.

O'Callaghan, C., & Colegrove, V. (1998). Effect of the music therapy introduction when engaging hospitalized cancer patents. *Music Therapy Perspectives, 16*(2), 67–74.

O'Callaghan, C., & Hiscock, R. (2007). Interpretative subgroup analysis extends modified grounded theory research findings in oncologic music therapy. *Journal of Music Therapy, 44*(3), 256–281.

O'Callaghan, C., & McDermott, F. (2004). Music therapy's relevance in a cancer hospital researched through a constructivist lens. *Journal of Music Therapy, 41*(2), 151–185.

O'Callaghan, C., & Turnbull, G. (1987). *The application of a neuropsychological knowledge base in the use of music therapy with severely brain damaged, adynamic, multiple sclerosis patients.* Paper presented at the Proceedings of the 13th Conference Australian Music Therapy Association Conference, Adelaide.

O'Callaghan, C., & Turnbull, G. (1988). *The application of a neuropsychological knowledge base in the use of music therapy with severely brain damaged, disinhibited, multiple sclerosis patients.* Paper presented at the Proceedings of the 14th Conference, Australian Music Therapy Association, Melbourne.

O'Kelly, J., & Koffman, J. (2007). Multidisciplinary perspectives of music therapy in adult palliative care. *Palliative Medicine, 2*(3), 235–241.

Pickett, E. (1987). Fibroid tumors and response to guided imagery: Two case studies. *Imagination, Cognition and Personality, 7*(2), 165–175.

Porchet-Munro, S. (1993). Music therapy perspectives in palliative care education. *Journal of Palliative Care, 9*(4), 39–42.

Post-White, J., & Bauer-Wu, S. (2005). Psychoneuroimmunology: The mind-body connection. In R. M. Carroll-Johnson, L. Gorman, & N. J. Bush (Eds.), *Psychosocial nursing care along the cancer continuum* (2nd ed.) (pp. 465–485). Pittsburgh, PA: Oncology Nursing Press.

Rainey, L. C. (1984). Death education for oncology professionals: A personal construct theory perspective. In R. A. Niemeyer (Ed.), *Personal meanings of death: Applications of personal construct theory to clinical practice* (pp. 195–210). New York: Hemisphere.

Reid, M. (2000). Cancer control and epidemiology. In C. H. Yarbro, M. H. Frogge, M. Goodman, & S. L. Groenwald (Eds.), *Cancer nursing principles and practice* (5th ed.) (pp. 60–81). Sudbury, MA: Jones and Bartlett.

Remen, R. N. (1996). *Kitchen table wisdom.* New York: Riverhead Books.

Richardson, J. L., Shelton, D. R., Krailo, M., & Levine, A. M. (1990). The effect of compliance with treatment on survival among patients with hematologic malignancies. *Journal of Clinical Oncology, 8*, 356–364.

Richardson, M. A., Post-White, J., Grimm, E. A., Moye, L. A., Singletary, S. E., & Justice, B. (1997). Coping, life attitudes, and immune responses to imagery and group support after breast cancer treatment. *Alternative Therapies, 3*(5), 62–70.

Richardson, M. A., Sanders, T., Palmer, J. L., Greisinger, A., & Singletary, S. E. (2000). Complementary/alternative medicine use in a comprehensive cancer center and the implications for oncology. *Journal of Clinical Oncology, 18*, 2505–2514.

Rider, M. S., & Achterberg, J. (1989). Effects of music-assisted imagery on neutrophils and lymphocytes. *Biofeedback and Self-Regulation, 14*, 247–257.

Rider, M. S., Achterberg, J., Lawlis, G. F., Goven, A., Toledo, R., & Butler, J. R. (1990). Effect of immune system imagery on secretory IgA. *Biofeedback and Self-Regulation, 15*, 317–333.

Rider, M. S., Floyd, J. W., & Kirkpatrick, J. (1985). The effect of music, imagery, and relaxation on adrenal corticosteroids and the re-entrainment of circadian rhythms. *Journal of Music Therapy, 22*, 46–58.

Rider, M., Mickey, C., Weldin, C., & Hawkinson, R. (1991). The effects of toning, listening, and singing on psychophysiological responses. In C. D. Maranto (Ed.), *Applications of music in medicine* (pp. 73–84). Washington, DC: National Association for Music Therapy.

Rieger, P. T. (1997). Myelosuppression. In C. Varricchio (Ed.), *A cancer source book for nurses* (7th ed.) (pp. 161–173). Atlanta, GA: American Cancer Society.

Rossman, M. L. (2003). *Fighting cancer from within*. New York: Henry Holt.

Rykov, M. (1999). Sometimes there are no reasons: Marco's song. In J. Hibben (Ed.), *Inside music therapy: Client experiences* (pp. 202–207). Gilsum, NH: Barcelona.

Rykov M. (2006). *Music at a time like this: Music therapy cancer support groups.* Unpublished doctoral dissertation, University of Toronto, Ontario.

Rykov, M. (2008). Experiencing music therapy cancer support. *Journal of Health Psychology, 13*(2), 190–200.

Rykov, M., & Salmon, D. (1998). Bibliography for music therapists in palliative care. *The American Journal of Hospice and Palliative Care, 15*(3), 174–180.

Sabo, C. E., & Rush Michael, S. (1996). The influence of personal message with music on anxiety side effects associated with chemotherapy. *Cancer Nursing, 19*(4), 283–289.

Sahler, O. R. Z., Hunter, B. C., & Liesveld, J. L. (2003). The effect of using music therapy with relaxation imagery in the management of patients undergoing bone marrow transplantation: A pilot feasibility study. *Alternative Therapies, 9*(6), 70–74.

Salmon, D. (2001). Music therapy as psychospiritual process in palliative care. *Journal of Palliative Care, 17*(3), 142–146.

Saperston, B. (1995). The effects of consistent tempi and physiologically interactive tempi on heart rate and EMG responses. In T. Wigram, B. Saperston, & R. West (Eds.), *Art and science of music therapy: A handbook* (pp. 58–79). Langhorne, PA: Harwood Academic.

Schlaug, G., Jancke, L., Huang, Y., & Steinmetz, H. (1995). In vivo evidence of structural brain asymmetry in musicians. *Science, 267*, 699–701.

Schön, D. A. (1991). *The reflective practitioner*. London: Temple Smith.

Scott, D. (1990). Practice wisdom: The neglected source of practice research. *Social Work, 35*(6), 564–568.

Sergent, J., Zuck, S., Tenial, S., & MacDonald, B. (1992). Distributed neural network underlying musical sightreading keyboard performance. *Science, 257*, 106–109.

Short, A. (2002). Guided Imagery and Music (GIM) in medical care. In K. E. Bruscia & D. E. Grocke (Eds.), *Guided Imagery and Music: The Bonny method and beyond* (pp. 151–170). Gilsum, NH: Barcelona

Skaggs, R. (1997). The Bonny method of Guided Imagery and Music in the treatment of terminal illness: A private practice setting. *Music Therapy Perspectives, 15*, 39–44.

Sourkes, B. M., Massie, M. J., & Holland, J. C. (1998). Psychotherapeutic issues. In J. C. Holland (Ed.), *Psycho-oncology* (pp. 694–700). New York: Oxford University Press.

Sparks, R. W., Helm, N., & Albert, M. (1974). Aphasia rehabilitation resulting from melodic intonation therapy. *Cortex, 10*, 313–316.

Spiegel, D., Bloom, J. R., & Yalom, I. (1981). Group support for patients with metastatic cancer: A randomized outcome study. *Archives of General Psychiatry, 38*, 527–533.

Stahl, C. (1997). Surgical oncology. In C. Varricchio (Ed.), *A cancer source book for nurses* (7th ed.) (pp. 80–90). Atlanta, GA: American Cancer Society.

Standley, J. (1992). Clinical applications of music and chemotherapy: The effects of nausea and emesis. *Music Therapy Perspectives, 10*, 27–35.

Strohl, R. A. (1999). Radiation therapy. In C. Miaskowski & P. Buchsel (Eds.), *Oncology nursing, assessment and clinical care* (pp. 59–81). St. Louis, MO: Mosby.

Summer, L., & Chong, H. J. (2006). Music and imagery techniques with an emphasis on the Bonny method of Guided Imagery and Music. In H. J. Chong (Ed.), *Music therapy: Techniques and models* [Korean language]. Seoul, Korea: Hakjisa.

Thomas, C. L. (Ed.). (1997). *Taber's cyclopedic medical dictionary*. Philadelphia: F. A. Davis.

Thompson, D. A., & Holland, E. J. (2003). Meaning making in the wake of public tragedy. In M. Lattanzi-Licht & K. J. Doka (Eds.), *Living with grief, coping with public tragedy* (pp. 165–178). New York: Hospice Foundation of America.

Thornton, S., & Brotchie, J. (1987). Reminiscence: A critical review of the empirical literature. *The British Psychological Society, 26*, 93–111.

Trichopoulos, D., Li, F. P., & Hunter, D. J. (1996). What causes cancer? *Scientific American, 275*(3), 80–87.

Tsao, C. C., Gordon, T., Maranto, C. D., Lerman, C., & Murasko, D. (1991). The effects of music and biological imagery on immune response (s-IgA). In C. D. Maranto (Ed.), *Applications of music in medicine* (pp. 85–121). Washington, DC: National Association for Music Therapy.

Uedo, N., Ishikawa, H., Morimoto, K., Ishihara, R., Narahara, H., Akedo, I., et al. (2004). Reduction in salivary cortisol level by music therapy during colonoscopic examination. *Hepato-Gastroenterology, 51*, 451–453.

Vaux, D. (2001, August 20). The great cancer myth. *The Age,* 13.

Ventre, M. (2002). The individual form of the Bonny method of Guided Imagery and Music (BMGIM). In K. E. Bruscia & D. E. Grocke (Eds.), *Guided Imagery and Music: The Bonny method and beyond* (pp. 29–36). Gilsum, NH: Barcelona.

Vickers, A. J., & Cassileth, B. R. (2001). Unconventional therapies for cancer and cancer-related symptoms. *Lancet Oncology, 2*, 226–232.

Waldon, E. (2001). The effects of group music therapy on mood states and cohesiveness in adult oncology patients. *Journal of Music Therapy, 38*, 212–238.

Weber, S., Nuessler, V., & Wilmanns, W. (1996). A pilot study on the influence of receptive music listening on cancer patients during chemotherapy. *International Journal of Arts Medicine, 5*(2), 27–35.

Weisman, A. D., & Worden, J. W. (1976). The existential plight in cancer: Significance of the first 100 days. *International Journal of Psychiatry in Medicine, 7*(1), 1–15.

Wellisch, D. K. (1979). Adolescent acting out when a parent has cancer. *International Journal of Family Therapy, 1*(3), 230–241.

West, T. (1994). Psychological issues in hospice music therapy. *Music Therapy Perspectives, 12,* 117–124.

Worden, J. W. (1991). *Grief counseling and grief therapy: A handbook for the mental health practitioner* (2nd ed.). New York: Springer.

Workman, M. L., & Visovsky, C. G. (1999). Cancer pathophysiology. In C. Miaskowski & P. Buchsel (Eds.), *Oncology nursing, assessment and clinical care* (pp. 11–28). St. Louis, MO: Mosby.

Yarbro, J. W. (2000). Carcinogenesis. In C. H. Yarbro, M. H. Frogge, M. Goodman, & S. L. Groenwald (Eds.), *Cancer nursing principles and practice* (5th ed.) (pp. 48–59). Sudbury, MA: Jones and Bartlett.

Yuska, C. M., & Nedved, P. G. (2000). Home care. In C. H. Yarbro, M. H. Frogge, M. Goodman, & S. L. Groenwald (Eds.), *Cancer nursing principles and practice* (5th ed.) (pp. 1661–1680). Sudbury, MA: Jones and Bartlett.

Zatorre, R. J., Evans, A. C., & Meyer, E. (1994). Neural mechanisms underlying melodic perception and memory for pitch. *Journal of Neuroscience, 14*(4), 1908–1919.

Zimmerman, L., Pozehl, B., Duncan, K., & Schmitz, R. (1989). Effects of music in patients who had chronic cancer pain. *Western Journal of Nursing Research, 11*(3), 298–309.

Appendix

Music Therapy in Adult Cancer Care: Across the Cancer Continuum

Dawn McDougal Miller, MME, MT-BC

Treatment Phase of Disease Continuum and Related Issues	Interdisciplinary Care Plan Issues	Music Therapy Goals	Music Therapy Interventions	Relevant Song Titles
	(adapted from National Cancer Institute, 2004)		Advanced training and certification required to utilize specific methods	Consider patient's preferred genres of music, age, and spiritual beliefs. Selections of music are primarily played live by the music therapist. Recorded music may be utilized if it is more appropriate to reproduce the style of the music, or to facilitate the music therapy technique.
Diagnosis				
Phase I: Initial Response	Shock, disbelief, numbness, denial and feelings of being overwhelmed Stigma of the word *cancer* Inability to process information clearly	Emotional support Establish trust and the therapeutic relationship	Education of therapeutic effects of music Song choice Provide familiar, predictable music	Familiar music from favorite genre "Rhosymedre" (Vaughan Williams, 2000, disc 2, track 8)
Phase II: Dysphoria period of time, sometimes lasting for 1 to 2 weeks, during which the patient is slowly acknowledging the reality of the cancer diagnosis (National Cancer Institute, 2004)	Emotional roller coaster: grief, fear, anger, lack of control, vulnerability, anguish, angst, disappointment, restlessness, inability to concentrate, insomnia, anxiety, and depression Myth of "good health" is shattered as patient faces own mortality "What if?" and "Why me?" questions Existential crisis Regression, bargaining, magical beliefs, and unrealistic hopes may occur (Lederberg, 1998)	Direct expression of emotions through verbal and non-verbal communication. Provide a catalyst or safe container for expressing intense emotions. Stress management.	Music listening or music improvisation to match and support emotional state, i.e., "This music sounds the way I feel." Music as a transitional object Drumming Upbeat music may be used as a brief respite from emotional turmoil	"Lean on Me" (Withers, 2000) "You've Got a Friend" (King, 1989) "You Raise Me Up" (Groban, 2003, track 12; Lovland & Graham, 2002) "Adagio for Strings" (Barber, 1996, track 11) "The Planets: Mars" (Holst, 1996, track 1) "Carmina Burana: excerpts" (Orff, 1996, tracks 3 & 4) "The Storm" (Boltz, 1994, track 7) "Hold Me Jesus" (Mullins, 1996, track 16) "He's My Son" (Schultz, 2000, track 3)

Treatment Phase of Disease Continuum and Related Issues	Interdisciplinary Care Plan Issues	Music Therapy Goals	Music Therapy Interventions	Relevant Song Titles
Phase III: Longer-term Adaptation	Gathering medical information and making informed decisions about treatment options Psychological distress (Holland, 2003; National Comprehensive Cancer Network, 2001) Heightened awareness of sense of time and threat of loss Loss of aspirations, hopes, and dreams	Patient will identify "tool box" of personal resources and support Encourage patient to mobilize effective coping strategies	Music listening and song analysis to support patient in identification of personal resources Individualized music-assisted relaxation techniques for centering and grounding If appropriate, utilize music to support humor and other positive coping strategies Education of therapeutic effects of music	"Bridge Over Troubled Water" (Simon, 1969) "The Anchor Holds" (Boltz, 1994, track 8) "Time in a Bottle" (Croce, 1974) "It's in Everyone of Us" (Pomeranz, 1994)

Treatment Phase of Disease Continuum and Related Issues	Interdisciplinary Care Plan Issues	Music Therapy Goals	Music Therapy Interventions	Relevant Song Titles
Treatment: Surgery				
Pre-surgery, pre-chemotherapy, or pre-radiation therapy	Anxiety, fear of the unknown, fear of side effects Anxiety regarding procedures Anticipatory nausea "Will they get it all?" "Will I need more treatment after surgery?" "Will I survive this?"	Patient will have opportunities to experience the "relaxation response" (Benson, 1976) Decrease anxiety	Provide live music during procedures such as blood draws or IV starts on day of surgery or treatment Explain use of music based on iso-principle to decrease anxiety Teach music-assisted relaxation techniques, such as progressive muscle relaxation, deep breathing, and autogenic relaxation Design individualized music imagery experiences, such as "peaceful place" or healing images Mandalas or improvisation as a tool for patient to express and explore anxiety and fears Create compilation of patient's personal motivational or inspirational songs to utilize during treatment	Improvised music based on isoprinciple and entrainment techniques Improvised music combined with music-focused relaxation cues Recorded music-focused relaxation: "Music Focused Relaxation: A Harp and Voice Meditation" (Cotter-Schaufele, 2004, CD) "Healing Blue Sky" (Miller, Holten, & Nielsen, 1999, CD) Relaxation music recordings: "Piano Dreamers" (Yallop, 1997, CD) "Tranquility" (Yallop, 1997, CD) "Canyon Trilogy" (Nakai, 2003, CD) "Going Home Again" (Kobialka, 1992, CD) "Silk Branches" (Kobialka, 1996, CD) "Flow" (Nielsen, 2003, CD) "Sacred Wind Calling" (Nielsen, 2003, CD) "Musical Massage" (Hoffman, 1993, CD) Relaxation music with environmental sounds
Immediate Post-surgical	Acute pain Nausea Need to rest	Decrease in patient's self-reported pain level and observable pain behaviors Pain and nausea management	Music and individualized pain management relaxation and imagery exercises Music to create healing environment	Patient's familiar, comforting, or sedative music

Treatment Phase of Disease Continuum and Related Issues	Interdisciplinary Care Plan Issues	Music Therapy Goals	Music Therapy Interventions	Relevant Song Titles
Post-surgical: physical rehabilitation	Increase activity level Pain with movement Adjustment to adaptive devices Fear and anxiety while awaiting results of pathology reports	Motivator and rhythmic stimulus for movement Increase endurance Encourage emotional expression and exploration of losses related to changes in body image (loss of breast, colon, larynx, etc.)	Neurologic Music Therapy techniques: gait training, Rhythmic Auditory Stimulation (RAS), Therapeutic Instrument Music Performance (TIMP), Patterned Sensory Enhancement (PSE) (Thaut, 1999) Coordinate goals with physical, occupational, and speech therapy. Entrainment of motor movements to multidimensional aspects of music	Marches, polkas, and other stimulative music genres such as rock or big band Improvised rhythmically music based on NMT techniques "Brown Eyed Girl" (Morrison, 1967) "In the Mood" (Garland, 1996) "Old Time Rock and Roll" (Jackson & Jones, 1996) For anxiety reduction or emotional support, utilize patient's familiar, comforting, or sedative music

Treatment Phase of Disease Continuum and Related Issues	Interdisciplinary Care Plan Issues	Music Therapy Goals	Music Therapy Interventions	Relevant Song Titles
Active Treatment: Curative Mode or "Cancer as a Chronic Disease"				
Chemotherapy (schedule may continue for days, months, or years)	Anxiety and dread about side effects and impacts of treatment process Side effects of nausea, vomiting, fatigue, and immuno-suppression Insomnia and restlessness due to side effects of chemotherapy pre-medications Hair loss and body image changes "Will I survive this?" Boredom during time-consuming procedures Difficulties in balancing rigorous outpatient chemotherapy treatment schedule and side effects, with home and work responsibilities	Decrease anxiety Induce "relaxation response" to potentially reduce onset and length of nausea post chemotherapy treatment (Frank, 1985; Standley, 1992) Emotional and spiritual support Create a healing environment and sacred space for healing Immune system enhancement Energy management strategies Patient will identify and increase awareness of personal resources Support patient's personal coping strategies Enhance quality of IV therapy treatment experiences	Active or receptive music experiences (singing, listening, and/or playing adapted instruments) Music listening, songwriting, song choice, or song analysis that affirms importance of support system, provides metaphors of losses, or explores images of hope and healing Music-assisted relaxation exercises and/or immune system enhancement imagery Bonny Method of Guided Imagery and Music (BMGIM) to explore personal healing images, emotions, and meaning-making of cancer experience Songwriting to support humor as a coping strategy for loss of hair or body image changes Provide opportunities for creativity and aesthetic expression that allow patient to tap into the normal, healthy "Self"	"Climb Every Mountain" (Rodgers & Hammerstein, 1997) or songs that represent a time when the patient has faced and survived adversity in life "Blowing in the Wind" (Dylan, 1989); rewrite words with patient to reflect cancer or chemotherapy process Improvised music (by therapist and/or patient) that represents and transports patient to personal image of a "peaceful place" Music that "sounds like cancer" or "sounds like healing" Sedative music selections listed in pre-chemotherapy category "One Day at a Time" (Wilkin & Kristofferson, 1996) "You'll Never Walk Alone" (Rodgers & Hammerstein, 1997)

Treatment Phase of Disease Continuum and Related Issues	Interdisciplinary Care Plan Issues	Music Therapy Goals	Music Therapy Interventions	Relevant Song Titles
Neurological effects "chemo brain" Not found in all cancer patients	Some chemotherapy agents, radiation, surgical anesthesia, or post-operative medications may cause temporary negative impacts on patients' short-term memory, decision-making, ability to concentrate or think clearly Brain tumors or metastases to the brain may also cause temporary or permanent neurological effects	Music for centering and focusing Decrease confusion Decrease agitation	Relaxation imagery techniques focused on centering and breathing Iso-principle Active music participation Structured reality-based music therapy techniques with familiar music	If cognitive changes are minimal and temporary, relaxation/sedative music may be utilized If patient has cognitive impairments, confusion or agitation, then patient's familiar preferred music may be more effective Music of the patient's young adult years
Neutropenia and protective isolation	Neutropenia, decreased immune functioning Institutional and sterile environment Isolation created by barriers of sterile physical environment Long inpatient hospitalization and boredom Loss of control, helplessness, emotional exhaustion, depression	Decrease feelings of isolation, helplessness, and depression Increase sense of control Increase emotional and spiritual support Mobilize inner coping resources (Brodsky, 1989) and provide means of self-expression Patient will identify people in his/her life that help support sense of hopefulness and positive attitude	Carefully adhere to infection control procedures, while "humanizing" the sterile environment Adaptive leisure skills/learning new instruments Song choice or songwriting focused on hope, support, and coping Opportunities for patient to make choices within structure of session Personalized music-assisted relaxation and imagery exercises and/or immune system enhancement imagery	"The River" (Shaw & Brooks, 1996) "Angels Among Us" (Hobbs & Goodman, 1996) "Crazy" (Nelson, 1991) "I'm So Lonesome, I Could Cry" (Williams, 1996) "Somewhere Over the Rainbow" (Arlen & Harburg, 1996; Cassidy, 1998, track 10) "You've Got a Friend" (King, 1989) "Precious Lord, Take My Hand" (Dorsey, 1938) "White Cliffs of Dover" (Kent & Burton, 1941) "Tomorrow" (Strouse & Charnin, 1997)

Treatment Phase of Disease Continuum and Related Issues	Interdisciplinary Care Plan Issues	Music Therapy Goals	Music Therapy Interventions	Relevant Song Titles
Cancer-related losses **Finding the "new normal"**	Hopelessness, powerlessness, "cancer victim" versus "cancer survivor" Change in physical status Decrease or change in quality of life Loss of dreams (Bowman, 1994)	Expression of pain, grief, depression, and/or anger related to losses and changes in lifestyle Finding the "new normal" Increase quality of life, hopefulness, and sense of control	Music to match emotions of grief and loss Music-based counseling techniques or music psychotherapy Music to acknowledge impact of life-changing experience of cancer Music as a transitional object	"Don't Get Around Much Anymore" (Ellington & Russell, 2003) "His Eye Is on the Sparrow" (Gabriel & Martin, 1985) "In the Garden" (Miles, 1985) "Amazing Grace" (Newton, 1985) "Wind Beneath My Wings" (Henley & Silbar, 2000) "The Rose" (McBroom, 2000) "You've Got a Friend" (King, 1989) "You'll Never Walk Alone" (Rodgers & Hammerstein, 1997) "Candle in the Wind" (John & Taupin, 1990) "On Eagle's Wings" (Joncas, 2000) "Dona Nobis Pacem" (Traditional, 1980)
Radiation therapy or radioactive implants	Fatigue increases as treatments continue Skin irritation, side effects of radiation Difficulties in balancing daily radiation treatments and side effects, with home and work responsibilities Fear of invisible, "radioactive" treatment Claustrophobia Physical isolation and need to remain motionless during treatment experience	Energy and fatigue management Coping with stresses of routine of daily radiation treatments Patient will explore personal images of healing to utilize during radiation treatments Decrease anxiety Patient will remain calm and motionless during treatment procedure	Music and personalized imagery for radiation Personalized relaxation and imagery for management of anxiety, panic attacks, or claustrophobic reactions	Sedative music selections listed in pre-radiation therapy category "Here Comes the Sun" (Harrison, 1991) Patient's familiar and preferred music
Discharge from hospital, or final chemo-therapy or radiation treatment	Celebration Preparation for return to home or to life without cancer treatment	Provide emotional closure Acknowledgment of life-changing experience Decrease anxiety regarding the end of treatments and remaining cancer-free	Personalized good-bye songs sung by music therapist and interdisciplinary team Encourage patient to select a song that represents hope, meaning, or encourages transition to life without cancer treatment	Words of songs can be personalized to reflect individual name and treatment process. "Every Long Journey" (Reed, 1986) "Happy Trails" (Evans, 1996) "Show Me the Way to Go Home" (King, 1991) "Till We Meet Again" (Whiting & Egan, 1994)

Treatment Phase of Disease Continuum and Related Issues	Interdisciplinary Care Plan Issues	Music Therapy Goals	Music Therapy Interventions	Relevant Song Titles
Repeated hospitaliza–tions, invasive medical procedures (i.e., bone marrow aspirations)	Pain and symptom management Compromised immune system Anxiety and fear about results of tests Change in condition, cancer may have metastasized Treatment approach may shift from curative to maintenance or palliative Possible discharge to new care environment	Provide support during anxious time of waiting for test results Stress reduction for patient, family members, and caregivers Provide musical focus to decrease patient's anxiety during invasive medical procedures such as bone marrow aspirations or IV starts Provide emotional and spiritual support as patient considers impact of changes in condition or treatment approach	Teach relaxation, centering, and grounding techniques to patient and family Iso-principle Live music during invasive medical procedures such as blood draws, IV starts, and bone-marrow aspirations Education of therapeutic effects of music	Sedative music listed in pre-surgery category. "You've Got a Friend" (King, 1989) "Lean on Me" (Withers, 2000) "Whispering Hope" (Hawthorne, 1983) "All Night, All Day" (Traditional spiritual, 1971) "Leaning on the Everlasting Arms" (Showalter & Hoffman, 1985)
Pain caused by metastases to bone or other factors	Determine patient's wishes for balance of pain management with desired level of alertness/sedation Pain management to acceptable level as determined by patient	Patient will report a decreased pain on 0 to 10 pain scale after music therapy intervention Decrease number of observable pain behaviors	If appropriate, provide brief explanation of pain etiology theories (such as Gate Control Theory of Pain) and music's role in decreasing pain perception Exploration of stimulative/ rhythmbased or sedative music to complement pain management	Improvised music and music-focused pain management relaxation techniques Sedative music listed in pre-surgery category. Familiar music "Make the World Go Away" (Cochran, 1963) becomes "Make my pain go away!" "Merciful Awareness: Natural Pain Management Techniques" (Levine, 1999)

Treatment Phase of Disease Continuum and Related Issues	Interdisciplinary Care Plan Issues	Music Therapy Goals	Music Therapy Interventions	Relevant Song Titles
Post Treatment				
Cancer in remission or cancer as a chronic disease	Celebration, sense of relief, and feelings of ambivalence Heightened distress and vulnerability due to decreased medical surveillance and cessation of active treatment	Patient will include relaxation and stress management within daily routines of life Acknowledgment of life-changing experience Discussion of energy management and finding new "rhythms of life"	Relaxation or imagery exercises for continued immune system enhancement Improvisation and drumming Songwriting or selection of songs to express gratitude and appreciation Follow-up "homework": • Explore, select, and utilize favorite sedative music • Utilize music-assisted relaxation techniques for 20 minutes, 3–6 times/week	"Oh What a Beautiful Morning" (Rodgers & Hammerstein, 1997) "I Can See Clearly Now" (Nash, 1978) "Looks Like I Made It" (Kerr & Jennings, 1996) "Morning Has Broken" (Haugen & Farjeon, 1994) "Shout to the Lord" (Zschech, 2000) "If Tomorrow Never Comes" (Brooks & Blazy, 1996) Music from Bonny Method of Guided Imagery programs
Tests and monitoring	Living with uncertainty Anxiety in waiting for test results Hyper-vigilance of health issues. Any new health change brings fears of "it must be cancer" Fears of cancer recurrence	Music as transitional object Decrease anxiety and fear Music for relaxation, centering, and hope	Music that provides assurance and comfort during times of anxiety and fear Personalized relaxation exercises to continue immune system enhancement and expression of emotions	Sedative music listed in pre-surgery category. "I Will Survive" (Ferkaris & Perren, 1978) "Day by Day" (Chain, Stordahl, & Weston, 1996) "One Day at a Time" (Wilkin & Kristofferson, 1996) "With a Little Help from My Friends" (Lennon & McCartney, 1991) "Because He Lives" (Gaither & Gaither, 1983)

Treatment Phase of Disease Continuum and Related Issues	Interdisciplinary Care Plan Issues	Music Therapy Goals	Music Therapy Interventions	Relevant Song Titles
Survivorship				
Survivorship issues	Finding the "new normal" Reconstruction of life goals "What does it mean to be a cancer survivor?" "How shall I live now?" Survivor "guilt"	Exploration of emotions and insights of cancer experience If cancer treatment will continue indefinitely, then patient may need to find ways to balance treatment routine with work and home responsibilities Some patients may identify positive benefits of their cancer experience (greater appreciation of life, reprioritizing of life values, strengthening of spiritual beliefs)	Music psychotherapy and counseling techniques to further explore patient's experience of cancer as a "wake-up" call to change unhealthy behavior patterns, relationships, and ways of being in life Music as a metaphor to recognize and summarize the process of negotiating, coping with, working through, and transcending the cancer experience (Abrams, 2001) Follow-up "homework:" • Find a song that reflects upon own cancer journey and new sense of meaning and priorities in life • Utilize music-assisted relaxation techniques within routines of daily life	"Let It Be" (Lennon & McCartney, 1991) "Every Long Journey" (Reed, 1986) "Both Sides Now" (Mitchell, 1970) "I Hope You Dance" (Sillers, 2000) "He Touched Me" (Gaither, 1983) "Amazing Grace" (Newton, 1985) "Forever Young" (Stewart, Cregan, Savigar, & Dylan, 1988) "Live Like You Were Dying" (McGraw, 2004, track 5)

Treatment Phase of Disease Continuum and Related Issues	Interdisciplinary Care Plan Issues	Music Therapy Goals	Music Therapy Interventions	Relevant Song Titles
Recurrence or Advanced Disease				
Recurrence (3 phases of adaptation are possible, similar to initial diagnosis)	Consideration of possible transition from curative treatment approach to cancer maintenance or palliative care focus Extreme emotional turmoil, similar to, but may be more intense than during initial diagnosis Shock, disbelief, denial, fear, dread, extreme anguish, and possible existential crisis Anger at God or Higher Power	Music as emotional and spiritual support Music to strengthen patient's current belief system, coping style and strategies, and internal and external resources and support	Using music as a catalyst and safe container for expression of intense emotions Music listening and discussion of lyrics and message of songs Exploring or writing songs that match emotions or represent hope	"Whispering Hope" (Hawthorne, 1983) "Send in the Clowns" (Sondheim, 1996) "Desperado" (Henley & Frey, 1994) "Amazing Grace" (Newton, 1985) Refer to music listed in diagnosis phases
Palliative Care: Treatment decisions are based upon potential effects on patient's quality of life. Focus is on restoring "wholeness," instead of curing patient of cancer.				
Task #1: Acknowledge the reality of the loss(es) Cancer has advanced to terminal diagnosis. Tasks are adapted from Worden's Tasks of Mourning (1991).	Decision to transition from curative treatment approach to a palliative care focus Possible hospice or palliative care referral Decision-making regarding wishes for further treatment and/or locations for care Emotions of shock, disbelief, and/or denial Existential crisis of impending death	Music to strengthen patient's current belief system, coping style and strategies, and internal and external resources and support	Musical life review with a focus on times when patient has faced loss and/or survived adversity in life Music listening and lyric analysis to remind patient of own strengths and personal resources	"Be Not Afraid" (Dufford, 1994) "Ave Maria" (Gounod, 1992; Schubert, 1992) "Today" (Sparks, 1996) "Fire and Rain" (Taylor, 1991)

Treatment Phase of Disease Continuum and Related Issues	Interdisciplinary Care Plan Issues	Music Therapy Goals	Music Therapy Interventions	Relevant Song Titles
Task #2: Experience and express the pain of grief	Extreme emotional anguish and turmoil. May be more intense than during initial diagnosis Anger at God or Higher Power Anticipatory grief for patient and family	Music as emotional and spiritual support	Using music as catalyst and safe container for expression of intense emotions Music listening and discussion of lyrics, musical elements, message, and meaning of songs Use of spiritually meaningful music Improvisation, drumming Writing songs that represent patient's life or process of facing death Music for rituals such as prayer services, goodbyes, life celebrations, or communion	Select music very carefully. The purpose of music is not to "fix" or find a solution for the patient's emotions, but to support the patient in expression of emotions. "Lean on Me" (Withers, 2000) "Bridge over Troubled Water" (Simon, 1969) "Just a Closer Walk" (Morris, 1996) "When It's All Been Said and Done" (Cowan, 1999, track 9) "Teach Me to Die" (Edwards, 1976) "Untitled Hymn" (Rice, 2003). "Sweet Hour of Prayer" (Bradbury & Walford, 1985) Refer to music listed in diagnosis phases

Treatment Phase of Disease Continuum and Related Issues	Interdisciplinary Care Plan Issues	Music Therapy Goals	Music Therapy Interventions	Relevant Song Titles
Task #3: Optimize quality of life in a "new reality" with heightened awareness of one's own mortality	Adjust to new physical limitations Focus on quality of life and unfinished business Specify future wishes for levels of medication for pain and sedation Specify wishes for a "safe and comfortable" dying process	Life review and reminiscence Validation of life experiences Specifying wishes for dying process and memorial service Aesthetic and creative experience Adaptive and/or shared leisure experience for patient and family Support patient in redefining hope. Patients may no longer hope for their cancer to be cured, but may instead define hope as having an acceptable quality of life up until their death.	Music Life Review utilizing songs from cultural background, decades of life and important life events (courtship, wedding, birth of children, funerals of family members, anniversaries, travel, military service) Songwriting to express gratitude, wishes, and goodbyes to family and friends Videotape sessions to leave a legacy Selecting music for memorial services and processing emotions that arise Create compilation of important songs in patient's life	"Live Like You Were Dying" (McGraw, 2004, track 5) "Sentimental Journey" (Green, Brown, & Homer, 1991) "Try to Remember" (Schmidt & Jones, 1997 "Those Were the Days" (Raskin, 1962) "My Way" (Revaux, Francois, Thibault, & Anka, 1996) "Some Enchanted Evening" (Rodgers & Hammerstein, 1997) "Love Me Tender" (Presley & Matson, 1991) "Anniversary Waltz" (Dubin & Franklin, 1941) "Danny Boy" (Weatherly, 1996) "Spanish Eyes" (Kaempfert, Singleton, & Snyder, 1991) "Moon River" (Mancini & Mercer, 1996) "Sunrise, Sunset" (Bock & Harnick, 1997) "Memory" (Webber & Nunn, 1997) "I Was There to Hear Your Borning Cry" (Ylvisaker, 1995) "Through the Years" (Youmans & Heyman, 1996) "If Tomorrow Never Comes" (Brooks & Blazy, 1996) "Seasons of Love" (Larson, 1997) "Shenandoah" (Traditional, 1996) "Oyfn pripetshok: On the hearth" (Warschafsky, 1994)

Treatment Phase of Disease Continuum and Related Issues	Interdisciplinary Care Plan Issues	Music Therapy Goals	Music Therapy Interventions	Relevant Song Titles
Death is imminent within days or hours **Task #4: Withdraw from life and reinvest energies in the transition**	Unresponsive patient, withdrawing from life and focusing inward Comfort care Anticipatory grief for family Need to provide care and optimize comfort in accordance with patient's self-determined wishes for a safe and comfortable dying process	Express messages of: "Forgive me," "I forgive you," "Thank you," "I love you," and/or "Goodbye" (Byock, 2004) Music to support transition from life to death Music as nonverbal communication and comfort	Family to choose special songs for patient, reminisce Entrainment of respiration rate to tempo of music and/or deepening of respiration volume and possible effects on Cheyne-Stokes respiration patterns Music to support images of dying in accordance with patient and family's spiritual belief systems	Familiar music of patient's spiritual belief system and/or sedative music "Leaving on a Jet Plane" (Denver, 1989) "Tears in Heaven" (Clapton & Lennings, 1991) "My Heart Will Go On" (Horner, 1997) "Goin' Home" (Dvorak & Fisher, 1922) "Red River Valley" (Traditional, 1996). "You Are My Sunshine" (Davis & Mitchell, 1930) "Down in the Valley" (Traditional, 1996) "Goodnight Irene" (Ledbetter & Lomax, 1950); substituting dying person's name in place of "Irene" "Silent Night" (Mohr & Gruber, 1996) "I'll Fly Away" (Brumley, 1983) "Peace in the Valley" (Dorsey, 1983) "Untitled Hymn" (Rice, 2003) "Softly and Tenderly" (Thompson, 1983) "Abide with Me" (Monk & Lyte, 1985) "Sweet By and By" (Webster & Bennett, 1985) "Beyond the Sunset" (Brock & Brock, 1985) "Rozhinkes mit mandln: Raisins and Almonds" (Goldfaden, 1994)

Treatment Phase of Disease Continuum and Related Issues	Interdisciplinary Care Plan Issues	Music Therapy Goals	Music Therapy Interventions	Relevant Song Titles
Bereavement				
Funeral or memorial service	Survivors are grieving; grief is often intense	To provide closure and enhance bereavement	Provide music for memorial service as appropriate (i.e., if the patient did not have a connection with a religious institution or if music therapy involvement is significant in the bereavement process for the survivors) Utilize community musicians or musicians connected with religious institutions for majority of memorial services rather than music therapist	Songs that represent the person who died Meaningful songs selected by patient or family "Ashokan Farewell" (Ungar, 1983) "Light a Candle" (Alexander, 1993) "Lake of Mercy" (Hesla, 2006)
Bereavement of family and friends	Grief can be a life-long process	To experience the emotions of loss To act as a catalyst for memories of the person who died	Explore music that facilitates special memories and an ongoing connection to the person who died Provide music for hospice or community memorial services	"I'll Be Seeing You" (Fain & Kahal, 1991) "You'll Be in My Heart" (Mancina & Collins, 1999, track 2) "Sand and Water" (Chapman, 1997, track 4) "Down to a River" (Kaldor, 1997, track 4) "The Living Years" (Rutherford & Robertson, 1988, track 2) "Circle of Life" (John & Rice, 1995, track 2) "Keep Me in Your Heart" (Zevon, 2003, track 11) Selections from "Oh, Brother, Where Art Thou?" (Burnett, 2000) "Angel" (McLachlan, 1997, track 7)

National Cancer Institute. (2004). *Situation-specific influences on adjustment.* Retrieved on November 30, 2004, from http://www.cancer.gov/cancertopics/pdq/supportivecare/adjustment/HealthProfessional/page2#Section_17

Discography and Printed Sources in Chart (combined)

Abrams, B. (2001). Music, cancer, and immunity. *Clinical Journal of Oncology Nursing, 5*(5), 1–3.

Alexander, P. (1993). *Light a candle* [Score]. Rockville Centre, NY: Paul Alexander Productions.

Arlen, H., & Harburg, E. Y. (1996). Somewhere over the rainbow [Score]. In C. Cuellar (Ed.), *Popular songs of inspiration* (pp. 10–13). Miami, FL: Warner Bros.

Barber, S. (1996). Adagio for strings. On *Music for the Imagination, Positive* [CD]. Gilsum, NH: Barcelona.

Benson, H. (1976). *The relaxation response*. New York: Avon Books.

Bock, J., & Harnick, S. (1997). Sunrise, sunset [Fake book]. In *The ultimate Broadway fake book* (4th ed.) (p. 204). Milwaukee, WI: Hal Leonard.

Boltz, R. (1994). The anchor holds. On *Allegiance* [CD]. New York: Word.

Boltz, R. (1994). The storm. On *Allegiance* [CD]. New York: Word.

Bradbury, W. B., & Walford, W. W. (1985). Sweet hour of prayer [Score]. In W. H. Goddard (Ed.), *Wonderful words of life* (p. 69). Carol Stream, IL: Hope.

Brock, B. K., & Brock, V. P. (1985). Beyond the sunset [Score]. In W. H. Goddard (Ed.), *Wonderful words of life* (p. 43). Carol Stream, IL: Hope.

Brodsky, W. (1989). Music therapy as an intervention for children with cancer in isolation rooms. *Music Therapy, 8*, 17–34.

Brooks, B., & Blazy, K. (1996). If tomorrow never comes [Fake book]. In T. Esposito & T. Roed (Eds.), *The world's greatest fake book* (p. 323). Miami, FL: Warner Bros.

Brumley, A. E. (1983). I'll fly away [Fake book]. In *Gospel's best words and music* (p. 129). Milwaukee, WI: Hal Leonard.

Burnett, T. B. (Producer). (2000). *Oh, brother, where art thou?* [CD]. Universal City, CA: Universal Music.

Byock, I. (2004). *The four things that matter most: A book about living.* New York: Free Press.

Cassidy, E. (1998). Over the rainbow. On *Songbird* [CD]. Gig Harbor, WA: Blix Street Records.

Chain, S., Stordahl, A., & Weston, P. (1996). Day by day [Fake book]. In T. Esposito & T. Roed (Eds.), *The world's greatest fake book* (p. 163). Miami, FL: Warner Bros.

Chapman, B. N. (1997). Sand and water. On *Sand and water* [CD]. Burbank, CA: Reprise Records.

Clapton, E., & Lennings, W. (1991). Tears in heaven [Score]. In *The best songs ever* (4th ed.) (pp. 222–226). Milwaukee, WI: Hal Leonard.

Cochran, H. (1963). Make the world go away [Fake book]. In *The ultimate country fake book* (4th ed.) (p. 339). Milwaukee, WI: Hal Leonard.

Cotter-Schaufele, S. (2004). *Music focused relaxation: A harp and voice meditation* [CD]. Chicago: Mitran Music. Available from Advocate Lutheran General Hospital Music Therapy at (847) 723-7265.

Cowan, J. (1999). When it's all said and done. On *Revival in Belfast* [CD]. Mobile, AL: Integrity.

Croce, J. (1974). Time in a bottle [Score]. In *Photographs and memories* (pp. 61–63). New York: Blendingwell Music.

Davis, J., & Mitchell, C. (1930). You are my sunshine [Fake book]. *The ultimate fake book* (3rd ed.) (p. 784). Milwaukee, WI: Hal Leonard.

Denver, J. (1989). Leaving on a jet plane [Fake book]. In R. Shipton (Ed.), *The complete guitar player song book* (Omnibus ed., Book 1) (p. 5). New York: Amsco.

Dorsey, T. A. (1938). Precious Lord, take my hand [Fake book]. In *The ultimate fake book* (3rd ed.) (p. 548). Milwaukee, WI: Hal Leonard.

Dorsey, T. A. (1983). Peace in the valley [Fake book]. In *Gospel's best words and music* (p. 223). Milwaukee, WI: Hal Leonard.

Dubin, A., & Franklin, D. (1941). The anniversary waltz [Fake book]. In *The ultimate fake book* (3rd ed.) (pp. 477–477). Milwaukee, WI: Hal Leonard.

Dufford, B. (1994). Be not afraid [Score]. In *Gather comprehensive* (Vol. 2) (p. 608). Chicago: GIA.

Dvorak, A., & Fisher, W. A. (1922). *Goin' home (Dvorak's Largo)* [Score]. Bryn Mawr, PA: Oliver Ditson.

Dylan, B. (1989). Blowing in the wind [Fake book]. In R. Shipton (Ed.), *The complete guitar player song book* (Omnibus ed., Book 1) (p. 6). New York: Amsco.

Edwards, D. E. (1976). Teach me to die [Fake book]. In D. E. Edwards (Ed.), *Peacebird* (p. 9). Los Angeles: Franciscan Communications Center.

Ellington, D., & Russell, B. (2003). Don't get around much anymore [Score]. In C. Cuellar (Ed.), *100 years of popular music 40s* (pp. 60–62). Miami, FL: Warner Bros.

Engelmann, H., & Glazer, T. (1942). Melody of love [Fake book]. In *The ultimate fake book* (3rd ed.) (p. 452). Milwaukee, WI: Hal Leonard.

Evans, D. (1996). Happy trails [Fake book]. In T. Esposito & T. Roed (Eds.), *The world's greatest fake book* (p. 253). Miami, FL: Warner Bros.

Fain, S., & Kahal, I. (1991). I'll be seeing you [Score]. In *The best songs ever* (4th ed.) (pp. 84–85). Milwaukee, WI: Hal Leonard.

Fekaris, D., & Perren, F. (1978). I will survive [Fake book]. In *The ultimate fake book* (3rd ed.) (p. 305). Milwaukee, WI: Hal Leonard.

Frank, J. M. (1985). The effects of music therapy and guided imagery. Oncology Nursing Forum, 12(5), 47–52.

Gabriel, C. H., & Martin, C. D. (1985). His eye is on a sparrow [Score]. In W. H. Goddard (Ed.), *Wonderful words of life* (p. 24). Carol Stream, IL: Hope.

Gaither, G., & Gaither, W. J. (1983). Because he lives [Fake book]. In *Gospel's best words and music* (p. 21). Milwaukee, WI: Hal Leonard.

Gaither, W. J. (1983). He touched me [Fake book]. In *Gospel's best words and music* (p. 84). Milwaukee, WI: Hal Leonard.

Garland, J. (1996). In the mood [Fake book]. In *The 200 of the best songs from swing era* (pp. 110–111). Milwaukee, WI: Hal Leonard.

Goldfaden, A. (1994). Rozhinkes mit mandln (Raisins and almonds). In H. Lefkowitch (Arr.) *Yiddish song favorites* (pp. 170–174). New York: Amsco.

Gounod, C. (1992). Ave Maria, meditation on prelude in C by J. S. Bach [Fake book]. In *The classical fake book* (p. 172). Milwaukee, WI: Hal Leonard.

Green, B., Brown, L., & Homer, B. (1991). Sentimental journey [Fake book]. In *The best fake book ever* (2nd ed.) (p. 618). Milwaukee, WI: Hal Leonard.

Groban, J. (2003). You raise me up. On *Closer* [CD]. Burbank, CA: Reprise Records.

Harrison, G. (1991). Here comes the sun [Fake book]. In *The best fake book ever* (2nd ed.) (p. 270). Milwaukee, WI: Hal Leonard.

Haugen, M., & Farjeon, R. (1994). Morning has broken [Score]. In *Gather comprehensive* (Vol. 3) (p. 756). Chicago: GIA.

Hawthorne, A. (1983). Whispering hope [Fake book]. In *Gospel's best words and music* (p. 304). Milwaukee, WI: Hal Leonard.

Henley, D., & Frey, G. (1994). Desperado [Lyrics and chords]. In *The tune book* (p. 193). San Anselmo, CA: Songs and Creations.

Henley, L., & Silbar, J. (2000). The wind beneath my wings [Score]. In C. Cuellar (Ed.), *Popular songs of inspiration* (pp. 3–13). Miami, FL: Warner Bros.

Hesla, B. (2006). Lake of mercy [Score]. In *Justice like a base of stone: Hymns of hope and transformation*. Minneapolis, MN: Augsburg Fortress.

Hobbs, B., & Goodman, D. (1996). Angels among us [Score]. In C. Cuellar (Ed.), *Popular songs of inspiration* (pp. 10–13). Miami, FL: Warner Bros.

Hoffman, J. (1993). *Musical massage* [CD]. Shawnee Mission, KS: Rhythmic Medicine.

Holland, J. C. (2003). Psychological care of patients: Psycho-oncology's contribution. *Journal of Clinical Oncology, 21*(23, Suppl.), 253s–265s.

Holst, G. (1996). The planets: Mars. On *Music for the imagination*: *Active* [CD]. Gilsum, NH: Barcelona.

Horner, J., & Jennings, W. (1997). My heart will go on [Fake book]. In *The ultimate fake book* (3rd ed.) (p. 477). Milwaukee, WI: Hal Leonard.

Jackson, G., & Jones, T. E. (1996). Old time rock and roll [Fake book]. In T. Esposito & T. Roed (Ed.), *The world's greatest fake book* (p. 492). Miami, FL: Warner Bros.

John, E., & Rice, T. (1995). Circle of life. On *Classic Disney*, Vol. I [CD]. Burbank, CA: Walt Disney Records.

John, E., & Taupin, B. (1990). Candle in the wind [Score]. In *Songs of the 80's* (pp. 10–16). Milwaukee, WI: Hal Leonard.

Joncas, M. (2000). On eagle's wings [Score]. In M. Zehnder (Ed.), *The best of the best in contemporary praise and worship* (p. 176). Phoenix, AZ: Fellowship.

Kaempfert, B., & Singleton, C., & Snyder, E. (1991). Spanish eyes [Fake book]. In *The best fake book ever* (2nd ed.) (p. 668). Milwaukee, WI: Hal Leonard.

Kaldor, C. (1997). Down to a river (Alan's song). On *Small café* [CD]. Cambridge, MA: Rounder Records.

Kent, W., & Burton, N. (1941). White cliffs of Dover [Fake book]. In *The ultimate fake book* (3rd ed.) (p. 760). Milwaukee, WI: Hal Leonard.

Kerr, R., & Jennings, W. (1996). Looks like we made it [Fake book]. In T. Esposito & T. Roed (Eds.), *The world's greatest fake book* (p. 409). Miami, FL: Warner Bros.

King, C. (1989). You've got a friend [Fake book]. In R. Shipton (Ed.), *The complete guitar player song book* [Omnibus ed., Book 2] (p. 47). New York: Amsco.

King, I. (1991). Show me the way to go home [Fake book]. In *The best fake book ever* (2nd ed.) (p. 637). Milwaukee, WI: Hal Leonard.

Kobialka, D. (1992). *Going home again* [CD]. Daly City, CA: Li-Sem Enterprises.

Kobialka, D. (1996). *Silk branches* [CD]. Daly City, CA: Li-Sem Enterprises.

Larson, J. (1997). Seasons of love [Fake book]. In *The ultimate Broadway fake book* (4th ed.) (pp. 634–635). Milwaukee, WI: Hal Leonard.

Ledbetter, H., & Lomax, J. A. (1950). Goodnight Irene [Fake book]. In *The ultimate fake book* (3rd ed.) (p. 227). Milwaukee, WI: Hal Leonard.

Lederberg, M. S. (1998). Oncology staff stress and related interventions. In J. C. Holland (Ed.), *Psycho-oncology* (pp. 1035–1048). New York: Oxford University Press.

Lennon, J., & McCartney, P. (1991). Let it be [Fake book]. In *The best fake book ever* (2nd ed.) (p. 426). Milwaukee, WI: Hal Leonard.

Lennon, J., & McCartney, P. (1991). With a little help from my friends [Fake book]. In *The best fake book ever* (2nd ed.) (pp. 820–821). Milwaukee, WI: Hal Leonard.

Levine, S. (1999). *Merciful awareness: Natural pain management techniques* [Cassette tape]. Boulder, CO: Sounds True.

Lovland, R., & Graham, B. (2002). *You raise me up* [Score]. Miami, FL: Warner Bros.

Mancina, M., & Collins, P. (1999). You'll be in my heart. On *Tarzan* [CD]. Burbank, CA: Burroughs/ Disney.

Mancini, H., & Mercer, J. (1996). Moon river [Fake book]. In T. Esposito & T. Roed (Eds.), *The world's greatest fake book* (p. 448). Miami, FL: Warner Bros.

McBroom, A. (2000). The rose [Score]. In C. Cuellar (Ed.), *Ultimate pop sheet music collection 2000* (pp. 274–277). Miami, FL: Warner Bros.

McGraw, T. (2004). Live like you were dying. On *Live like you were dying* [CD]. Nashville, TN: Curb Records.

McLachlan, S. (1997). Angel. On *Surfacing* [CD]. New York: Arista Records.

Miles, C. A. (1985). In the garden [Score]. In W. H. Goddard (Ed.), *Wonderful words of life* (p. 59). Carol Stream, IL: Hope.

Miller, D. M., Holten, S., & Nielsen, C. (1999). *Healing blue sky* [CD]. Minneapolis, MN: Christian Nielsen Music Therapy Productions. Available from www.nielsenmtbc.com or (952) 221-1857.

Miller, D. M., & Pansch, B. (1997, November). *Going home: A rationale for music therapy in hospice.* Presentation at the annual conference of the American Music Therapy Association, Los Angeles.

Mitchell, J. (1970). Both sides now [Score]. In M. Okun (Ed.), *The New York Times great songs of the sixties* (Vol. 1) (pp. 50–52). New York: Cherry Lane Music.

Mohr, J., & Gruber, F. (1996). Silent night [Fake book]. In T. Esposito & T. Roed (Eds.), *The world's greatest fake book* (p. 563). Miami, FL: Warner Bros.

Monk, W. H., & Lyte, H. F. (1985). Abide with me [Score]. In W. H. Goddard (Ed.), *Wonderful words of life* (p. 98). Carol Stream, IL: Hope.

Morris, K. (1996). Just a closer walk [Fake book]. In T. Esposito & T. Roed (Eds.), *The world's greatest fake book* (pp. 368). Miami, FL: Warner Bros.

Morrison, V. (1967). *Brown eyed girl* [Score]. Miami, FL: Warner Bros.

Mullins, R. (1996). Hold me, Jesus. On *Songs* [CD]. Nashville, TN: Arista Records.

Nakai, R. C. (2003). Canyon trilogy [CD]. Phoenix, AZ: Canyon Records.

Nash, J. (1978). I can see clearly now [Score]. In M. Okun (Ed.), *Great songs of the 70s* (pp. 106–107). New York: Times Books.

National Cancer Institute. (2004). *Situation-specific influences on adjustment.* Retrieved November 30, 2004, from http://www.cancer.gov/cancertopics/pdq/supportivecare/adjustment/HealthProfessional/page2#Section_17

National Comprehensive Cancer Network. (2001). Distress management practice guidelines. *Cancer Control, 8*(6, Suppl. 2), 88–93.

Nelson, W. (1991). Crazy [Score]. In *The best songs ever* (4th ed.) (pp. 48–49). Milwaukee, WI: Hal Leonard.

Newton, J. (1985). Amazing grace [Score]. In W. H. Goddard (Ed.), *Wonderful words of life* (p. 88). Carol Stream, IL: Hope.

Nielsen, C. (2003). *Flow* [CD]. Minneapolis, MN: Christian Nielsen Music Therapy Productions. Available from www.nielsenmtbc.com or (952) 221-1857.

Nielsen, C. (2003). *Sacred wind calling* [CD]. Minneapolis, MN: Christian Nielsen Music Therapy Productions. Available from www.nielsenmtbc.com or (952) 221-1857.

O'Hara, J. (1991). Grandpa [Fake book]. In *The best fake book ever* (2nd ed.) (p. 242). Milwaukee, WI: Hal Leonard.

Orff, C. (1996). Carmina burana, excerpts. On *Music for the imagination: Active* [CD]. Gilsum, NH: Barcelona.

Pomeranz, D. (1994). It's in every one of us [Fake book]. In *The tune book* (p. 131A). San Anselmo, CA: Songs and Creations.

Presley, E., & Matson, V. (1991). Love me tender [Score]. In *The best songs ever* (4th ed.) (pp. 124–125). Milwaukee, WI: Hal Leonard.

Raskin, G. (1962). Those were the days [Fake book]. In *The ultimate fake book* (3rd ed.) (p. 703). Milwaukee, WI: Hal Leonard.

Reed, A. (1986). Every long journey [Fake book]. In *Ann Reed song book* (pp. 27–30). Minneapolis, MN: Turtlecub Productions.

Revaux, J., Francois, C., Thibault, G., & Anka, P. (1996). My way [Fake book]. In T. Esposito & T. Roed (Eds.), *The world's greatest fake book* (p. 465). Miami, FL: Warner Bros.

Richardson, S. (1997). *Shakuhachi meditation music* [CD]. Boulder, CO: Sounds True.

Rodgers, R., & Hammerstein, O. (1997). Climb every mountain [Score]. In *The ultimate Broadway fake book* (4th ed.) (p. 533). Milwaukee, WI: Hal Leonard.

Rodgers, R., & Hammerstein, O. (1997). Oh, what a beautiful morning [Fake book]. In *The ultimate Broadway fake book* (4th ed.) (p. 436–437). Milwaukee, WI: Hal Leonard.

Rodgers, R., & Hammerstein, O. (1997). Some enchanted evening [Fake book]. In *The ultimate Broadway fake book* (4th ed.) (pp. 548–549). Milwaukee, WI: Hal Leonard.

Rodgers, R., & Hammerstein, O. (1997). You'll never walk alone [Fake book]. In *The ultimate Broadway fake book* (4th ed.) (p. 140). Milwaukee, WI: Hal Leonard.

Rutherford, M., & Robertson, B.A. (1988). The living years. [Recorded by Mike and the Mechanics]. On *Living years* [CD]. New York: Atlantic Records.

Schmidt, H., & Jones, T. (1997). Try to remember [Fake book]. In *The ultimate Broadway fake book* (4th ed.) (p. 198). Milwaukee, WI: Hal Leonard.

Schubert (1992). Ave Maria [Fake book]. In *The classical fake book* (p. 310). Milwaukee, WI: Hal Leonard.

Schultz, M. (2000). He's my son. On *Mark Schultz* [CD]. New York: Word Entertainment.

Shaw, V., & Brooks, G. (1996). The river [Score]. In C. Cuellar (Ed.), *Popular songs of inspiration* (pp. 55–59). Miami, FL: Warner Bros.

Showalter, A. J., & Hoffman, E. A. (1985). Leaning on the everlasting arms [Score]. In W. H. Goddard (Ed.), *Wonderful words of life* (p. 86). Carol Stream, IL: Hope.

Sillers, T., & Sanders, M.D. (2000). *I hope you dance* [Score]. Milwaukee, WI: Hal Leonard.

Simon, P. (1969). Bridge over troubled water [Score]. In *Simon and Garfunkel's greatest hits* (pp. 40–44). London: Music Sales.

Sondheim, S. (1996). Send in the clowns [Fake book]. In T. Esposito & T. Roed (Eds.), *The world's greatest fake book* (p. 545). Miami, FL: Warner Bros.

Sparks, R. (1996). Today [Fake book]. In T. Esposito & T. Roed (Eds.), *The world's greatest fake book* (p. 641). Miami, FL: Warner Bros.

Standley, J. (1992). Clinical applications of music and chemotherapy: The effects of nausea and emesis. *Music Therapy Perspectives, 10*, 27–35.

Stewart, R., Cregan, J., Savigar, K., & Dylan, B. (1988). Forever young [Fake book]. In *The ultimate fake book* (3rd ed.) (p. 208). Milwaukee, WI: Hal Leonard.

Strouse, C., & Charnin, M. (1997). Tomorrow [Fake book]. In *The ultimate Broadway fake book* (4th ed.) (p. 83). Milwaukee, WI: Hal Leonard.

Taylor, J. (1991). Fire and rain [Fake book]. In *The best fake book ever* (2nd ed.) (pp. 208–209). Milwaukee, WI: Hal Leonard.

Thaut, M. (1999). *Training manual for Neurologic Music Therapy*. Center for Biomedical Research in Music, Colorado State University, Ft. Collins.

Thompson, W. L. (1983). Softly and tenderly [Fake book]. In *Gospel's best words and music* (p. 248). Milwaukee, WI: Hal Leonard.

Traditional. (1980). Dona nobis pacem [Score]. In L. Dallin & L. Dallin (Eds.), *Heritage songster* (2nd ed.) (p. 186). Boston: McGraw Hill.

Traditional folk song. (1996). Down in the valley [Fake book]. In T. Esposito & T. Roed (Eds.), *The world's greatest fake book* (p. 188). Miami, FL: Warner Bros.

Traditional folk song. (1996). Red river valley [Fake book]. In T. Esposito & T. Roed (Eds.), *The world's greatest fake book* (p. 526). Miami, FL: Warner Bros.

Traditional folk song. (1996). Shenandoah [Fake book]. In T. Esposito & T. Roed (Eds.), *The world's greatest fake book* (p. 557). Miami, FL: Warner Bros.

Traditional spiritual. (1971). All night, all day [Score]. In C. F. Brown (Ed.), *Sing 'n' celebrate* (p. 79). Waco, TX: Word Music.

Ungar, J. (1983). *Ashokan farewell* [Score]. Hurley, NY: Swinging Door Music.

Vaughan-Williams, R. (2000). Rhosymedre. On *Hickox conducts Vaughan Williams* [CD]. London: EMI Records.

Warschafsky, M. (1994). Oyfn pripetshok (On the hearth). In *Yiddish song favorites* (pp. 112–115). New York: Amsco.

Weatherly, F. (1996). Danny boy [Fake book]. In T. Esposito & T. Roed (Eds.), *The world's greatest fake book* (p. 162). Miami, FL: Warner Bros.

Webber, A. L., & Nunn, T. (1997). Memory [Fake book]. In *The ultimate Broadway fake book* (4th ed.) (p. 156). Milwaukee, WI: Hal Leonard.

Webster, J. P., & Bennett, S. F. (1985). Sweet by and by [Score]. In W. H. Goddard (Ed.), *Wonderful words of life* (p. 35). Carol Stream, IL: Hope.

Whiting, R. A., & Egan, R. B. (1994). Till we meet again [Fake book]. In *The ultimate fake book* (3rd ed.) (p. 709). Milwaukee, WI: Hal Leonard.

Wilkin, M., & Kristofferson, K. (1996). One day at a time [Fake book]. In T. Esposito & T. Roed (Eds.), *The world's greatest fake book* (p. 499). Miami, FL: Warner Bros.

Williams, H. (1996). I'm so lonesome, I could cry [Fake book]. In T. Esposito & T. Roed (Eds.), *The world's greatest fake book* (p. 332). Miami, FL: Warner Bros.

Withers, B. (2000). Lean on me [Score]. In C. Cuellar (Ed.), *Ultimate pop sheet music collection 2000* (pp. 212–217). Miami, FL: Warner Bros.

Worden, J. W. (1991). *Grief counseling and grief therapy: A handbook for the mental health practitioner* (2nd ed.). New York: Springer.

Yallop, T. (Producer). (1997). *Piano dreamers* [CD]. Sausalito, CA: Real Music.

Yallop, T. (Producer). (1997). *Tranquility* [CD]. Sausalito, CA: Real Music.

Yallop, T. (Producer). (2001). *Quiet days* [CD]. Sausalito, CA: Real Music.

Ylvisaker, J. (1995). I was there to hear your borning cry [Score]. In *With one voice* (pp. 770–771). Minneapolis, MN: Augsburg Fortress.

Youmans, V., & Heyman, E. (1996). Through the years (Kenny Rogers) [Fake book]. In T. Esposito & T. Roed (Eds.), *The world's greatest fake book* (p. 634). Miami, FL: Warner Bros.

Zevon, Warren (2003). Keep me in your heart. On *The wind* [CD]. New York: Artemis Records.

Zschech, D. (2000). Shout to the Lord [Score]. In M. Zehnder (Ed.), *The best of the best in contemporary praise and worship* (pp. 198–199). Phoenix, AZ: Fellowship.

Section III:

Resources

GLOSSARY OF TERMS

Abruptio placenta – the premature separation of a normally implanted placenta from the uterus after 20 weeks of gestation. It is an obstetric emergency.

Acute – a disease with sudden onset, short duration, and rapid progression, contrasted with "subacute," which refers to a longer duration or less rapid progression, and "chronic," which refers to an infinite duration or very little change.

Adjuvant – a substance or therapy used in addition to a drug or treatment.

Adrenal-medullary – center part of the adrenal gland that consists of cells that secrete epinephrine and norepinephrine.

Adrenaline (epinephrine) – a hormone that increases heart rate and contracts blood vessels, dilates air passages, and participates in the fight-or-flight response of the sympathic nervous system.

Adynamia – lack of strength or vigor due to a pathological condition. It is often associated with a range of neurological diseases such as multiple sclerosis and medial-frontal lobe lesions.

Analgesia (analgesic) – a drug that reduces pain without the loss of consciousness.

Antepartum – the period before childbirth.

Antiemetic – a drug taken to reduce nausea and vomiting.

Anxiolytic – something that relieves anxiety; usually a medication, but can also include the use of music or sound.

Aphasia – an acquired language disorder in which there is an impairment of any language modality. This may include difficulty in producing or comprehending spoken or written language.

Apnea – suspension of external breathing.

Arterial constriction – the narrowing or obstruction of blood vessels transporting blood from the heart to other areas of the body.

Audioanalgesia – the use of sound or music to reduce pain.

Autogenic relaxation – a relaxation technique involving visual imagery and body awareness; focus is on mentally repeated words or suggestions and awareness of physical sensations such as relaxed breathing, slower heart rate, and progressive relaxation of muscles.

Biologic therapy (also biotherapy) – includes a wide range of medicinal products such as vaccines, blood and blood components, allergenics, somatic cells, gene therapy, tissues, and recombinant therapeutic proteins created by biological processes.

Biomarker – biochemical characteristic that can indicate the progress of disease or effects of treatment.

Breech – delivery in which the baby is bottom- or foot-first; more likely to harm the mother or child than a head-first delivery.

Carcinogen – any substance, radionuclide or radiation, that is an agent directly involved in the exacerbation of cancer or in the increase of its propagation.

Cardiology – medical specialty dealing with disorders of the heart.

Cardiothoracic – diseases affecting organs inside the thorax (the chest), generally the heart and lungs.

Cerebrovascular accident (stroke) – the rapidly developing loss of brain function(s) due to disturbance in the blood supply to the brain, caused by a blocked or burst blood vessel.

Cheyne-Stokes – an abnormal pattern of breathing characterized by oscillation of ventilation between apnea and tachypnea with a crescendo-decrescendo pattern in the depth of respirations, to compensate for changing serum partial pressures of oxygen and carbon dioxide.

Co-morbidity – either the presence of one or more disorders (or diseases) in addition to a primary disease or disorder, or the effect of such additional disorders or diseases.

Contact isolation – used to prevent the spread of diseases that can be spread through contact with open wounds. Health care workers making contact with a patient on contact isolation are required to wear gloves and, in some cases, a gown.

Coronary Artery Bypass Grafting (CABG) – a surgical procedure performed to relieve angina and reduce the risk of death from coronary artery disease.

Curative – treatments with a focus on healing and recovery.

Debrided – the medical removal of a patient's dead, damaged, or infected tissue to improve the healing potential of the remaining healthy tissue.

DNR (Do Not Resucitate) – a legal, binding document that states resuscitation should not be attempted if a person suffers cardiac or respiratory arrest.

Doula – a non-medical assistant who provides a mother with physical and emotional support before, during, and after the childbirth process.

Dyspnea – difficulty in breathing or shortness of breath.

Effaced (Cervical effacement) – the softening and thinning of the cervix for birth.

Endocrinology – concerned with the study of the biosynthesis, storage, chemistry, and physiological function of hormones and with the cells of the endocrine glands and tissues that secrete them.

Endorphin – hormones that work as natural pain relievers.

Entrainment – a phenomenon in which the dominant rhythmic vibrations of one object will cause the less powerful vibrations of another object to oscillate at the rate of the dominant rhythm.

Epidural analgesia – a form of regional anesthesia involving injection of drugs through a catheter placed into the epidural space. The injection can cause both a loss of sensation (anesthesia) and a loss of pain (analgesia), by blocking the transmission of signals through nerves in or near the spinal cord.

Epinephrine (adrenaline) – a substance secreted by the adrenal medulla as a response to a stressor; part of the fight-or-flight response.

Extubation – the process of removing a tube from a hollow organ or passageway, often from the airway.

Fetus – an unborn baby from the eighth week after conception until the moment of birth; the term *embryo* is used prior to the eighth week.

Gastroenterology – medicine whereby the digestive system and its disorders are studied.

Gate Control Theory – the idea that physical pain is not a direct result of activation of pain receptor neurons, but rather its perception is modulated by interaction between different neurons. The idea that a gate control system modulates sensory input from the skin before it evokes pain perception and response.

Gustatory – the sensory system for the sense of taste.

Hematology – internal medicine concerned with the study of blood.

Hematopoiesis – the production of blood cells in the bone marrow.

Hypochondria – an excessive preoccupation or worry about having a serious illness.

Immunocompetence – the ability to produce normal immune responses.

Immunocompromised – the inability to produce a normal immune response; usually caused by disease, treatment, or malnutrition.

Immunology – a broad branch of biomedical science that covers the study of all aspects of the immune system in all organisms.

Immunotherapy – treatment of disease by inducing, enhancing, or suppressing an immune response.

Implantable ports – a central venous line that does not have an external connector; instead, it has a small reservoir that is covered with silicone rubber and is implanted under the skin. Medication is administered intermittently by placing a small needle through the skin, piercing the silicone, into the reservoir. When the needle is withdrawn, the reservoir cover reseals itself.

Induction – starting of labor using drugs.

Intrapartum –occurring during labor and delivery.

Intubation – the process of putting a tube into an organ, airway, or other passageway.

Iso principle – the technique of matching the musical elements (e.g., tempo, dynamics, melodic contour) to the current physical and/or emotional behavior of the patient and then gradually changing the musical elements to facilitate a change in physical and/or emotional behavior in a desired direction.

Ketoacidosis – a feature of uncontrolled diabetes that is characterized by an increase in the acidity and ketone bodies in the blood; symptoms can include difficulty breathing, increased frequency of urination, confusion, and loss of consciousness.

Metastasis (metastasize) – the spread of cancer cells from the location of the original tumor to other areas of the body.

Methicillin-resistant Staphylococcus aureus (MRSA) – a type of staph bacteria resistant to antibiotics; often occurs when the entrance site of a catheter becomes infected.

Midwife – a person trained to assist a woman during childbirth, often at the woman's home or a special birthing center.

Musicogenic epilepsy – a form of reflex or affective epilepsy; involves autonomic, behavioral, cognitive, and emotional reactions to selected musical stimuli.

Musculoskeletal – system involving or made up of both the muscles and bones.

Myocardial – relating to the muscle tissue of the heart.

NG tube – nasogastric feeding tube, passed through the nares (nostril), down the esophagus and into the stomach.

Necrosis – the death of cells or tissues, sometimes due to restricted blood flow.

Neoplasm – a tumor, or abnormal growth of tissue, which may be benign or malignant.

Nephrology – the study of the function and diseases of the kidney.

Neuro-oncology – cancer of the central nervous system.

Neutrophil – a type of white blood cell that fights infection in the body by killing and digesting microorganisms.

Norepinephrine (noradrenaline) – a substance secreted by the adrenal medulla that narrows blood vessels and raises blood pressure.

Nurse-midwife – a person trained in both nursing and midwifery; certified by the American College of Nurse-Midwives.

Obstetrician – a physician whose specialty is managing pregnancy and delivering babies.

Olfactory – the sense of smell.

Oncology/hematology – the branch of medicine that deals with tumors (cancer).

Palliative care – treatments with a focus on reducing the severity of a disease, slowing its progress, and lowering pain levels.

Peripherally inserted central catheters (PIC line) – a form of intravenous access that can be used for a prolonged period of time.

Pitocin – U.S. brand name of the drug oxytocin that stimulates contraction of uterine smooth muscle cells. Uterine sensitivity to oxytocin increases throughout pregnancy.

Placenta – a temporary organ joining a fetus and its mother; transmits nutrients and oxygen to the fetus and removes waste and carbon dioxide.

Placenta previa – when the placenta is attached in the lower half of the uterus, covering the mouth of the uterus; risks include maternal hemorrhage; requires cesarean section delivery.

Postpartum – occurring after birth.

Pre-eclampsia – a condition in the third trimester of pregnancy in which the mother experiences sudden high blood pressure, swelling of the hands and feet, high levels of protein in the urine, and other abnormal symptoms; if untreated, it can lead to coma and seizures, putting both the mother and fetus in danger.

Premature labor – labor that begins after the 20th week of gestation and before the 37th week (considered full term); requires prompt medical attention, medications, and bed rest to stop the labor.

Prognosis – the expected course of a disease, and the patient's chance of recovery.

Progressive muscle relaxation – a relaxation technique in which each muscle group is tensed and relaxed in turn; the purpose is awareness of the physical sensations of stress and relaxation.

Psychoneuroimmunology (PNI) – the study of the interrelationships between psychological, behavioral, neural, endocrinal, and immune processes.

Pulmonology – the specialty that deals with diseases of the lungs and the respiratory tract.

Respiratory isolation – required for diseases that are spread through particles that are exhaled.

Reticular Activating System – an area of the brain responsible for regulating arousal and sleep-wake transitions.

Rheumatology – medical specialization in rheumatic diseases.

Ruptured membranes – occasionally, the membranes (amniotic and chorionic sac) rupture before labor begins, and amniotic fluid leaks through the cervix and vagina. Also know as premature rupture of membranes (PROM), when the amniotic sac breaks prior to labor; if prior to the 37th week, it is considered a preterm PROM; the only symptom is leaking or gushing fluid from the vagina, but infection is possible if delivery is delayed.

Strict contact isolation – used for the most contagious diseases spread through the air and, in some cases, by contact. Patient is kept in a room separate from other patients, health care staff contact is minimal, and, in some cases, visitors are not allowed.

Sympathetic nervous system (SNS) – one of the three parts of the autonomic nervous system, along with the enteric and parasympathetic systems. Its general action is to mobilize the body's resources under stress, to induce the flight-or-fight response. It is, however, constantly active at a basal level in order to maintain homeostasis.

Toxemia – a generic term for poisoning by bacterial toxins in the blood. Infection increases risk of obstetric complications and problems in the fetus. The toxins released by bacteria can enter the blood stream and can move throughout the body without any bacteria entering the blood stream.

Tracheotomy – surgical procedure on the neck to open a direct airway through an incision in the trachea (the windpipe).

Transverse – delivery in which the fetus lies horizontally in the uterus so that the shoulder enters the birth canal first; can lead to injury of the uterus.

Vascular Access Device (central venous catheter) – a long, thin, flexible tube used to give medicines, fluids, nutrients, or blood products over a long period of time, usually several weeks or more. A catheter is often inserted in the arm or chest through the skin into a large vein. The catheter is threaded through this vein until it reaches a large vein near the heart.

Venous constriction – the narrowing or obstruction of blood vessels transporting blood to the heart from other areas of the body.

Ventilator – any machine designed to mechanically move breatheable air into and out of the lungs, to provide the mechanism of breathing for a patient who is physically unable to breathe, or is breathing insufficiently.

Visualization – a relaxation technique that focuses on imagining multisensory mental images in order to create a calming place or situation.

COMPREHENSIVE BIBLIOGRAPHY

Adults

Obstetrics

Browning, C. A. (2000). Using music during childbirth. *Birth: Issues in Perinatal Care, 27*, 272–276.

Browning, C. A. (2001). Music therapy in childbirth: Research in practice. *Music Therapy Perspectives, 19*, 74–81.

Cervasco, A. M. (2008). The effects of mothers' singing on full-term and preterm infants and maternal emotional responses. *Journal of Music Therapy, 45*, 273–306.

Chang, S., & Chen, C. (2005). Effects of music therapy on women's physiologic measures, anxiety, and satisfaction during cesarean delivery. *Research in Nursing and Health, 28*, 453–461.

Clark, M., McCorkle, R., & Williams, S. (1981). Music therapy-assisted labor and delivery. *Journal of Music Therapy, 18*, 88–100.

Clark, M. E. (1986). Music therapy-assisted childbirth: A practical guide. *Music Therapy Perspectives, 3*, 34–41.

Durham, L., & Collins, M. (1986). The effect of music as a conditioning aid in prepared childbirth education. *Journal of Obstetric, Gynecologic, and Neonatal Nursing, 15*, 268–270.

Elliott, S. A., Anderson, M., Brough, D. I., Watson, J. P., & Rugg, A. J. (1984, April). Relationship between obstetric outcome and psychological measures in pregnancy and the postnatal year. *Journal of Reproductive and Infant Psychology, 2*(1), 18–32.

Elliott, T. R., Shewchuk, R., Richeson, C., Pickelman, H., & Franklin, K. W. (1996). Problem-solving appraisal and the prediction of depression during pregnancy and in the postpartum period. *Journal of Counseling and Development, 74*, 645–651.

Elster, A. B., & Roberts, D. (1985). The financial impact of a comprehensive adolescent pregnancy program on a university hospital. *Journal of Adolescent Health Care, 6*, 17–20.

Federico, G. F., & Whitwell, G. E. (2001). Music therapy and pregnancy. *Journal of Prenatal and Perinatal Psychology and Health, 15*, 299–311.

Ferketich, S. L., & Mercer, R. T. (1990). Effects of antepartal stress on health status during early motherhood. *Scholarly Inquiry for Nursing Practice: An International Journal, 4*(2), 127–149.

Geden, E. A., Lower, M., Beattie, S., & Beck, N. (1989). Effects of music and imagery on physiologic and self-report of analogued labor pain. *Nursing Research, 38*, 37–41.

Gonzalez, C. E. (1989). The music therapy-assisted childbirth program: A study evaluation. *Journal of Prenatal and Perinatal Psychology and Health, 4*, 111–124.

Guttmacher Institute. (2004). *U.S. teenage pregnancy statistics national and state trends and trends by race and ethnicity.* Retrieved October 16, 2009, from http://www.guttmacher.org/pubs/2006/09/12/USTPstats.pdf

Hanser, S. B., Larson, S. D., & O'Connell, A. S. (1983). The effect of music on relaxation of expectant mothers during labor. *Journal of Music Therapy, 22*, 50–58.

Kerschner, J., & Schenck, V. (1991). Music therapy-assisted childbirth. *International Journal of Childbirth Education, 6*(3), 32–33.

Lex, J. P., Pratt, R. R., Abel, H. H., & Spintge, R. (1996). Effects of music listening and biofeedback interventions on cardiac chronotropic control of women in childbirth. *Music Medicine, 2*, 182–192.

Liebman, S. S., & MacLaren, A. (1991). The effects of music and relaxation on third trimester anxiety in adolescent pregnancy. *Journal of Music Therapy, 28*, 89–100.

Maloni, J. A., Brezinski-Tomasi, J. E., & Johnson, L. A. (2001). Antepartum bed rest: Effect upon the family. *Journal of Obstetrics, Gynecology, and Neonatal Nursing, 30*(2), 165–173.

McKinney, C. H. (1990). Music therapy in obstetrics: A review. *Music Therapy Perspectives, 8*, 57–60.

Olson, S. L. (1998). Bedside musical care: Applications in pregnancy, childbirth, and neonatal care. *Journal of Obstetric, Gynecologic, and Neonatal Nursing, 27*, 569–575.

Phumdoung, S., & Good, M. (2003). Music reduces sensation and distress of labor pain. *Pain Management Nursing, 4*, 54–61.

Reza, M., Ali, S. M., Saeed, K., Abul-Qasim, A., & Reza, T. H. (2007). The impact of music on postoperative pain and anxiety following cesarean section. *Middle East Journal of Anesthesiology, 19*, 573–586.

Sidorenko, V. N. (2000). Clinical application of Medical Resonance Therapy Music in high-risk pregnancies. *Integrative Physiological and Behavioral Science, 35*, 199–207.

Stevens, K. M. (1992). My room, not theirs! A case study of music during childbirth. *Journal of the Australian College of Midwives, 5*(3), 27–30.

Whitwell, G. E. (1999). The importance of prenatal sound and music. *Journal of Prenatal and Perinatal Psychology and Health, 13*, 255–262.

Zeanah, C. H., Keener, M. A., Anders, T. F., & Vieira-Baker, C. C. (1987). Adolescent mothers' perceptions of their infants before and after birth. *American Journal of Orthopsychiatry, 57*(3), 351–360.

Zwelling, E., Johnson, K., & Allen, J. (2006). How to implement complementary therapies for laboring women. *The American Journal of Maternal Child Nursing, 31*, 364–372.

Intensive Care

Aasgaard, T. (1999). Music therapy as milieu in the hospice and paediatric oncology ward. In D. Aldridge (Ed.), *Music therapy in palliative care: New voices* (pp. 29–42). London: Jessica Kingsley.

Ahmad, H., Brophy, K., Grant, G. R., & Brandstetter, R. D. (1999). Benefit of music therapy for our intensive care unit (ICU) patients. *Heart & Lung: The Journal of Critical Care, 28*, 79–80.

Aldridge, D. (2006). Music therapy and spirituality: A transcendental understanding of suffering. In D. Aldridge & J. Fachner (Eds.), *Music and altered states: Consciousness, transcendence, therapy and addictions* (pp. 155–171). Philadelphia: Jessica Kingsley.

Almerud, S., & Petersson, K. (2003). Music therapy: A complementary treatment for mechanically ventilated intensive care patients. *Intensive and Critical Care Nursing, 19*, 21–30.

Bally, K., Campbell, D., Chesnick, K., & Tranmer, J. E. (2003). Effects of patient-controlled music therapy during coronary angiography on procedural pain and anxiety distress syndrome. *Critical Care Nursing, 23*, 50–58.

Bright, R. (1995). Music therapy as a facilitator in grief counseling. *The art and science of music therapy: A handbook* (pp. 309–323). Newark, NJ: Harwood Academic.

Cardozo, M. (2004). Harmonic sounds: Complementary medicine for the critically ill. *British Journal of Nursing, 13*, 1321–1324.

Chlan, L. L. (1998). Effectiveness of a music therapy intervention on relaxation and anxiety for patients receiving ventilatory assistance. *Heart & Lung: The Journal of Critical Care, 27*, 169–176.

Chlan, L. L. (2000). Music therapy as a nursing intervention for patients supported by mechanical ventilation. *American Association of Critical-Care Nurses Clinical Issues, 11*(1), 128–138.

Chlan, L. L., Engeland, W. C., Anthony, A., & Guttormson, J. (2007). Influence of music on the stress response in patients receiving mechanical ventilatory support: A pilot study. *American Journal of Critical Care, 16*, 141–145.

Coughlan, A. (1994). Music therapy in the ICU. *Nursing Times, 90*(17), 35.

Dileo, C., & Starr, R. (2005). Cultural issues in music therapy at end of life. In C. Dileo & J. V. Loewy (Eds.), *Music therapy at the end of life* (pp. 85–94). Cherry Hill, NJ: Jeffrey Books.

Emery, C. F., Hsiao, E. T., Hill, S. M., & Frid, D. J. (2003). Short-term effects of exercise and music on cognitive performance among participants in a cardiac rehabilitation program. *Heart & Lung, 32*, 368–373.

Ferguson, S. L., & Voll, K. V. (2004). Burn pain and anxiety: The use of music relaxation during rehabilitation. *Journal of Burn Care & Rehabilitation, 25*, 8–14.

Hamel, W. J. (2001). The effects of music intervention on anxiety in the patient waiting for cadiac cathetorization. *Intensive Critical Care Nursing, 17*(5), 279–285.

Lee, O. K. A., Chung, Y. F. L., Chan, M. F., & Chan, W. M. (2005). Music and its effect on the physiological responses and anxiety levels of patients receiving mechanical ventilation: A pilot study. *Journal of Clinical Nursing, 14*, 609–620.

Magee, W. L. (2007). Development of a music therapy assessment tool for patients in low awareness states. *Neurorehabiliation, 22*(4), 319–324.

Magee, W. L., & Davidson, J. W. (2002). The effect of music therapy on mood states in neurological patients: A pilot study. *Journal of Music Therapy, 39*, 20–29.

Mandel, S. E., Hanser, S. B., & Ryan, L. J. (2010). Effects of a music-assisted relaxation and imagery compact disc recording on health-related outcomes in cardiac rehabilitation. *Music Therapy Perspectives, 28*, 11–21.

Metzger, L. K. (2004). Assessment of use of music by patients participating in cardiac rehabilitation. *Journal of Music Therapy, 41*, 55–69.

O'Sullivan, R. J. (1991). A musical road to recovery: Music in intensive care. *Intensive Care Nursing, 7*, 160–163.

Rider, M. S. (1985). Entrainment mechanisms are involved in pain reduction, muscle relaxation, and music-mediated imagery. *Journal of Music Therapy, 22*(4), 183–192.

Robb, S. L. (2000). Music assisted progressive muscle relaxation, progressive muscle relaxation, music listening, and silence: A comparison of relaxation techniques. *Journal of Music Therapy, 37*(1), 2–21.

Sendelbach, S. E., Halm, M. A., Doran, K. A., Miller, E. H., & Gaillard, P. (2006). Effects of music therapy on physiological and psychological outcomes for patients undergoing cardiac surgery. *Journal of Cardiovascular Nursing, 21*, 194–200.

Stubbs, T. (2005). Experiences and perceptions of music therapy in critical illness. *Nursing Times, 101*(45), 34–36.

Thompson, A. B., Arnold, J. C., & Murray, S. E. (1990). Music therapy assessment of the cerebrovascular accident patient. *Music Therapy Perspectives, 8*, 23–29.

Tse, M. M. Y., Chan, M. F., & Benzie, I. F. F. (2005). The effect of music therapy on postoperative pain, heart rate, systolic blood pressure and analgesic use following nasal surgery. *Journal of Pain and Palliative Care Pharmacotherapy, 19*, 21–29.

Updike, P. (1990). Music therapy results for ICU patients. *Dimensions of Critical Care Nursing, 9*, 39–45.

Voss, J. A., Good, M., Yates, B., Baun, M. M., Thompson, A., & Hertzog, M. (2004). Sedative music reduces anxiety and pain during chair rest after open-heart surgery. *Pain, 112*, 197–203.

Wheeler, B. L., Shiflett, S. C., & Nayak, S. (2003). Effects of number of sessions and group or individual music therapy on the mood and behavior of people who have had strokes or traumatic brain injuries. *Nordic Journal of Music Therapy, 12*, 139–151.

Wilkins, M. K., & Moore, M. L. (2004). Music intervention in the intensive care unit: A complementary therapy to improve patient outcomes. *Evidence-Based Nursing, 7*, 103–104.

General Medical/Surgical

Allen, K., Golden, L. H., Izzo, J. L., Jr., Ching, M. L., Forrest, A., Niles, C. R., et al. (2001). Normalization of hypertensive responses during ambulatory surgical stress by preoperative music. *Psychosomatic Medicine, 63*, 487–492.

Augustin, P., & Hains, A. A. (1996). Effect of music on ambulatory surgery patients' preoperative anxiety. *Association of periOperative Registered Nurses Journal, 63*, 750–758.

Ayoub, C. M., Rizk, L. B., Yaacoub, C. I., Gaal, D., & Kain, Z. N. (2005). Music and ambient operating room noise in patients undergoing spinal anesthesia. *Anesthesia and Analgesia, 100*, 1316–1319.

Barnason, S., Zimmerman, L., & Nieveen, J. (1995). The effects of music interventions on anxiety in the patient after coronary artery bypass grafting. *Heart & Lung: The Journal of Critical Care, 24*, 124–132.

Broscious, S. K. (1999). Music: An intervention for pain during chest tube removal after open heart surgery. *American Journal of Critical Care, 8*, 410–415.

Brunges, M. J., & Avigne, G. (2003). Music therapy for reducing surgical anxiety. *Association of perOperative Registered Nurses Journal, 78*, 816–818.

Byers, J. F., & Smyth, K. A. (1997). Effect of a music intervention on noise annoyance, heart rate, and blood pressure in cardiac surgery patients. *American Journal of Critical Care, 6*, 183–191.

Chan, M. F. (2007). Effects of music on patients undergoing a C-clamp procedure after percutaneous coronary interventions: A randomized controlled trial. *Heart & Lung: The Journal of Critical Care, 36*, 431–439.

Christenberry, E. B. (1979). The use of music therapy with burn patients. *Journal of Music Therapy, 16*, 138–148.

Cirina, C. (1994). Effects of sedative music on patient preoperative anxiety. *Today's OR Nurse, 16*(3), 15.

Cooke, M., Chaboyer, W., Schluter, P., & Hiratos, M. (2005). The effect of music on preoperative anxiety in day surgery. *Journal of Advanced Nursing, 52*, 47–55.

Cornell, E. L. (1948). Music as a diverter in local and spinal anesthesia and analgesia. *American Journal of Obstetrics and Gynecology, 56*, 582–583.

Cowan, D. S. (1991). Music therapy in the surgical arena. *Music Therapy Perspectives, 9*, 42–45.

Cruise, C. J., Chung, F., Yogendran, S., & Little, D. (1997). Music increases satisfaction in elderly outpatients undergoing cataract surgery. *Canadian Journal of Anaesthesia, 44*, 43–48.

Cunningham, M. F., Monson, B., & Bookbinder, M. (1997). Introducing a music program in the perioperative area. *Association of periOperative Registered Nurses Journal, 66*, 674–682.

Eisenman, A., & Cohen, B. (1995). Music therapy for patients undergoing regional anesthesia. *Association of periOperative Registered Nurses Journal, 62*, 947–950.

Engen, R. L. (2005). The singer's breath: Implications for treatment of persons with emphysema. *Journal of Music Therapy, 42*, 20–48.

Evans, D. (2002). The effectiveness of music as an intervention for hospital patients: A systematic review. *Journal of Advanced Nursing, 37*, 8–18.

Ferguson, S. L., & Voll, K. V. (2004). Burn pain and anxiety: The use of music relaxation during rehabilitation. *The Journal of Burn Care and Rehabilitation, 25*, 8–14.

Fratianne, R. B., Prensner, J. D., Huston, M. J., Super, D. M., Yowler, C. J., & Standley, J. M. (2001). The effect of music-based imagery and musical alternate engagement on the burn debridement process. *Journal of Burn Care & Rehabilitation, 22*, 47–53.

Gaberson, K. B. (1995). The effect of humorous and musical distraction on preoperative anxiety. *Association of periOperative Registered Nurses Journal, 62*, 784–789.

Giaquinto, S., Cacciato, A., Minasi, S., Sostero, E., & Amanda, S. (2006). Effects of music-based therapy on distress following knee arthroplasty. *British Journal of Nursing, 15*, 576–579.

Goloff, M. S. (1981). The responses of hospitalized medical patients to music therapy. *Music Therapy, 1*, 51–56.

Good, M. (1995). A comparison of the effects of jaw relaxation and music on postoperative pain. *Nursing Research, 44*, 52–57.

Good, M. (1996). Effects of relaxation and music on postoperative pain: A review. *Journal of Advanced Nursing, 24*, 905–914.

Good, M., Anderson, G. C., Ahn, S., Cong, X., & Stanton-Hicks, M. (2005). Relaxation and music reduce pain following intestinal surgery. *Research in Nursing and Health, 28*, 240–251.

Good, M., Anderson, G. C., Stanton-Hicks, M., Grass, J. A., & Makii, M. (2002). Relaxation and music reduce pain after gynecologic surgery. *Pain Management Nursing, 3*, 61–70.

Hanser, S. B., & Mandel, S. E. (2005). The effects of music therapy in cardiac healthcare. *Cardiology in Review, 13*, 18–23.

Harikumar, R., & Kumar, S. (2007). Colonoscopy and the role of music therapy: How to go about an ideal protocol? *World Journal of Gastroenterology, 13*, 3272–3273.

Hunter, B. C., Olivia, R., Sahler, O. J. Z., Gassier, D., Salipante, D. M., & Arezina, C. H. (2010). Music therapy as an adjunctive treatment in the management of stress for patients being weaned from mechanical ventiation. *Journal of Music Therapy, 47*(3), 198–219.

Ikonomidou, E., Rehnström, A., & Naesh, O. (2004). Effect of music on vital signs and postoperative pain. *Association of periOperative Registered Nurses Journal, 80*, 269–274.

Kenny, D. T., & Fraunce, G. (2004). The impact of group singing on mood, coping, and perceived pain in chronic pain patients attending a multidisciplinary pain clinic. *Journal of Music Therapy, 41*, 241–258.

Leardi, S., Pietroletti, R., Angeloni, G., Necozione, S., Ranalletta, G., & Del Gusto, B. (2007). Randomized clinical trial examining the effect of music therapy in stress response to day surgery. *British Journal of Surgery, 94*, 943–947.

Madson, A. T., & Silverman, M. J. (2010). The effect of music therapy on relaxation, anxiety, pain perception, and nausea in adult solid organ transplant patients. *Journal of Music Therapy, 47*(3), 220–232.

Mandel, S. E., Hanser, S. B., Secic, M., & Davis, B. A. (2007). Effects of music therapy on health-related outcomes in cardiac rehabilitation: A randomized controlled trial. *Journal of Music Therapy, 44*(3), 176–197.

McCaffrey, R., & Locsin, R. (2006). The effect of music on pain and acute confusion in older adults undergoing hip and knee surgery. *Holistic Nursing Practice, 20*, 218–226.

Metzger, L. K. (2004). Assessment of use of music by patients participating in cardiac rehabilitation. *Journal of Music Therapy, 41*, 55–69.

Miluk-Kolasa, B., Obminski, Z., Stupnicki, R., & Golec, L. (1994). Effects of music treatment on salivary cortisol in patients exposed to pre-surgical stress. *Experimental and Clinical Endocrinology, 102*, 118–120.

Mitchell, L. A., & MacDonald. R. A. R. (2006). An experimental investigation of the effects of preferred and relaxing music listening on pain perception. *Journal of Music Therapy, 43*(4), 295–314.

Moss, V. A. (1987). The effect of music on anxiety in the surgical patient. *Perioperative Nursing Quarterly, 3*(1), 9–16.

Ovayolu, N., Ucan, O., Pehlivan, S., Pehlivan, Y., Buyukhatipoglu, H., Savas, M.C., et al. (2006). Listening to Turkish classical music decreases patients' anxiety, pain, dissatisfaction, and the dose of sedative and analgesic drugs during colonoscopy: A prospective randomized controlled trial. *World Journal of Gastroenterology, 12*, 7532–7536.

Palakanis, K. C., DeNobile, J. W., Sweeney, W. B., & Blankenship, C. L. (1994). Effect of music therapy on state anxiety in patients undergoing flexible sigmoidoscopy. *Diseases of the Colon and Rectum, 37*, 478–481.

Pellino, T. A., Gordon, D. B., Engelke, Z. K., Busse, K. L., Collins, M. A., Silver, C. E., & Norcross, N. J. (2005). Use of nonpharmacologic interventions for pain and anxiety after total hip and total knee arthroplasty. *Orthopaedic Nursing, 24*, 182–190.

Prensner, J. D., Yowler, C. J., Smith, L. F., Steele, A. L., & Fratianne, R. B. (2001). Music therapy for assistance with pain and anxiety management in burn treatment. *The Journal of Burn Care & Rehabilitation, 22*, 83–88.

Richards, T., Johnson, J., Sparks, A., & Emerson, H. (2007). The effect of music therapy on patients' perception and manifestation of pain, anxiety, and patient satisfaction. *Medical-Surgical Nursing Journal, 16*, 7–14.

Robb, S. L., Nichols, R. J., Rutan, R. L., Bishop, B. L., & Parker, J. C. (1995). The effects of music assisted relaxation on preoperative anxiety. *Journal of Music Therapy, 32*, 2–21.

Rodgers, L. (1995). Music for surgery. *Advances, 11*(3), 49–57.

Rudin, D. (2006). Frequently overlooked and rarely listened to: Music therapy in gastrointestinal endoscopic procedures. *World Journal of Gastroenterology, 13*, 4533.

Rudin, D., Kiss, A., Wetz, R. V., & Sottile, V. M. (2007). Music in the endoscopy suite: A meta-analysis of randomized controlled studies. *Endoscopy, 39*, 507–510.

Schmidt, K., & Ernst, E. (2004). Music therapy for patients with cardiovascular diseases: A systematic review. *Perfusio, 17*, 136–144.

Standley, J. M. (1996). Music research in medical/dental treatment: An update of prior meta-analysis. In C. E. Furman (Ed.), *Effectiveness of music therapy procedures: Documentation of research and clinical practice* (pp. 1–60). Silver Spring, MD: National Association for Music Therapy.

Triller, N., Erzen, D., Duh, S., Petrinec Primozic, M., & Kosnik, M. (2006). Music during bronchoscopic examination: The physiological effects. A randomized trial. *Respiration, 73*, 95–99.

Tse, M. M., Chan, M. F., & Benzie, I. F. (2005). The effect of music therapy on postoperative pain, heart rate, systolic blood pressures and analgesic use following nasal surgery. *Journal of Pain and Palliative Care Pharmacotherapy, 19*(3), 21–29.

Tusek, D. L., Church, J. M., Strong, S. A., Grass, J. A., & Fazio, V. W. (1997). Guided imagery: A significant advance in the care of patients undergoing elective colorectal surgery. *Diseases of the Colon and Rectum, 40*, 172–178.

Twiss, E., Seaver, J., & McCaffrey, R. (2006). The effect of music listening on older adults undergoing cardiovascular surgery. *Nursing in Critical Care, 11*, 224–231.

Updike, P. A., & Charles, D. M. (1987). Music Rx: Physiological and emotional responses to taped music programs of preoperative patients awaiting plastic surgery. *Annals of Plastic Surgery, 19*, 29–33.

Verheecke, G., & Troch, E. (1980). Music while you wait: Patient acceptance of music in the preanesthetic period. *Acta Anaesthesiologica Belgica, 31*, 61–67.

White, C. S., Dolwick, M. F., Gravenstein, N., & Paulus, D. A. (1989). Incidence of oxygen desaturation during oral surgery outpatient procedures. *Journal of Oral and Maxillofacial Surgery, 47*, 147–149.

Winter, M. J., Paskin, S., & Baker, T. (1994). Music reduces stress and anxiety of patients in the surgical holding area. *Journal of Post Anesthesia Nursing, 9*, 340–343.

Cancer Care

Beck, S. L. (1991). The therapeutic use of music for cancer-related pain. *Oncology Nursing Forum, 18*, 1327–1337.

Bozcuk, H., Artac, M., Kara, A., Ozdogan, M., Sualp, Y., Topcu, Z., et al. (2006). Does music exposure during chemotherapy improve quality of life in early breast cancer patients? A pilot study. *Medical Science Monitor, 12*, 200–205.

Burns, D. S. (2001). The effect of the Bonny method of Guided Imagery and Music on the mood and life quality of cancer patients. *Journal of Music Therapy, 38*, 51–65.

Burns, D. S., Sledge, R. B., Fuller, L. A., Daggy, J. K., & Monahan, P. O. (2005). Cancer patients' interest and preferences for music therapy. *Journal of Music Therapy, 42*, 185–199.

Cassileth, B. R., Vickers, A. J., & Magill, L. A. (2003). Music therapy for mood disturbance during hospitalization for autologous stem cell transplantation: A randomized controlled trial. *Cancer, 98*, 2723–2729.

Clark, M., Isaacks-Downton, G., Wells, N., Redlin-Frazier, S., Eck, C., Hepworth, J. T., et al. (2006). Use of preferred music to reduce emotional distress and symptom activity during radiation therapy. *Journal of Music Therapy, 43*, 247–265.

Ernst, E., & Cassileth, B. R. (1998). The prevalence of complementary/alternative medicine in cancer: A systematic review. *Cancer, 83*, 777–782.

Ferrer, A. J. (2007). The effect of live music on decreasing anxiety in patients undergoing chemotherapy treatment. *Journal of Music Therapy, 44*(3), 242–255.

Hanser, S. (2006). Music therapy in adult oncology: Research issues. *Journal of the Society for Integrative Oncology, 4*(2), 62–66.

Johnston, K., & Rohaly-Davis, J. (1996). An introduction to music therapy: Helping the oncology patient in the ICU. *Critical Care Nursing Quarterly, 18*(4), 54–60.

Knight, W. E. J., & Rickard, N. S. (2001). Relaxing music prevents stress-induced increases in subjective anxiety, systolic blood pressure, and heart rate in healthy males and females. *Journal of Music Therapy, 38*(4), 254–272.

Kwekkeboom, K. L. (2003). Music versus distraction for procedural pain and anxiety in patients with cancer. *Oncology Nursing Forum, 30*, 433–440.

Núñez, M., Mañá, P., Liñares, D., Riveiro, M. R., Balboa, J., Suárez-Quintanilla, J., et al. (2002). Music, immunity, and cancer. *Life Sciences, 71*, 1047–1057..

O'Brien, E. (2005). Songwriting with adult patients in oncology and clinical hematology. In F. Baker & T. Wigram (Eds.), *Songwriting methods, techniques and clinical applications for music therapy clinicians, educators and students* (pp. 185–205). London: Jessica Kingsley.

O'Brien, E. (2006). Opera therapy: Creating and performing a new work with cancer patients. *Nordic Journal of Music Therapy, 15*(1), 89–103.

O'Callaghan, C. (Guest ed.). (2006). Music therapy supplement. *Journal of the Society for Integrative Oncology, 4*(2), 57–81.

O'Callaghan, C. C., & Colegrove, V. (1998). Effect of the music therapy introduction when engaging hospitalized cancer patients. *Music Therapy Perspectives, 16*(2), 67–74.

O'Callaghan, C., & Magill, L. (2009). Effect of music therapy on oncologic staff bystanders: A substantive grounded theory. *Palliative and Supportive Care, 7*, 219–228.

O'Callaghan, C., & McDermott, F. (2004). Music therapy's relevance in a cancer hospital researched through a constructivist lens. *Journal of Music Therapy, 41*, 151–185.

O'Callaghan, C., & McDermott, F. (2007). Discourse analysis reframes oncology music therapy research findings. *Arts in Psychotherapy, 34*, 398–408.

Petterson, M. (2001). Music for healing: The creative arts program at the Ireland Cancer Center. *Alternative Therapies, 7*(1), 88–89.

Pothoulaki, M., MacDonald, R., & Flowers, P. (2005). Music interventions in oncology settings: A systematic literature review. *British Journal of Music Therapy, 19*, 75–83.

Slivka, H. H., & Magill, L. (1986). The cojoint use of social work and music therapy with children of cancer patients. *Music Therapy, 6A*(1), 30–40.

Smith, M., Casey, L., Johnson, D., Gwede, C., & Riggin, O. Z. (2001). Music as a therapeutic intervention for anxiety in patients receiving radiation therapy. *Oncology Nursing Forum, 28*, 855–862.

Standley, J. M. (1992). Clinical applications of music and chemotherapy: The effects on nausea and emesis. *Music Therapy Perspectives, 10*(1), 27–35.

Waldon, E. G. (2001). The effects of group music therapy on mood states and cohesiveness in adult oncology patients. *Journal of Music Therapy, 38*, 212–238.

Palliative Care

Aldridge, D. (2003). Music therapy references relating to cancer and palliative care. *British Journal of Music Therapy, 17*, 17–25.

Clements-Cortes, A. (2004). The use of music in facilitating emotional expression in the terminally ill. *American Journal of Hospice and Palliative Medicine, 21*, 255–260.

Dileo, C., & Loewy, J. (Eds.). (2005). *Music therapy at the end of life*. Cherry Hill, NJ: Jeffrey Books.

Gallagher, L. M., Huston, M. J., Nelson, K. A., Walsh, D., & Steele, A. L. (2001). Music therapy in palliative medicine. *Support Care in Cancer, 9*, 156–161.

Gallagher, L. M., Lagman, R., Walsh, D., Davis, M. P., & Legrand, S. B. (2006). The clinical effects of music therapy in palliative medicine. *Support Care Cancer, 14*(8), 859–866.

Gallagher, L. M., & Steele, A. L. (2001). Developing and using a computerized database for music therapy in palliative medicine. *Journal of Palliative Care, 17*, 147–154.

Groen, K. M. (2007). Pain assessment and management in end of life care: A survey of assessment and treatment practices of hospice music therapy and nursing professionals. *Journal of Music Therapy, 44*, 90–112.

Halstead, M. T., & Roscoe, S. T. (2002). Restoring the spirit at the end of life: Music as an intervention for oncology nurses. *Clinical Journal of Oncology Nursing, 6*, 332–336.

Hartley, N. A. (2001). On a personal note: A music therapist's reflections on working with those who are living with a terminal illness. *Journal of Palliative Care, 17*, 135–141.

Hilliard, R. E. (2001). The use of music therapy in meeting the multidimensional needs of hospice patients and families. *Journal of Palliative Care, 17*, 161–166.

Hilliard, R. E. (2003). The effects of music therapy on the quality and length of life of people diagnosed with terminal cancer. *Journal of Music Therapy, 41*, 266–281.

Hilliard, R. E. (2004). Hospice administrators' knowledge of music therapy: A comparative analysis of surveys. *Music Therapy Perspectives, 22*, 104–108.

Hilliard, R. E. (2004). A post-hoc analysis of music therapy services for residents in nursing homes receiving hospice care. *Journal of Music Therapy, 41*, 266–281.

Hilliard, R. E. (2005). Music therapy in hospice and palliative care: A review of the empirical data. *Evidence-Based Complementary and Alternative Medicine, 2*, 173–178.

Hilliard, R. E. (2006). The effect of music therapy sessions on compassion fatigue and team building of professional hospice caregivers. *Arts in Psychotherapy, 33*, 395–402.

Hogan, B. (1998). Approaching the end of life: A role for music therapy within the context of palliative care models. *Australian Journal of Music Therapy, 9*, 18–34.

Hogan, B., & Cockayne, M. (2003). Striking a chord: Consolidating music therapy's future in palliative care. *Australian Journal of Music Therapy, 14*, 50–62.

Horne-Thompson, A. (2003). Expanding from hospital to home based care: Implications for music therapists working in palliative care. *Australian Journal of Music Therapy, 14*, 38–49.

Horne-Thompson, A., Daveson, B., & Hogan, B. (2007). A project investigating music therapy referral trends within palliative care: An Australian perspective. *Journal of Music Therapy, 44*(2), 139–155.

Horne-Thompson, A., & Grocke, D. (2008). *The effect of music therapy on anxiety in patients who are terminally ill patients. Journal of Palliative Medicine, 11*(4), 582–590.

Krout, R. E. (2001). The effects of single-session music therapy interventions on the observed and self-reported levels of pain control, physical comfort, and relaxation of hospice patients. *The American Journal of Hospice and Palliative Care, 18*, 383–390.

Krout, R. E. (2003). Music therapy with imminently dying hospice patients and their families: Facilitating release near the time of death. *The American Journal of Hospice and Palliative Care, 20*, 129–134.

Krout, R. E. (2004). A synerdisciplinary music therapy treatment team approach for hospice and palliative care. *Australian Journal of Music Therapy, 15*, 33–45.

Magill, L. (2001). The use of music therapy to address the suffering in advanced cancer pain. *Journal of Palliative Care, 17*, 167–172.

Magill, L. (2005). Music therapy: Enhancing spirituality at the end of life. In C. Dileo & J. V. Loewy (Eds.), *Music therapy at the end of life* (pp. 3–17). Cherry Hill, NJ: Jeffery Books.

Magill, L. (2006). Music therapy and spirituality and the challenges of end-stage illness. In D. Aldridge & J. Fachner (Eds.), *Music and altered states: Consciousness, transcendence, therapy and addictions* (pp. 172–183). Philadelphia: Jessica Kingsley.

Mandel, S. E. (1993). The role of the music therapist on the hospice/palliative care team. *Journal of Palliative Care, 9*, 37–39.

Mramor, K. M. (2001). Music therapy with persons who are indigent and terminally ill. *Journal of Palliative Care, 17*, 182–187.

Munro, S., & Mount, B. (1978). Music therapy in palliative care. *Canadian Medical Association Journal, 119*, 1029–1034.

O'Callaghan, C. (1993). Communicating with brain-impaired palliative care patients through music therapy. *Journal of Palliative Care, 9*, 53–55.

O'Callaghan, C. (1996). Lyrical themes in songs written by palliative care patients. *Journal of Music Therapy, 33*(2), 74–92.

O'Callaghan, C. (1996). Pain, music creativity and music therapy in palliative care. *The American Journal of Hospice and Palliative Care, 13*(2), 43–49.

O'Callaghan, C. (1997). Therapeutic opportunities associated with the music when using song writing in palliative care. *Music Therapy Perspectives, 15*(1), 32–38.

O'Callaghan, C. (2001). Bringing music to life: A study of music therapy and palliative care experiences in a cancer hospital. *Journal of Palliative Care, 17*, 155–160.

O'Callaghan, C. (2004). Music therapy in palliative care. In G. Hanks, N. MacDonald, N. Cherny, & K. Calman (Eds.), *The Oxford textbook of palliative medicine* (3rd ed.) (pp. 1041–1046). Oxford, England: Oxford University Press.

O'Callaghan, C. (2005). Song writing in threatened lives. In C. Dileo & J. Loewy (Eds.), *Music therapy at the end of life care* (pp. 117–128). Cherry Hill, NJ: Jeffrey Books.

O'Callaghan, C. (2008). Lullament: Lullaby and lament therapeutic qualities actualized through music therapy. *American Journal of Hospice and Palliative Medicine, 25*(2), 93–99.

O'Kelly, J. (2002). Music therapy in palliative care: Current perspectives. *International Journal of Palliative Nursing, 8*(3), 130–136.

O'Kelly, J., & Koffman, J. (2007). Multidisciplinary perspectives of music therapy in adult palliative care. *Palliative Medicine, 21*, 235–241.

Porchet-Munro, S. (1988) Music therapy in support of cancer patients. *Recent Results in Cancer Research, 108*, 289–294.

Renz, M., Schütt Mao, M., & Cerny, T. (2005). Spirituality, psychotherapy and music in palliative cancer care: Research projects in psycho-oncology at an oncology center in Switzerland. *Supportive Care in Cancer, 13*, 961–966.

Rykov, M., & Salmon D. (Guest eds.). (2001). Moments musicaux: Music therapy in palliative care [Special issue]. *Journal of Palliative Care, 17*(3), 133–192.

Salmon, D. (1989). Partage: Groupwork in palliative care. In J. A. Martin (Ed.), *Next step forward: Music therapy with the terminally ill* (pp. 47–51). New York: Calvary Hospital.

Salmon, D. (1993). Music and emotion in palliative care. *Journal of Palliative Care, 9*, 48–52.

Salmon, D. (2001). Music therapy as psychospiritual process in palliate care. *Journal of Palliative Care, 17*, 142–146.

Starr, R. J. (1999). Music therapy in hospice care. *The American Journal of Hospice and Palliative Care, 16*, 739–742.

Trauger-Querry, B., & Haghighi, K. R. (1999). Balancing the focus: Art and music therapy for pain control and symptom management in hospice care. *The Hospice Journal, 14*, 25–38.

West, T. M. (1994). Psychological issues in hospice music therapy. *Music Therapy Perspectives, 12*(2), 117–124.

Wlodarczyk, N. (2007). The effect of music therapy on the spirituality of persons in an in-patient hospice unit as measured by self-report. Journal of Music Therapy, 44, 113–122.

SAMPLE MUSIC THERAPY INTERVENTION PLANS

Population/Age Range: Adults

Title: *Music-Assisted Relaxation* (MAR)

Estimated Time for Implementation: 10–30 minutes

Goals: To facilitate relaxation, to decrease perception of pain, to promote sedation, to improve compliance during procedures

Objective(s):

1. Pt. will demonstrate stability or reduction in heart rate and respiration rate.
2. Pt. will demonstrate increase in deep inhalations.
3. Pt. will demonstrate decrease in physical tension.
4. Pt. will report less pain.
5. Pt. will fall asleep.
6. Pt. will tolerate painful procedures with minimal stress behaviors.

Response Definition:

1. Therapist will record baseline heart rate (HR) and/or respiratory rate (RR) and will observe/record changes during session.
2. Therapist will observe depth of breathing (shallow frequent breaths vs. deep, slow inhalations).
3. Therapist will note changes to observable signs of tension (clenched fists, wincing, contracted arms or legs).
4. Therapist will record pt.'s reported level of pain (use Wong-Baker FACES scale).
5. Therapist will observe behavior state and vital sign indications of sleep (maintenance or decrease in HR and/or RR).
6. Therapist will note pt.'s compliance with procedural requirements (e.g., holding affected limb still for blood draw or IV start).

Materials: Quiet portable accompanying instrument (usually guitar, keyboard, or folk harp); optional: sound effects percussion (ocean drum, rainstick), improvised or pre-composed sedative music representative of various genres of music

Procedural Steps:

1. Introduce self to pt.; assess developmental level, current mood state, and level of reported pain or anxiety.
2. Assess baseline measures of HR, RR, behavior state, observable physical tension, and pain (if applicable).
3. Decide upon relaxation method based on assessment of pt.'s developmental level, pain level, anxiety level, and procedural requirements (e.g., sedative music listening, music-facilitated deep breathing, music and guided imagery, active or passive progressive muscle relaxation).
4. Begin sedative music accompaniment approximating tempo of breathing (depending on MT-BC's assessment of pt., therapist may choose to begin with voice alone first, then add gentle accompaniment).
5. Assess pt.'s tolerance of auditory stimuli by observing responses to music and add voice (or accompaniment) quietly if stimuli are well-tolerated.
6. Gradually slow tempo if pt. is currently agitated.
7. Begin cues for chosen relaxation method (e.g., cues for breathing in and out or visualization to assist with deep inhalations, cues for imagery, or prompts to tighten and release muscle groups for active progressive muscle relaxation or imagery for muscle groups if using passive progressive muscle relaxation).
8. Assess changes in vital signs and observable behaviors.
9. If vital signs or observable behaviors are moving toward preferred direction for sedation, continue with current relaxation method.
10. If there is no change in vital signs or observable behaviors, either discontinue verbal prompts, repeat current cues, or change to alternate relaxation method.
11. If vital signs or observable behaviors change in negative direction, reduce complexity of auditory stimuli, wait for stabilization of vital signs or behaviors, then either repeat current relaxation method or try an alternate method.
12. When concluding relaxation method, phase out if pt. appears to be asleep or help pt. gradually transition back to being aware of surroundings.
13. Leave pt.'s room quietly; if appropriate, ask pt.'s nurse or other staff members to close the door or put up a "please do not disturb" sign.

Measurement Tools:

1. Heart rate (HR) and/or respiratory rate (RR)
2. Changes in breathing pattern
3. Observable signs of tension
4. Pain level as measured on Wong-Baker FACES analog scale

5. Behavior state
6. Pt. verbalizations
7. Amount of pain or sedation medication required for procedure
8. Pt. level of compliance with procedure

Possible Adaptations: The relaxation method chosen within the MAR technique will vary depending on patient's developmental, pain, and anxiety levels, as well as upon the ultimate goal of intervention (e.g., relaxation, procedural compliance, sleep). The technique also requires adaptation or adjustment throughout, depending upon patient responses. The patient can be asked to describe a relaxing scene or image while the therapist improvises music based on patient's description. The image does not have to be visual, but could be a smell, taste, sound, color, feeling, energy awareness, or kinesthetic sensation.

Population/Age Range: Adults

Title: *Music-Assisted or Music-Focused Relaxation (music and individualized relaxation script)*

Estimated Time for Implementation: 30–60 minutes

Goals: To achieve the relaxation response

Objective(s):

1. Pt. will report a decrease of 1 or more points on a self-rating scale of 0–10, with 10 = most tense or stressed, to 0 = most relaxed.

Response Definition:

1. Therapist will observe changes in pt.'s respiration rate and volume, muscle tension, physical positioning, response to specific relaxation cues, and other indicators of completeness and duration of relaxation response.
2. Therapist will ask pt. to rate level of stress/relaxation on a 0–10 scale, before and after the relaxation intervention.
3. At the end of the session, therapist will ask pt. to describe any changes in his/her mind, body, or spiritual status.

Materials: Music accompaniment instrument (guitar, piano keyboard, or harp) or pre-recorded sedative music and compact disc player, handouts of relaxation instructions and overview of relaxation techniques, wind instruments (e.g., Native American flutes, recorders) or recording of environmental sounds (e.g., waves, rain, wind, birds)

Procedural Steps:

1. If pre-recorded music is going to be used, the pt. can be given a choice to close his/her eyes and listen to brief samples of several different types of relaxation music (e.g., solo piano, harp, Native American flute, or pt.'s preferred pre-recorded selections).
2. Allow pt. to give feedback regarding the optimal volume level for the music.
3. At the end of the initial relaxation session, give pt. both verbal and written information (e.g., basic relaxation instructions/techniques or descriptions of sedative music/resources) to encourage and reinforce his/her independent practice of relaxation techniques at home.

Measurement Tools: Pt.'s self-reported stress/relaxation levels (before and after treatment) and therapist observation

Possible Adaptations: A variety of relaxation techniques can also be utilized during the session: deep breathing, autogenic relaxation, progressive muscle relaxation, mindfulness meditation techniques, guided imagery, or immune system enhancement imagery. Providing the patient with a recording that contains a music-focused relaxation exercise with the familiar voice of the music therapist can also be a wonderful resource.

Population/Age Range: Adults

Title: *Music-Facilitated Imagery (music and personalized imagery script)*

Estimated Time for Implementation: 30–60 minutes

Goals: To achieve the relaxation response; to support coping abilities during prolonged hospitalization, illness, and procedures

Objective(s):

1. Pt. will report a decrease of 1 or more points on a self-rating scale of 0–10 with 10 = most tense or stressed, to 0 = most relaxed.
2. Pt. will have the opportunity to explore and experience images of a peaceful place, the cancer, chemotherapy or other treatments, and the healing process.

Response Definition:

1. Therapist will observe changes in pt.'s respiration rate and volume, muscle tension, physical positioning, response to specific relaxation cues, and other indicators of completeness and duration of relaxation response.
2. Therapist will ask pt. to rate level of stress/relaxation on a 0-10 scale, before and after the relaxation intervention.
3. At the end of the session, therapist will ask pt. to describe any changes in his/her mind, body, or spiritual status.
4. Therapist will ask pt. to describe and discuss specific images explored during the imagery.

Materials: Music accompaniment instrument (guitar, piano keyboard, or harp) or pre-recorded sedative music and compact disc player, handouts of relaxation instructions and overview of relaxation techniques, wind instruments (e.g., Native American flutes, recorders) or recording of environmental sounds (e.g., waves, rain, wind, birds)

Procedural Steps:

1. If the scripted imagery will be focused on "peaceful place," the therapist can ask the pt. to identify the important sensory qualities of his/her imagined or real peaceful place.
2. Therapist can take written notes to enable the use of the pt.'s own words and descriptors within the imagery cues.
3. Music used to create environment as support for scripted imagery.

Measurement Tools: Pt.'s self-reported stress/relaxation levels (before and after treatment), therapist observation.

Possible Adaptations: Different imagery focuses can be used: (1) peaceful place imagery scene, (2) general healing imagery, (3) immune system enhancement, (4) exploration of the emotional and spiritual meaning of illness (Bonny Method of Guided Imagery is recommended; additional training is required).

Population/Age Range: Adults (group or individual)

Title: *The Sounds of Healing Improvisation*

Estimated Time for Implementation: 10–15 minutes (therapist should assess pt.'s physical status and energy level to determine timeframe)

Goals: To provide a medium for nonverbal expression, to explore and express feelings, to facilitate acceptance of treatment and healing process

Objective(s):

1. Pt. will make choices of instruments that represent various aspects of his/her medical experience.
2. Pt. will create a musical improvisation that will represent various aspects of his/her medical experience.
3. Following a expressive or receptive music improvisation experience, pt. will discuss personal associations between the music and his/her illness, treatment, and healing process.

Response Definition:

1. Therapist will note which instruments pt. chooses and to what aspect of the medical experience each is assigned.
2. Therapist will note what aspects of the medical experience the pt. chooses to represent through expressive improvisation.
3. Therapist will note what personal associations the pt. verbalizes following the expressive or receptive music experience and facilitate discussion that focuses on exploring and expressive feelings about the illness, treatment, and healing process.

Materials: Orff instruments, hand-held percussion instruments, and traditional accompaniment instruments (piano keyboard, guitar, dulcimer, harp, etc.)

Procedural Steps:

1. If appropriate, ask pt. to briefly discuss topics of his/her personal medical experience, including diagnosis, treatment, and healing process.
2. Explain the concept of representing emotions and experiences through music.
3. Demonstrate musical examples and techniques by playing various instruments.
4. Provide pt. with choices of an active music-making improvisational experience (playing instruments) alone or with the therapist, or a receptive experience (therapist plays instrument based on specific information and directions from the patient).

5. Ask the pt. to play music that represents his/her experiences, e.g., receiving a medical diagnosis, enduring medical treatment, related images of healing, etc.
6. If the pt. prefers to have a receptive improvisational experience, the therapist can manipulate various musical elements (e.g., timbre, tempo, meter, rhythm, melody, melodic intervals, harmony, dynamics, articulation, form, lyrics) to represent the pt.'s personal medical experience (Gardstrom, 2001).
7. Ask the pt. for reflections, feedback, and suggestions, incorporating changes into another instrumental improvisation. Offer open-ended questions to allow pt. to verbally process his/her emotions.

Measurement Tools: Observation of pt. choices and verbalizations about improvisation and associations with illness, treatment, and healing

Possible Adaptations: The therapist can involve the patient's family members and/or significant others into the intervention. Referential improvisation can be used to focus on nonverbal communication (e.g., "Play what it is like to be a caregiver"). Nonreferential inmprovisation can also be used. This technique is based strictly on musical considerations, without a predetermined focus or outside reference. Nonreferential improvisation can be utilized to encourage creativity, self-expression, emotional expression, and aesthetic experiences (Bruscia, 1987).

References

Bruscia, K. (1987). *Improvisational models of music therapy*. Springfield, IL: C. C. Thomas.

Gardstrom, S. C. (2001). Practical techniques for the development of complementary skills in musical improvisation. *Music Therapy Perspectives, 19*, 82–87.

Population/Age Range: Adults

Title: *Songwriting (structured or improvised)*

Estimated Time for Implementation: 15–45 minutes

Goals: Facilitate verbal or nonverbal communication, improve self-esteem, decrease anxiety, improve choice-making and control, alleviate depression, improve coping with illness and hospitalization

Objective(s):

1. Pt. will demonstrate active participation in songwriting to extent capable.
2. Pt. will express self verbally or nonverbally depending upon ability.
3. Pt. will demonstrate improved self-esteem as exhibited by positive self-statements or positive comments about the songwriting process or product.
4. Pt. will demonstrate choice-making during songwriting interaction.
5. Pt. will demonstrate decrease in anxious behaviors.
6. Pt. will demonstrate improvement in frequency or quality of positive affect.
7. Pt. will demonstrate awareness of one positive strategy for coping with illness and hospitalization.

Response Definition:

1. Therapist will assess pt.'s level of active participation (e.g., frequency/duration of eye contact, level of verbal engagement, level of musical engagement).
2. Therapist will note frequency of pt.'s verbal or nonverbal communication attempts.
3. Therapist will note frequency of pt.'s positive self-statements or positive comments about the songwriting process or product.
4. Therapist will note frequency of pt.'s choice-making.
5. Therapist will observe changes in frequency of pt.'s anxious behaviors before and during intervention.
6. Therapist will observe pt.'s frequency and quality of positive affect before, during, and after songwriting.
7. Therapist will note pt.'s ability to verbalize positive skills for coping with illness and hospitalization.

Materials: Accompanying instrument that allows pt. participation (e.g., strumming on guitar, Q chord, portable keyboard); novel and attractive instruments such as rainstick, thunder tube, ocean drum, chimes, triangle, shaker eggs, and drums; optional: puppets or toy props for songs (must be immediately washable or owned by the pt.)

Procedural Steps:

1. Introduce self to pt.; assess developmental level, current mood state, and level of anxiety (if not already accomplished during a different intervention).
2. Based on assessment of pt.'s developmental level, attention span, and anxiety level, either directly offer choices for songwriting participation or begin by demonstrating instruments to facilitate engagement in:
    a. spontaneous song (improvised song, usually follows naturally from pt.'s active participation in music interaction, may or may not include lyrics).
    b. fill-in-the-blank (a.k.a. Cloze Technique) songwriting (pt. offers words or short phrases to complete lyrics provided by therapist, or lyrics of a familiar song).
    c. song parody (pt. rewrites lyrics of familiar, pre-existing song).
    d. blues songwriting (original lyrics created following the blues lyrical structure of AAB).
    e. musical poems (pt. and therapist create original music to original or pre-existing poetry).
    f. original song (pt. creates original lyrics and music).
3. Depending upon pt.'s developmental level and level of active participation, MT-BC may explain the specific songwriting technique, or may shape a pt.'s verbal and nonverbal responses to form the song without explaining the technique.
4. Offer pt. suggestions for broad subject areas if creating lyrics (e.g., song about something that has happened while in the hospital, song about a favorite place, song about favorite things to do, song about an imaginary place, song about a doll or toy on pt.'s bed).
5. Once a broad subject area is chosen, identify pt.'s choices for accompaniment style (e.g., accompanying instrument, fast/slow, quality such as happy/sad/angry/tired).
6. Identify pt.'s choices for musical participation (e.g., singing, speaking, playing rhythm instruments, assisting MT-BC with accompanying instrument).
7. Pt. may choose who will initiate the music.
8. For open-ended lyric writing techniques, the MT-BC may sing or speak prompts such as "I've been in this hospital for . . . ," "If I could be anywhere right now I'd be . . . ," etc.
9. Continue with one of the aforementioned songwriting techniques, prompting pt. for responses and choice-making whenever possible.
10. Support and validate pt. responses (e.g., while singing, therapist echoes back significant pt. verbalizations or themes).
11. Validate pt.'s negative feelings during songwriting, then gradually guide pt. to identifying solutions to conflicts or negative feelings that arise during songwriting.
12. Cue pt. to bring closure to the song by deciding how he/she wants it to end.

13. If a parental consent for audio recording has been signed and pt. desires, pt. and/or therapist may create a recorded version of the completed song for the pt. to keep.
14. After finishing song and listening to a final version, assist pt. in making connections between themes in the song and conflicts/emotions experienced that are related to hospitalization or illness, when developmentally appropriate.
15. Discuss positive coping techniques that pt. could use, as developmentally appropriate.
16. Segue into a closing ritual to help pt. transition out of activity (e.g., singing the completed song once more for family or staff members if desired, singing a favorite familiar song, MAR, and/or good-bye song).
17. Schedule future sessions with pt., family, and staff when appropriate.

Measurement Tools:

1. Frequency and quality of physical participation
2. Frequency and quality of verbal and nonverbal communication efforts
3. Frequency of positive self-statements or positive comments about song or songwriting process
4. Frequency of choice-making
5. Observable signs of anxiety
6. Pt. affect
7. Pt. verbalizations

Possible Adaptations: Patients who will be hospitalized for longer than 1 week may engage in longer-term songwriting projects. An example might be the creation of a personal song to affirm identity or give hope and the creation of a CD recording of this song. Any songwriting technique chosen should flow naturally from the patient's engagement in music making. Songwriting techniques with higher levels of structure (e.g., fill-in-the-blank songwriting, blues songwriting) may be more effective with patients who are reluctant to participate verbally. The music therapist will vary the amount of prompting used to elicit patient responses, and the amount of structure provided, depending upon the patient's level of verbal participation. Group songwriting can include the patient as well as family groups. Relatives, friends, or caregivers can be invited to write a song for the patient.

Population/Age Range: Children-adults (individual or group)

Title: *Therapeutic Music Instruction and Performance*

Estimated Time for Implementation: 15 minutes – several sessions

Goals: To promote self-efficacy

Objective(s):

1. Pt. will engage in a successful musical experience using traditional or adaptive musical instruments within the physical limitations of the medical environment (e.g., pt. on bed rest, barriers of IV, oxygen or catheter tubing, etc.).

Response Definition:

1. Therapist will assess pt.'s positive affect, eye contact, and level of musical engagement.

Materials: Any instrument on which one can give instruction: drums, tuned percussive instruments, Orff instruments, autoharp, Q-chord (updated omnichord), mouth organ keyboard, recorder, guitar, electric piano keyboard, or blinking lights piano keyboard (adaptive instrument)

Procedural Steps:

1. Therapist can use a preferred teaching model, allowing for interspersed opportunities for music-based counseling.
2. Prompt vocal performance while considering the pitch and volume of the instrument being used to promote expression.
3. If pt. has had previous experience with music lessons, discuss the difference between music therapy's goal of playing music to express one's emotions or engage in a positive sensory experience versus a performance goal.
4. If it does not appear to be a successful experience for the pt., provide adaptive techniques, devices, or other instruments to promote pt.'s success.

Measurement Tools:

1. Pt.'s level of engagement in music intervention
2. Pt.'s affect and eye contact

Possible Adaptations: Patient may be assisted while playing a musical instrument (e.g., patient strums strings while the therapist plays the chords on an autoharp or Q-chord).

Population/Age Range: Adults (individual or group

Title: *Musical Profiles (reviewing one's life through music)*

Estimated Time for Implementation: part of a session – many sessions

Goals: To improve communication with significant others, to increase self-expression

Objective(s):

1. Pt. will illustrate significant memories, transitions, or milestones of his/her life.
2. Pt. will identify and discuss personal regrets, losses, relationships, hopes, and dreams.

Response Definition:

1. Therapist will note patient's ability to identify music that represents significant memories, transitions, or milestones of his/her life.
2. Therapist will note patient's verbal expressions and facilitate discussion

Materials: Recording device, videos, recorded music, pictures (possibly magazine and newspaper archives as well), and personal photos

Procedural Steps:

1. Therapist assesses pt.'s energy level and desire to participate in the music therapy experience and determines the extent to which the pt.'s musical life will be examined.
2. Therapist helps pt. identify significant life events or themes.
3. Therapist helps pt. identify and discuss his/her favorite songs that represent different periods during his/her lifetime and/or listen to a variety of songs together, choosing ones that describe memories or hold meaning for the pt. (this process can be an important catalyst for emotional expressional, discussion of meaning, and insights).
4. From the selected songs, a CD is compiled by the pt. and therapist. A cover can be designed with notes included to summarize each song and its role in the pt.'s life.
5. The finished CD can be given to the pt.'s friends, family members, or other health professionals to promote the pt.'s legacy after his/her illness or death.

Measurement Tools:

1. Pt.'s specific choices of music and events the music represents
2. Pt.'s verbalizations

Possible Adaptations: The end product can be enhanced with video or audio recordings of the patient talking about each musical milestone. Patient reflections could be compiled in a "scrapbook" with accompanying photos and relevant archival media clippings. If there is not enough time to create or leave the CD with the patient, recorded or live music may be listened to, sung along with, and/or reflect upon as elicited memories are shared within the session.

APPENDICES

Appendix A

MUSIC THERAPY AND MEDICINE

"I certainly think that every institution should have its music therapy and its music therapists."

— Oliver Sacks, MD, Neurologist

What Is Music Therapy?

Music therapy is the clinical and evidence-based use of music interventions to accomplish individualized goals within a therapeutic relationship by a credentialed professional who has completed an approved music therapy program. It is an established health service similar to occupational therapy and physical therapy and consists of using music therapeutically to address physical, psychological, cognitive and/or social functioning for patients of all ages. Because music therapy is a powerful and non-invasive medium, unique outcomes are possible. In addition to its applications with hospital patients, music therapy is used successfully with persons of all ages and disabilities.

How Does Music Therapy Make a Difference for Medical Patients?

Music therapy has been shown to be an efficacious and valid treatment option for medical patients with a variety of diagnoses. Music therapy can be used to address patient needs related to respiration, chronic pain, physical rehabilitation, diabetes, headaches, cardiac conditions, surgery, and obstetrics, among others. Research results and clinical experiences attest to the viability of music therapy even in those patients resistant to other treatment approaches. Music is a form of sensory stimulation, which provokes responses due to the familiarity, predictability, and feelings of security associated with it.

What Do Music Therapists Do?

Music therapists use music activities, both instrumental and vocal, designed to facilitate changes that are non-musical in nature. Music therapy programs are based on individual assessment, treatment planning, and ongoing program evaluation. Frequently functioning as members of an interdisciplinary team, music therapists implement programs with groups or individuals addressing a vast continuum of outcomes, including reduction of pain and anxiety, stress management, communication, and emotional expression.

What Can One Expect From a Music Therapist?

Music therapy utilized in a medical setting complies with the expectations and requirements inherent in the medical model of treatment. Professionally trained music therapists design and utilize individualized music experiences to assess, treat, and evaluate patients. Music therapy patient objectives are specific and relevant to medical diagnosis, course of treatment, and discharge timeline. Benefits are described in medical, and not musical, terms.

Through a planned and systematic use of music and music activities, the music therapist provides opportunities for:

- Anxiety and stress reduction
- Non-pharmacological management of pain and discomfort
- Positive changes in mood and emotional states
- Active and positive patient participation in treatment
- Decreased length of stay

In addition, music therapy may allow for:

- Emotional intimacy with families and caregivers
- Relaxation for the entire family
- Meaningful time spent together in a positive, creative way

Who Is Qualified as a Music Therapist?

Graduates of colleges or universities from more than 70 approved music therapy programs are eligible to take a national examination administered by the Certification Board for Music Therapists (CBMT), an independent, non-profit certifying agency fully accredited by the National Commission for Certifying Agencies. After successful completion of the CBMT examination, graduates are issued the credential necessary for professional practice, Music Therapist-Board Certified (MT-BC). In addition to the MT-BC credential, other recognized professional designations are Registered Music Therapists (RMT), Certified Music Therapists (CMT), and Advanced Certified Music Therapist (ACMT) listed with the National Music Therapy Registry. Any individual who does not have proper training and credentials is not qualified to provide music therapy services.

Where Do Music Therapists Work?

Music therapists offer services in medical hospitals, skilled and intermediate care facilities, rehabilitation hospitals, adult day care centers, senior centers, hospices, psychiatric treatment centers, drug and alcohol programs, schools and other facilities. In the medical setting, music therapists work with a variety of patient needs, and may work in many different hospital units, including ICU, NICU, Pre- and Post-Op, surgery, chronic pain management, cardiac care, obstetrics, emergency, pediatrics, physical rehabilitation, and outpatient programs. Some therapists are self-employed and work on the basis of independent contracts, while others are salaried hospital employees.

How Does Music Therapy Help Patients and Health Care Staff?

Dr. Walter Quan, Jr., Oncologist-Hematologist of St. Luke's Medical Center in Cleveland, Ohio, attests that:

> *"Music therapy has a wide range of applications. We see some patients whose blood pressure does come down and seems to stay down through regular use of music therapy. Another important aspect is the use in the labor and delivery room. We know that patients, who go through Lamaze training for instance, can also use music therapy to help them relax and to have pain relief in terms of labor pains."*

Music therapy is quantifiable and qualitative. Dr. Quan continues:

> *"...[I]n general as a physician you only use those things that you can measure or that have a number related to [them]... but there are a number of disciplines, and music therapy is one of them, where there is a qualitative effect which can give a lot of benefit for patients."*

Music therapists complete assessments for each patient and collect extensive data in order to write a complex patient history and develop a client-centered treatment plan. The music therapist is then able to evaluate the patient during the course of treatment. All of this contributes to the quantifiability of music therapy treatment.

Music therapy interventions are favored for the ability to meet quality of life needs. As quality of life issues and patient choice are pushed to the forefront of the national healthcare agenda, music therapy is being increasingly recognized for its unique contribution to patient quality of life.

Music therapy can help to relieve pain and reduce stress and anxiety for the patient, resulting in physiological changes, including:

- Improved respiration
- Lower blood pressure
- Improved cardiac output
- Reduced heart rate
- Relaxed muscle tension

Music therapy has been shown to have a significant effect on a patient's perceived effectiveness of treatment, self reports of pain reduction, relaxation, respiration rate, behaviorally observed and self-reported anxiety levels, and patient choice of anesthesia and amount of analgesic medication.

Why Music Therapy?

William Frohlich, President, Beth Abraham Health Services in New York, talks about music therapy as part of the total treatment modality:

> *"I think that the therapist plays an integral team role when you are talking about a team of physicians, a team of nurses, therapists, physical or occupational therapists and so on... included in that team needs to be a music therapist. The observations where a patient may be singing where they could not speak before or they may be walking or dancing where they could not move before – that is important for the music therapist to bring to the occupational therapist or physical therapist to become part of the total treatment modality."*

Dr. Walter Quan, Jr., Hematologist-Oncologist, St. Luke's Medical Center in Cleveland, Ohio, on music therapy in the treatment of cancer:

> *"The mind/body relationship is particularly important in terms of looking at the immune system to treat cancer. We believe that patients who are under less stress, who are in a brighter mood, appear to do better in terms of their anti-cancer therapy. I think that music therapy and imaging and immune therapy of cancer all tie together... I think it can be helpful in conjunction with biologic therapy for cancer. A study done just relatively recently on cancer patients showed that approximately three quarters of cancer patients that had their usual pain medicines but also had the additional music therapy experienced less pain then previously... Music therapy in helping patients relax could possibly be beneficial in raising the innate immune system which could have therapeutic implications for cancer."*

Susan Shurin, M.D., Chief of Pediatric-Hematology, Oncology at the Ireland Cancer Center in Cleveland, Ohio, comments on the effectiveness of music therapy in treatment of neurological impairments:

> *"Music therapy enables people to sometimes put words together in ways that are hard for them to do otherwise. ...[I]t often seems to be easier if [the patient] has the rhythm and cadence that comes along with music. Particularly with people with certain kinds of neurological deficits I think that [music therapy] can be very helpful. The music seems to get through to the patient and in many ways it enables [the patient] to get through to us which [may be] very hard to do with any other modality."*

Joseph Arezzo, PhD, Vice Chair, Department of Neuroscience, Albert Einstein College of Medicine, New York, talks about music therapy's role in restorative neurology:

> *"[T]he degree to which function can be recovered is phenomenal and we are just tapping into the extent that we can get recovery following stroke or injury or disease. We hope that music might play a particularly important role in helping [the regeneration of] those cells, in helping the individual learn to interpret the pattern and essentially to help that person learn again."*

What Is AMTA?

The American Music Therapy Association (AMTA) represents over 5,000 music therapists, corporate members, and related associations worldwide. AMTA's roots date back to organizations founded in 1950 and 1971. Those two organizations merged in 1998 to ensure the progressive development of the therapeutic use of music in rehabilitation, special education, and medical and community settings. AMTA is committed to the advancement of education, training, professional standards, and research in support of the music therapy profession. The mission of the organization is to advance public knowledge of music therapy benefits and increase access to quality music therapy services. Currently, AMTA establishes criteria for the education and clinical training of music therapists. Members of AMTA adhere to a Code of Ethics and Standards of Practice in their delivery of music therapy services.

Related Resources Available from AMTA:

- *Effective Clinical Practice in Music Therapy: Medical Music therapy for Pediatrics*, edited by Deanna Hanson-Abromeit and Cynthia Colwell
  2008. ISBN #978-1-884914-225
- *Medical Music Therapy,* edited by Jayne M. Standley
  2005. ISBN #1-884914-14-4
- *Music Therapy in Pediatric Healthcare*, edited by Sheri L. Robb
  2003. ISBN #1-884914-10-1
- *Clinical Guide to Music Therapy in Adult Physical Rehabilitation Settings*, written by Elizabeth H. Wong
  2004. ISBN #1-884914-11-X
- *Music Therapy with Premature Infants*, written by Jayne M. Standley
  2003. ISBN #1-884914-09-8
- *Music Therapy & Medicine*, edited by Cheryl Dileo
  1999. ISBN #1-884914-00-4

How Can You Find a Music Therapist or Get More Information?

American Music Therapy Association
8455 Colesville Road, Suite 1000
Silver Spring, MD 20910
Phone (301) 589-3300
Fax (301) 589-5175
Web: www.musictherapy.org
Email: info@musictherapy.org

Appendix B

MUSIC THERAPY IN THE TREATMENT AND MANAGEMENT OF PAIN

What is Music Therapy?

Music therapy is the clinical and evidence-based use of music interventions to accomplish individualized goals within a therapeutic relationship by a credentialed professional who has completed an approved music therapy program. Music therapy is an established health profession that uses music and the therapeutic relationship to address physical, psychological, cognitive and/or social functioning for patients of all ages and disabilities. Because music therapy is a powerful and non-invasive medium, unique outcomes are possible when interventions are directed to reduce pain, anxiety, and depression. These outcomes appear to be mediated through the individual's emotional, cognitive and interpersonal responsiveness to the music and/or the supportive music therapy relationship.

Annotated Bibliography of Research: 1992–2003

- **Reviews of Music Therapy in medical settings.**

Standley, J. M. (1992). Meta analysis of research in music and medical treatment. Effect size as a basis for comparisons across multiple dependent and independent variables. In R. Spintge & R. Droh (Eds), *MusicMedicine*, St Louis, MO: MMB.

Standley, J. M. (2000). Music research in medical treatment. In D. Smith (Ed.), *Effectiveness of music therapy procedures: Documentation of research and clinical practice.* Silver Spring, MD: American Music Therapy Association.

- **Music Therapy reduces pain.**

Colwell, C. (1997). Music as distraction and relaxation to reduce chronic pain and narcotic ingestion: A case study. *Music Therapy Perspectives, 15*, 24–31.

Edwards, J. (1998). Music therapy for children with severe burn injury. *Music Therapy Perspectives, 16*, 21–26.

Fratianne, R. B, Presner, J. D., Houston, M. J., Super, D. M., Yowler, C. J., & Standley, J. M. (2001). The effect of music-based imagery and musical alternate engagement on the burn debridement process. *Journal of Burn Care & Rehabilitation, 22*(1), 47–53.

Good, M., Anderson, G. C., Stanton-Hicks, M., Grass, J. A., & Makil, M. (2002). Relaxation and music reduce pain after gynecologic surgery. *Pain Management Nursing, 3*(2), 61–70.

Loewy, J. (1997). Music therapy pediatric pain management: Assessing and attending to the sounds of hurt, fear and anxiety. In J. Loewy (Ed.), *Music therapy and pediatric pain* (pp. 45–56). Jeffrey Books.

- **Music Therapy reduces physiological indicators of anxiety and reduces need for sedation and analgesia, increases completion rate, and shortens examination time during colonoscopy.**

Smolon, D., Topp, R., & Singer, L. (2002). The effect of self-selected music during colonoscopy on anxiety, heart, rate, and blood pressure. *Applied Nursing Research, 15*(3), 126–136.

Schiemann, U., Gross, M., Reuter, R., & Kellner, H. (2002). Improved procedure of colonoscopy under accompanying music therapy. *European Journal of Medical Research, 7*(3), 131–134.

- **Music Therapy reduces physiological indicators of pre-operative stress.**

Miluk-Kolasa, B., Matejek, M., & Stupnicki R. (1996). The effects of music listening on changes in selected physiological parameters in adult pre-surgical patients. *Journal of Music Therapy, 33*, 208–218.

Robb, S. L., Nichols, R. J., Rutan, R. L., & Bishop B. L. (1995). The effects of music assisted relaxation on preoperative anxiety. *Journal of Music Therapy, 32*, 2–21.

- **Music Therapy reduces cortisol in healthy adults.**

McKinney, C. H., Antoni, M. H., Kumar, M., Tims, F. C., & McCabe, P. M. (1997). Effects of Guided Imagery and Music (GIM) therapy on mood and cortisol in healthy adults. *Health Psychology, 16*(4), 390–400.

- **Music Therapy reduces physiological and psychological indicators of distress in post-operative cardiac patients.**

Cadigan, M. E., Caruso, N. A., Halderman, S. M., McNamara, M. E., Noyes, D. A., Spadafora, M. A., & Carrol, D. L. (2001). The effect of music on cardiac patients on bed rest. *Progress in Cardiovascular Nursing, 16*(1), 5–13.

- **Engaging in group music therapy and listening to music reduces anxiety associated with chemotherapy and radiotherapy.**

Cai, G., Qiao, Y., Li, P., & Lu, L. (2001). Music therapy in treatment of cancer patients. *Chinese Mental Health Journal, 15*(3), 179–181.

Harper, E. I. (2001). *Reducing treatment-related anxiety in cancer patients: Comparison of psychological interventions.* Doctoral dissertation, Southern Methodist University.

Sabo, C. E., & Michael, S. R. (1996). The influence of personal message with music on anxiety and side effects associated with chemotherapy. *Cancer Nursing, 19*(4), 283–289.

- **Listening to music reduces nausea and emesis for patients receiving chemotherapy.**

Standley, J. M. (1992). Clinical applications of music and chemotherapy: The effects on nausea and emesis. *Music Therapy Perspectives, 10*, 27–35.

- **Participating in Music Therapy sessions increases comfort and motivates bone marrow transplant patients during treatment.**

  Boldt, S. (1996). The effects of music therapy on motivation, psychological well-being, physical comfort, and exercise endurance of bone marrow transplant patients. *Journal of Music Therapy, 33*, 164–188.

- **Listening to music alleviates pain, fatigue, and anxiety of hospice cancer patients.**

  Longfield, V. (1995). *The effects of music therapy on pain and mood in hospice patients.* Unpublished master's thesis: Saint Louis University.

- **Music Therapy serves to decrease behavioral distress among pediatric oncology patients during needle sticks.**

  Malone, A. B. (1996). The effects of live music on the distress of pediatric patients receiving intravenous starts, venipunctures, injections, and heel sticks. *Journal of Music Therapy, 33*(1), 19–33.

- **Music provides an environment for engaging behaviors and decreasing distress behaviors for isolated pediatric oncology patients.**

  Robb, S. L. (2000). The effect of therapeutic music interventions on the behavior of hospitalized children in isolation: developing a contextual support model of music therapy. *Journal of Music Therapy, 37*(2), 118–146.

How Does Music Therapy Make a Difference?

Music therapy has been shown to be an efficacious and valid treatment option for patients experiencing pain related to a variety of diagnoses. Music therapy interventions can focus on pain management for physical rehabilitation, cardiac conditions, medical and surgical procedures, obstetrics, oncology treatment, and burn debridement, among others. Music is a form of sensory stimulation, which provokes responses due to the familiarity, predictability, and feelings of security associated with it. Research results and clinical experiences attest to the viability of music therapy even in those patients resistant to other treatment approaches.

What Do Music Therapists Do?

Music therapy utilized in the treatment and management of pain complies with the expectations and requirements inherent in the medical model of treatment. Music therapy programs are based on individual assessment and collection of extensive data for the development of complex patient histories and client-centered treatment plans. Patient objectives are specific and relevant to medical diagnosis, course of treatment, and discharge timeline.

Once goals and objectives are established, music therapists use music activities, both instrumental and vocal, designed to facilitate changes that are non-musical in nature. Through a planned and systematic use of music and music strategies, the music therapist provides opportunities for:

- Anxiety and stress reduction
- Non-pharmacological management of pain and discomfort
- Positive changes in mood and emotional states
- Active and positive patient participation in treatment
- Decreased length of stay

Functioning as members of an interdisciplinary team, music therapists also evaluate the patients during the course of treatment, implement changes that are indicated by the patient's response, and document benefits in medical, not musical, terms.

How Does Music Therapy Help Patients?

Music therapy can help to relieve pain and reduce stress and anxiety for the patient, resulting in physiological changes, including:

- Improved respiration
- Lower blood pressure
- Improved cardiac output
- Reduced heart rate
- Relaxed muscle tension

Music therapy has been shown to have a significant effect on a patient's perceived effectiveness of treatment, self-reports of pain reduction, relaxation, respiration rate, behaviorally observed and self-reported anxiety levels, and patient choice of anesthesia and amount of analgesic medication.

Music Therapy Protocol for Pain Management

"[This protocol]... is based on a cognitive behavioral model of therapy, which posits that new thoughts, feelings and body states may be conditioned to replace dysfunctional patterns. Specifically, a relaxed body and pleasant visual images may replace tension and worry when they are conditioned as a response to familiar, calming music. The conditioning process takes place when listening to this music is paired with deep relaxation through repeated practice. Over time, the music alone cues the response...

The music therapy protocol is designed to perform several functions:

1. To direct attention away from pain or anxiety, distracting the listener with comforting music.
2. To provide a musical stimulus for rhythmic breathing.
3. To offer a rhythmic structure for systematic release of body tension.
4. To cue positive visual imagery.

5. To condition a deep relaxation response.
6. To change mood.
7. To focus on positive thoughts and feelings and to celebrate life."

—Professor Suzanne Hanser, EdD, MT-BC, Berklee College of Music

Who is Qualified as a Music Therapist?

Graduates of colleges or universities from more than 70 approved music therapy programs are eligible to take a national examination administered by the Certification Board for Music Therapists (CBMT), an independent, non-profit certifying agency fully accredited by the National Commission for Certifying Agencies. After successful completion of the CBMT examination, graduates are issued the credential necessary for professional practice, Music Therapist-Board Certified (MT-BC). In addition to the MT-BC credential, other recognized professional designations are Registered Music Therapists (RMT), Certified Music Therapists (CMT), and Advanced Certified Music Therapist (ACMT) listed with the National Music Therapy Registry. Any individual who does not have proper training and credentials is not qualified to provide music therapy services.

Where Do Music Therapists Work?

Music therapists offer services in medical hospitals, skilled and intermediate care facilities, rehabilitation hospitals, adult day care centers, senior centers, hospices, psychiatric treatment centers, drug and alcohol programs, schools and other facilities. In pain management applications, music therapists can work in many different hospital units, including ICU, NICU, Pre- and Post-Op, surgery, cardiac care, obstetrics, emergency, pediatrics, physical rehabilitation, and outpatient programs. Some therapists are self-employed and work on the basis of independent contracts, while others are salaried hospital employees.

How Can You Find a Music Therapist or Get More Information?

American Music Therapy Association
8455 Colesville Road, Suite 1000
Silver Spring, MD 20910
Phone: (301) 589-3300
Fax: (301) 589-5175
Web: www.musictherapy.org
Email: info@musictherapy.org

AMTA Monograph Series
Effective Clinical Practice in Music Therapy:
Medical
Music Therapy
for
Pediatrics
in
Hospital Settings
Using Music to Support Medical Interventions
Editors
Deanna Hanson-Abromeit, PhD, MT-BC
Cynthia Colwell, PhD, MT-BC